SIMPLIFIED MECHANICS
AND
STRENGTH OF MATERIALS

BOOKS BY HARRY PARKER

Simplified Design of Reinforced Concrete
      Third Edition

Simplified Design of Roof Trusses for Architects and Builders
      Second Edition

Simplified Design of Structural Steel
      Third Edition

Simplified Design of Structural Timber
      Second Edition

Simplified Engineering for Architects and Builders
      Fourth Edition

Simplified Mechanics and Strength of Materials
      Second Edition

Simplified Site Engineering for Architects and Builders
      By Harry Parker and John W. MacGuire

Kidder-Parker Architects' and Builders' Handbook
      By the late Frank E. Kidder and Harry Parker
      Eighteenth Edition

Materials and Methods of Architectural Construction
      By Harry Parker, the late Charles Merrick Gay, and John W. MacGuire
      Third Edition

New York • London • Sydney

JOHN WILEY & SONS, INC.

SIMPLIFIED MECHANICS
AND
STRENGTH OF MATERIALS

SECOND EDITION

HARRY PARKER, M.S.

Emeritus Professor of Architectural Construction
School of Fine Arts
University of Pennsylvania

SECOND EDITION

13   14   15

Library of Congress Catalog Card Number: 61-15405

Printed in the United States of America

ISBN 0 471 66561 4

to Tony

PREFACE

The purpose and scope of this book are given in the preface to the first edition. The first preface, therefore, is again printed.

The basic laws of equilibrium are, of course, unchanging, but in the field of engineering new materials and alloys are constantly being developed. In addition, engineering societies and building codes alter, from time to time, the allowable unit stresses to be used in design as well as the specified design requirements. Therefore, because of these changes, books that deal with engineering subjects must be revised periodically if their usefulness is to be retained. It is because of these changes that the second edition of this book is presented.

This is not an advanced treatise; the purpose of this book is to provide basic practicable information in the field of mechanics and strength of materials without the use of advanced mathematics. A knowledge of arithmetic and algebra is sufficient preparation. Theory and derivations of certain fundamental formulas are presented to explain to the reader the reason for and the logic of present-day methods of design. A great portion of this book is devoted to illustrative examples; these examples, whenever possible, are of a practical nature. Following the examples, similar problems to be solved by the student are added. All these examples and problems have been modified to conform to present-day requirements.

Besides the changes in working stresses, certain additions have been made in the book. Among the items are structural aluminum; the investigation of reactions, shear, and bending moments for continuous beams with concentrated loads; the derivation of the deflection formula for simple beams with uniformly distributed loads; the design of solid wood columns to conform with current building-code requirements; the design of spaced columns; high-strength bolts; and numerous changes in the chapters relating to reinforced concrete in accordance with current working stresses and design requirements.

This book has been entirely reset. The American standard abbreviations for engineering terms are now employed, tables have been revised wherever necessary, and new tables have been added.

Because of their kindness in granting permission to reproduce tables and other data from their publications, I am indebted to The American Institute of Steel Construction, The American Concrete Institute, The National Lumber Manufacturers Association, The Timber Engineering Company, and The Aluminum Company of America. Their tables of properties of structural shapes as well as allowable working unit stresses constitute an essential part of this type of book.

In its new form this volume should continue to provide valuable basic information to all those who seek usable knowledge relating to the action of forces on bodies and to the design of structural members.

HARRY PARKER

High Hollow
Southampton
Bucks County, Pennsylvania
July 1961

PREFACE TO FIRST EDITION

Since engineering design is based on the science of mechanics, it is impossible to overemphasize the importance of a thorough knowledge of this basic subject. Regardless of the particular field of engineering in which a student is interested, it is essential that he understand fully the fundamental principles that deal with the action of forces on bodies and the resulting stresses.

Each of the other volumes of this "simplified" series has, in general, dealt with the design of a particular material, structural steel, timber, and reinforced concrete. In each of these books is included only pertinent material, relating to the principles of mechanics, in the accompanying discussions and explanations. Obviously, such discussions and explanations are brief and limited in scope and many important items are necessarily omitted. Students in engineering will find that the knowledge gained from a study of mechanics and strength of materials will enable them to understand more fully the theory of the design of structural members regardless of the material involved.

This is an elementary treatment written for those who have had limited preparation. The best books on the subject of mechanics and strength of materials make use of physics, calculus, and trigonometry. Such books are useless for many ambitious men. Consequently, this book has been prepared for the student who has not obtained a practical appreciation of mechanics or advanced mathematics. A working knowledge of algebra and arithmetic is sufficient to enable him to comprehend the mathematics involved in this volume.

This book has been written for use as a textbook in courses in mechanics and strength of materials and for use by practical men interested in mechanics and construction. Because it is elementary, the material has been arranged so that it may be used for home study. For those who have had previous training it will serve as a refresher course in reviewing the most important of the basic principles of structural design.

One of the most important features of this book is a detailed explanation of numerous illustrative examples. In so far as possible, the examples relate to problems encountered in practice. The explanations are followed by problems to be solved by the student.

The designer of structural members must have at hand tables of allowable stresses, properties of sections, and other tables giving engineering data. Such tables are included in this book, and reference books are not required. The author is indebted to The American Concrete Institute, The American Institute of Steel Construction, The National Lumber Manufacturers Association, and the Timber Engineering Company for their kindness and cooperation in granting permission to reproduce tables and other data from their publications.

This book presents no short-cuts to a knowledge of the fundamental principles of mechanics and strength of materials. There is nothing unique in the presentation, for the discussions follow accepted present-day design procedure. It is the belief of the author, however, that a thorough understanding of the material contained herein will afford a foundation of practical information and serve as a step to further study.

HARRY PARKER

High Hollow
Southampton
Bucks County, Pennsylvania
May 1951

Martin D. Kravik

CONTENTS

CHAPTER 1   MECHANICS AND STRENGTH OF MATERIALS   **1**

    1–1.   Mechanics   1
    1–2.   Strength of Materials   1
    1–3.   Abbreviations   2
    1–4.   Suggestions for Study   2

CHAPTER 2   FORCES   **4**

    2–1.   Forces   4
    2–2.   Compression   5
    2–3.   Tension   5
    2–4.   Shear   5
    2–5.   Vectors   6
    2–6.   Elements of a Force   6
    2–7.   Motion   7
    2–8.   Equilibrium   7
    2–9.   Resultant and Components   8
    2–10. Parallelogram of Forces   9
    2–11. Combined Resultants   11
    2–12. Equilibrant   12
    2–13. Force Polygon   13
    2–14. Bow's Notation   14
    2–15. Use of the Force Polygon   15
    2–16. Stresses in Frames   16
    2–17. Funicular Polygon   17
    2–18. Mechanical Couple   18
    2–19. Three Forces in Equilibrium   20
    2–20. Resultant Found by Funicular Polygon   .   .   .   20
    2–21. Resultant of Parallel Forces   21
    2–22. Reactions Found Graphically   25

2–23. Parallel Truss Reactions 26
2–24. Truss Reactions, Roller at One End . . . 28
2–25. Truss Reactions, Three Forces in Equilibrium . . 29
2–26. Stress Diagram for Trusses 31
2–27. Character of Stresses in Truss Members . . . 34

CHAPTER 3   **FORCES ACTING ON BODIES**   37

3–1. Free Body Diagram 37
3–2. Two-Force Members 38
3–3. Three-Force Members 39
3–4. The Inclined Plane 40
3–5. Forces Exerted by Spheres 41
3–6. Force Required to Produce Motion 43

CHAPTER 4   **MOMENTS OF FORCES**   47

4–1. Moment of a Force 47
4–2. Increasing Moments 48
4–3. Moment of a Mechanical Couple 49
4–4. Moments of Forces on a Beam 49
4–5. Basic Laws of Equilibrium 51
4–6. Reactions Found by Moments 55
4–7. Relation of Reactions to Loads 60
4–8. Forces Found by Moments 61

CHAPTER 5   **STRESSES AND DEFORMATIONS**   65

5–1. Mechanical Properties of Materials . . . 65
5–2. Strength 66
5–3. Stiffness 66
5–4. Elasticity 66
5–5. Ductility 67
5–6. Malleability 67
5–7. Materials Used in Construction 67
5–8. Deformation 69
5–9. Elastic Limit, Yield Point, and Ultimate Strength . . 70
5–10. Modulus of Elasticity 73
5–11. Factor of Safety 75
5–12. Allowable Unit Stresses 77

CHAPTER 6   **PROPERTIES OF SECTIONS**   85

6–1. Centroids 85
6–2. Moment of Inertia 89
6–3. Moment of Inertia of Rectangles, Circles, and
Triangles 91

6–4.   Transferring Moments of Inertia **94**
6–5.   Section Modulus **98**
6–6.   Radius of Gyration **100**
6–7.   Properties of Sections **103**
6–8.   Aluminum Sections **113**

CHAPTER 7   SHEARING STRESSES IN BEAMS   114

7–1.   Types of Beams **114**
7–2.   Kinds of Loads **115**
7–3.   Vertical Shear   .   .   .   .   **11€**
7–4.   Shear Diagram   .   .   .   .   **11€**
7–5.   Horizontal Shear **123**
7–6.   Shearing Stresses in Steel Beams **127**
7–7.   Shearing Stresses in Built-Up Beams   .   .   .   **12€**

CHAPTER 8   BENDING MOMENTS IN BEAMS   133

8–1.   Moment of a Force **133**
8–2.   Bending Moment and Bending Moment Diagram   .   **133**
8–3.   Bending Moments for Typical Loadings   .   .   .   **139**
8–4.   Uniformly Distributed Load on a Simple Beam   .   **14C**
8–5.   Concentrated Load at Center of Span of a Simple Beam **142**
8–6.   Equal Concentrated Loads at Third Points of Span   .   **143**
8–7.   Equal Concentrated Loads at Fourth Points of Span   .   **144**
8–8.   Cantilever Beam with Uniformly Distributed Load   .   **145**
8–9.   Cantilever Beam with Load at Unsupported End   .   **147**
8–10.   Triangular Load on a Simple Beam   .   .   .   **148**
8–11.   Overhanging Beam, Negative Bending Moments   .   **150**
8–12.   Moving Loads **154**
8–13.   Bending Moment Determined by Shear Diagram   .   **157**

CHAPTER 9   CONTINUOUS AND RESTRAINED BEAMS   159

9–1.   Continuous Beams, Theorem of Three Moments   .   .   **159**
9–2.   Continuous Beam with Equal Spans **160**
9–3.   Continuous Beam with Unequal Spans   .   .   .   **162**
9–4.   Continuous Beam with Concentrated Loads   .   .   **164**
9–5.   Continuous Beam with Three Spans **166**
9–6.   Restrained Beams **167**

CHAPTER 10   DEFLECTION OF BEAMS   172

10–1.   Deflection of Beams **172**
10–2.   Deflection Formulas **172**

CHAPTER 11 BENDING STRESSES, DESIGN OF BEAMS 178

11-1. Bending Stresses 178
11-2. Resisting Moment 179
11-3. Flexure Formula 180
11-4. Moment of Inertia of a Rectangle . . . 182
11-5. Design of Beams 183
11-6. Computation of Safe Loads 186
11-7. Investigation of Beams 187

CHAPTER 12 BUILT-UP BEAMS OF TWO MATERIALS 190

12-1. Beams of Two Materials 190

CHAPTER 13 COLUMNS 193

13-1. Columns and Posts 193
13-2. Slenderness Ratio 193
13-3. End Conditions of Columns 194
13-4. Solid Wood Columns 194
13-5. Spaced Columns 196
13-6. Slenderness Ratio of Steel Columns . . 198
13-7. Formulas for Steel Columns 199
13-8. Eccentrically Loaded Columns 201
13-9. Principle of the Middle Third . . . 205

CHAPTER 14 RIVETS AND WELDS 210

14-1. Connections 210
14-2. Rivets 210
14-3. Failure of a Riveted Joint 210
14-4. Shearing Stresses in a Rivet . . . 211
14-5. Bearing Stress in a Rivet 212
14-6. Tensile Stress in a Plate 213
14-7. Double Bearing 213
14-8. Allowable Working Values for Rivets . . 215
14-9. Design of Riveted Joints 217
14-10. Welding 219
14-11. Fillet Welds 219
14-12. Butt Welds 224
14-13. Plug and Slot Welds 225
14-14. High Strength Bolts 227

CHAPTER 15 TORSIONAL STRESS, SHAFTS, AND HORSEPOWER 229

15–1. Torsion 229
15–2. Torsion Formula 230
15–3. Keys in Pulleys 232
15–4. Shaft Couplings 233
15–5. Work, Horsepower 234

CHAPTER 16 STRESSES IN PIPES AND TANKS 236

16–1. Stresses in Pipes and Tanks 236

CHAPTER 17 REINFORCED CONCRETE 239

17–1. Theoretical Assumptions 239
17–2. Notation Used in Reinforced Concrete . . . 240
17–3. Flexure Formulas for Rectangular Reinforced Concrete Beams and Slabs 241
17–4. Summary of Flexure Formulas 244
17–5. Allowable Stresses in Concrete and Steel . . . 245
17–6. Modulus of Elasticity of Concrete 247
17–7. Formula Coefficients for Rectangular Sections . . 247
17–8. Design of a Rectangular Reinforced Concrete Beam for Flexure 249
17–9. Design of a Reinforced Concrete Slab . . . 254
17–10. Diagonal Tension, Web Reinforcement . . . 255
17–11. Portion of Beam Requiring Stirrups . . . 257
17–12. Spacing of Stirrups 258
17–13. Bond Stress 261
17–14. Reinforced Concrete Columns 264

CHAPTER 18 RETAINING WALLS AND DAMS 268

18–1. General Considerations 268
18–2. Earth Pressure 269
18–3. Resultant of Weight of Wall and Earth Pressure . 270
18–4. Stability of Retaining Walls 271
18–5. Design of a Dam 273
18–6. Design of a Retaining Wall with Surcharge . . 276

INDEX 281

CHAPTER 1

MECHANICS AND STRENGTH
OF MATERIALS

1–1. Mechanics. A knowledge of the basic principles of *mechanics* is of great importance to those interested in determining the size of bodies to resist forces. Practically all engineering design is based on the science of mechanics. *Mechanics* is the science that treats of the action of forces on material bodies. *Statics* treats of forces in equilibrium or of bodies held in equilibrium by the forces acting on them. *Kinetics* treats of the relations between forces acting on bodies in motion. This book deals with bodies held in equilibrium by forces, bodies in which there is no motion.

1–2. Strength of Materials. When a force acts on a body, two things happen. First, internal forces that resist the external forces are set up in the body. These internal resisting forces are called *stresses*. Second, the external forces produce *deformations*, changes in shape of the body.

Strength of materials is the study of the properties of material bodies that enable them to resist the action of external forces, the study of the stresses within the bodies and the deformations that result from the external forces.

In general, an architect or engineer is confronted with two distinct types of problems, *design* and *investigation*. Design problems are problems in which the material, shape, and size of a body are to be determined in order that external forces may be resisted economically. Problems of investigation give as data the kind of material and its size and shape as well as the loads to be resisted by the body. The architect or engineer computes the magnitudes of the internal resisting forces (stresses) set up in the body in order to determine whether or not the size of the member is sufficiently large. The great majority of problems that come to the engineer are design problems. Throughout this book will be found many examples and problems, most of which illustrate problems of design.

1–3. Abbreviations. An abbreviation is a shortened form of a name or expression. Abbreviations are used in texts and tabulations; they should not be used in equations. They should never be used where the meaning would not be clear. If there is doubt concerning the sense or significance, the name should be spelled out.

Throughout this text abbreviations are used constantly. Those employed are as follows:

Names	*Abbreviations*
cubic foot	cu ft
cubic inch	cu in.
cubic yard	cu yd
foot	ft
foot-pound	ft-lb
horsepower	hp
inch	in.
inch-pound	in-lb
linear foot	lin ft
pound	lb
pounds per cubic foot	lb per cu ft
pounds per square foot	psf
pounds per square inch	psi
revolutions per minute	rpm
square foot	sq ft
square inch	sq in.
thousand pounds	kip
weight	wt
yard	yd

The same abbreviation is used for both the singular and the plural. Thus "one foot" and "eight feet" are written 1 ft and 8 ft, respectively.

1–4. Suggestions for Study. It is assumed that those who use this book are serious in their efforts to gain useful knowledge.

With this in mind, the author recommends that the following suggestions be followed:

For those who are unfamiliar with the subject it is important that each item be taken up in the sequence in which it is presented. Most of the discussions are based on principles that were explained previously.

On first reading a problem to be solved, do not be confused by details. Determine the essentials. What information is given as data? What is to be determined?

Given data should be written down as part of the solution. In almost every instance a free-hand sketch can be made to show the forces and their positions on the member. *Always make such sketches.* Frequently the diagram itself will indicate the procedure to be employed in the solution of the problem.

The solution of a problem involves some basic principle or law of equilibrium. What is the principle involved? This is the key to the solution. Perhaps the fundamental principle can be expressed by an equation. Write it down. Now substitute the known quantities; the unknown factor may be the answer to the problem. Some problems are complex and require several steps. Nevertheless, follow the above procedure for it will always serve as an aid in solving problems.

There is one more important suggestion. From the beginning form the habit of writing the denominations or names of the quantities; do not be content with merely the magnitude. Thus we may write 50,000 lb (fifty thousand pounds), 30 cu in. (thirty cubic inches), 20 sq in. (twenty square inches), 3000 psi (three thousand pounds per square inch), 20,000 in-lb (twenty thousand inch-pounds), etc. Observing this suggestion is certain to aid in avoiding unnecessary errors.

FORCES

2–1. Forces. A *force* is that which produces, or tends to produce, motion or a change of motion of bodies. The force by which all bodies are attracted toward the center of the earth is the *force of*

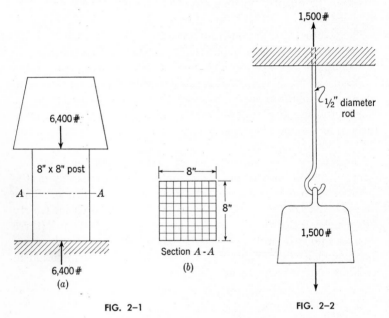

FIG. 2–1   FIG. 2–2

gravity. The magnitude of the force of gravity is the *weight* of the body. The amount of material in a body is its *mass.* The English unit of force is the *pound.*

Figure 2–1(*a*) represents a block of metal weighing 6400 lb supported on a short piece of wood having an 8 x 8 in. cross-sectional area. The wood in turn is supported on a base of masonry. The force of the metal block exerted on the wood is 6400 lb. Note that the wood transfers a force of equal magnitude (ignoring the weight of the wood block) to the masonry base. If there is to be no motion (equilibrium), there must be an equal upward force in the base. Force actions exist in pairs. In this instance the magnitude of the force is 6400 lb, and the resisting force offered by the masonry is also 6400 lb. The wood block has a cross-sectional area of 8 x 8 in., or 64 sq in. (sixty-four square inches), as indicated in Fig. 2–1(*b*), and, if the weight of the block is distributed uniformly over the piece of wood, each square inch of cross section of wood must have a stress of 6400 ÷ 64, or 100 psi (one hundred pounds per square inch). *A stress is an internal resistance to an external force.* It should be noted that the total stress in the masonry directly under the wood block is also 6400 lb, a unit stress of 100 psi. A *unit stress* is the stress per unit of area.

2–2. Compression. In general, there are two types of force, compression and tension. When a force acts on a body in a manner that tends to shorten the body or to push the parts of the body together, the force is a *compressive* force and the stresses within the body are compressive stresses. The block weighing 6400 lb acting on the piece of wood, shown in Fig. 2–1, is a compressive force and the resulting stresses are compressive stresses.

2–3. Tension. Figure 2–2 represents a $\frac{1}{2}$-in. diameter steel rod suspended from a ceiling. A weight of 1500 lb is attached to the lower end of the rod. The weight of 1500 lb is a tensile force, with respect to the rod, a *tensile* force being a force that tends to lengthen the body on which it acts. Since the rod has a diameter of $\frac{1}{2}$ in., its cross-sectional area is πr^2, or $3.1416 \times 0.25^2 = 0.196$ sq in. Hence the tensile unit stress in the rod is 1500 ÷ 0.196, or 7655 psi.

2–4. Shear. Consider the two steel bars held together by a $\frac{3}{4}$-in. diameter rivet as shown in Fig. 2–3. The force exerted on the rivet is 5000 lb. In addition to the bearing action of the bars on the rivet, there is a tendency for the rivet to fail by a cutting action at the plane at which the two bars are in contact. This is called *shear;* it results when two parallel forces having opposite directions act on a body, tending to cause one part of the body to slide past an adjacent part. A $\frac{3}{4}$-in. rivet has a cross-sectional area of 0.4418 sq in.; hence the unit shearing stress in the rivet is 5000 ÷ 0.4418, or 11,317 psi. Note particularly that this example illustrates the computation of a shearing stress. The 5000-lb forces shown act away from each other, but the shearing stress on the rivet would be of the same magnitude if the forces acted toward each other.

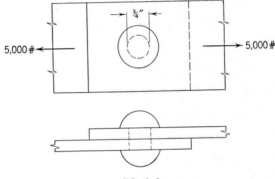

FIG. 2–3

2–5. Vectors. A quantity that combines both magnitude and direction is a *vector* quantity, whereas a *scalar* quantity involves magnitude but no direction. Forces, velocity, and acceleration are vector quantities, and energy, time, and mass are scalar quantities. Any vector quantity may be represented graphically by a drawn line; the solutions of problems involving forces are frequently accomplished by the construction of diagrams, the forces being represented by straight lines.

2–6. Elements of a Force. To identify a force, we must know its three elements, *magnitude, direction,* and *line of action.* If a force acts on a body, the point of contact with the body is called the *point of application.* Obviously, the point of application is some point on the line of action of the force. As forces are vector quantities, they may be represented by lines. As an example, two forces, P_1 and P_2, have an angle of 90° between their lines of action. P_1 is a horizontal force of 175 lb and its direction is from left to right. P_2 is a vertical downward force and its magnitude is 100 lb. The point O is common to their lines of action. This system of forces may be represented graphically by adopting a suitable scale, as, for example, 1 in. = 200 lb. Then, referring to Fig. 2–4, P_1, the solid line, is drawn horizontally from point O; its length is $\frac{7}{8}$ in. The arrow on the right end of the line indicates that the direction of the force is from left to right. From point O, the left end of force P_1, P_2, the solid line, is drawn vertically. Since its magnitude is 100 lb, its length is $\frac{1}{2}$ in., and the arrow is drawn pointing downward, the direction of the force. This diagram represents graphically the given system of forces; the system might also have been represented by the dotted lines shown on the same figure.

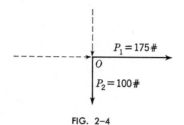

FIG. 2–4

Many problems involving forces require that a single force (the resultant) be found that has the same effect as the various forces acting simultaneously. Problems of this kind may be solved arithmetically, trigonometrically, or graphically, the last by representing the forces by vectors. The results obtained by mathematics are probably more exact, but solutions found graphically are often performed more rapidly, the accuracy of the solution depending on the accuracy employed in constructing the diagrams. Only the graphical solutions are discussed in this chapter.

2–7. Motion. A force may be defined as that which produces or tends to produce motion or a change of motion of bodies. *Motion* is a change of position with respect to some object regarded as having a fixed position. When the path of a moving point is a straight line, the point has *motion of translation*. When the path of a point is curved, the point has *curvilinear motion* or *motion of rotation*. Problems in this book deal with *coplanar forces*, forces lying in the same plane. When the path of a point lies in a plane, the point has *plane motion*. Other motions are *space motions*.

2–8. Equilibrium. A body is in *equilibrium* when it is in a state of rest or of uniform motion. When a system of forces acting on a body produces no motion in the body, the system of forces is said to be in equilibrium.

A simple example of equilibrium is illustrated in Fig. 2–5(a). Two equal, opposite, and parallel forces, having the same line of action, P_1 and P_2, act on a body. We say that the two forces *balance* each other; the body does not move and the system of forces is in equilibrium. These two forces are *concurrent*. If the lines of action of a system of forces have a point in common, the forces are concurrent.

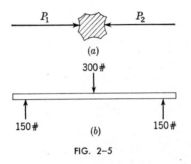

(a)

300#

(b)

150#   150#

FIG. 2–5

Another example of forces in equilibrium is illustrated in Fig. 2–5(b). A vertical downward force of 300 lb acts at the mid-point in the length of a beam. The two upward vertical forces of 150 lb each (the reactions) act at the ends of the beam. The system of three forces is in equilibrium. The forces are parallel and, not having a point in common, *nonconcurrent*.

2–9. Resultant and Components. The *resultant* of a system of forces is the simplest system (usually a single force) that has the same effect as the various forces in the system acting simultaneously. The lines of action of any system of two nonparallel forces must have a point in common, and the resultant of the two forces will pass through this common point. The resultant of two nonparallel forces may be found graphically by constructing a *parallelogram of forces*.

The *components* of a force are the two or more forces that, acting together, have the same effect as the given force. Referring to Fig. 2–7(a), suppose that we are given the force of 112 lb. The vertical component of this force is 50 lb, and the horizontal component is 100 lb. Thus any force is the resultant of its components.

2–10. Parallelogram of Forces. The *parallelogram law* may be stated thus: two nonparallel forces are laid off at any scale (of so many pounds to the inch) with both forces pointing toward or both forces pointing away from the point of intersection of their lines of action. A parallelogram is then constructed with the two forces as adjacent sides. The diagonal of the parallelogram passing through the common point is the resultant in magnitude, direction, and line of action, the direction of the resultant being similar to that of the given forces, toward or away from the point in common. In Fig. 2–6(a) P_1 and P_2 represent two nonparallel forces

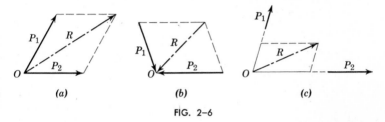

(a)   (b)   (c)

FIG. 2–6

whose lines of action intersect at point O. The parallelogram is drawn, and the diagonal R is the resultant of the given system. In this illustration note that the two forces point *away* from the point in common, hence the resultant also has its direction away from point O. It is a force upward to the right. Notice that the resultant of forces P_1 and P_2 shown in Fig. 2–6(b) is R; its direction is *toward* the point in common.

Forces may be considered to act at any points on their lines of action. In Fig. 2–6(c) the lines of action of the two forces P_1 and P_2 are extended until they meet at point O. At this point the parallelogram of forces is constructed, and R, the diagonal, is the resultant of the forces P_1 and P_2. In determining the magnitude of the resultant, the scale used is, of course, the same scale used in laying off the given system of forces.

Example. A vertical force of 50 lb and a horizontal force of 100 lb, as shown in Fig. 2–7(a), have an angle of 90° between their lines of action. Determine the resultant.

SOLUTION. The two forces are laid off from their point of intersection at a scale of 1 in. = 80 lb. The parallelogram is drawn, and the diagonal is the resultant. Its magnitude scales approximately 112 lb, its direction is upward to the right, and its line of action passes through the point of intersection of the lines of action of the two given forces. By use of a protractor, it is found that the angle between the resultant and the force of 100 lb is approximately $26\frac{1}{2}°$.

Example. The angle between two forces of 40 and 90 lb, as shown in Fig. 2–7(*b*), is 60°. Determine the resultant.

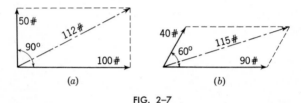

(*a*)   (*b*)

FIG. 2–7

SOLUTION. The forces are laid off from their point of intersection at a scale of 1 in. = 80 lb. The parallelogram of forces is constructed, and the resultant is found to be a force of approximately 115 lb, its direction is upward to the right, and its line of action passes through the common point of the two given forces. The angle between the resultant and the force of 90 lb is approximately $17\frac{1}{2}°$.

Attention is called to the fact that the two problems above have been solved graphically by the construction of diagrams. Mathematics might have been employed. For many practical problems graphical solutions give sufficiently accurate answers and frequently require far less time. Do not make diagrams too small. Remember that greater accuracy is obtained by using larger parallelograms of forces.

Problems 2–10–A–B–C–D–E–F. By constructing the parallelogram of forces, determine the resultants for the pairs of forces shown in Figs. 2–8(*a*), (*b*), (*c*), (*d*), (*e*), and (*f*).

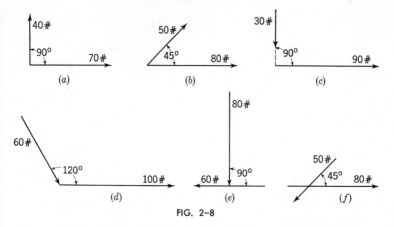

FIG. 2–8

2–11. Combined Resultants. The resultant of more than two nonparallel forces may be obtained by finding the resultants of pairs of forces and finally the resultant of the resultants.

Example. Let it be required to find the resultant of the concurrent forces P_1, P_2, P_3, and P_4 shown in Fig. 2–9.

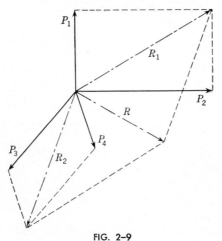

FIG. 2–9

SOLUTION. By constructing the parallelogram of forces, the resultant of P_1 and P_2 is found to be R_1. Similarly, the resultant of P_3 and P_4 is R_2. Finally, the resultant of R_1 and R_2 is R, the resultant of the four given forces.

Problems 2–11–A–B–C. Find, by graphical methods, the resultants of the systems of concurrent forces shown in Figs. 2–10(a), (b), and (c).

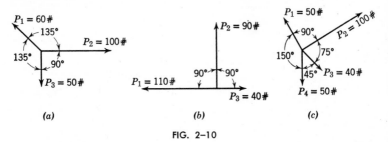

FIG. 2–10

2–12. Equilibrant. The force required to maintain a system of forces in equilibrium is called the *equilibrant* of the system. Suppose that we are required to investigate the system of two forces, P_1 and P_2, as shown in Fig. 2–11. The parallelogram of forces is

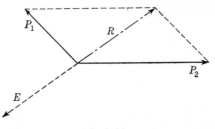

FIG. 2–11

constructed, and the resultant is found to be R. The system is not in equilibrium. The force required to maintain equilibrium is force E, shown by the dotted line. E, the equilibrant, is equal to the resultant in magnitude and opposite in direction and has the same line of action. The three forces, P_1 and P_2 and E, constitute a system in equilibrium.

If two forces are in equilibrium, they must be equal in magnitude and opposite in direction and have the same line of action. Either of the two forces may be said to be the equilibrant of the other. The resultant of a system of forces in equilibrium is zero.

2–13. Force Polygon. The resultant of a system of concurrent forces may be found by constructing a *force polygon*. To draw the force polygon, begin with a point and lay off, at a convenient scale, a line parallel to one of the forces, equal to it in magnitude and having the same direction. From the termination of this line draw similarly another line corresponding to one of the remaining forces and continue in the same manner until all the forces in the given system are accounted for. If the polygon does not close, the system of forces is not in equilibrium, and the line required to close the polygon *drawn from the starting point* is the resultant in magnitude and direction. If the forces in the given system are concurrent, the line of action of the resultant passes through the point they have in common. If they are not concurrent, the line of action of the resultant may be found by constructing a funicular polygon as explained in Art. 2–20.

If the force polygon for a system of concurrent forces closes, the system is in equilibrium and the resultant is zero.

Example. Let it be required to find the resultant of the four concurrent forces, P_1, P_2, P_3, and P_4, shown in Fig. 2–12(a). This

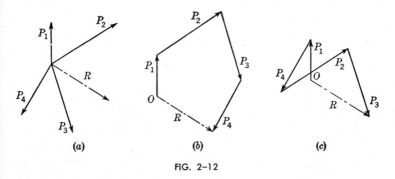

(a)   (b)   (c)

FIG. 2–12

diagram is called the *space diagram;* it shows the relative positions of the forces in a given system.

SOLUTION. Beginning with some point such as point O, shown in Fig. 2–12(b), draw the upward force P_1. At the upper extremity of the line representing P_1 draw P_2, continuing in a like manner with P_3 and P_4. The polygon does not close; therefore the system is not in equilibrium. The resultant R, shown by the dot-and-dash line, is the resultant of the given system. Note that its direction is *from* the starting point O, downward to the right. The line of action of the resultant of the given system shown in Fig. 2–12(a) has its line of action passing through the point they have in common, its magnitude and direction having been found in the force polygon.

In drawing the force polygon, the forces may be taken in any sequence. In Fig. 2–12(c) a different sequence is taken, but the resultant R is found to have the same magnitude and direction as previously found in Fig. 2–12(b).

2–14. Bow's Notation. Thus far forces have been identified by the symbols P_1, P_2, etc. A system of identifying forces, known as Bow's notation, affords many advantages. In this system of lettering letters are placed in the space diagram on each side of a force and a force is identified by two letters. *The sequence in which the letters are read is important.* Figure 2–13(a) shows the space

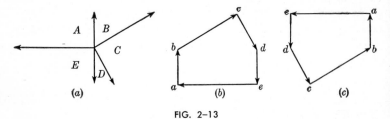

FIG. 2–13

diagram of five concurrent forces. Reading about the point in common *in a clockwise manner* the forces are AB, BC, CD, DE, and EA. When a force in the force polygon is represented by a line, a letter is placed at each end of the line. As an example, the vertical upward force in Fig. 2–13(a) is read AB (note that this is read clockwise about the common point); in the force polygon [Fig. 2–13(b)] the letter a is placed at the bottom of the line representing the force AB and the letter b is at the top. We shall use capital letters to identify the forces in the space diagrams and lower-case letters in the force polygon. From point b in the force polygon we draw force bc, then cd, and continue with de and ea. Since the force polygon closes, the five concurrent forces are in equilibrium.

In reading forces, a clockwise manner is used in all the following discussions. It is important that this method of identifying forces be thoroughly understood. To make this clear, suppose that we are asked to draw the force polygon for the five forces shown in Fig. 2–13(a), *reading the forces counterclockwise.* Then the vertical upward force is read *BA* (not *AB* as before), and the force polygon is shown in Fig. 2–13(c). Either direction may be employed, but, to avoid confusion, we shall read forces in a clockwise fashion.

2–15. Use of the Force Polygon. Two ropes are attached to a ceiling and their lower ends connected to a ring, making the angles shown in Fig. 2–14(a). From this ring is hung a weight of 100 lb.

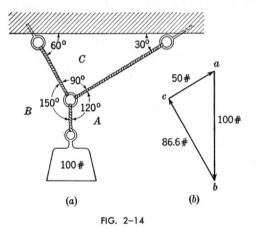

(a)   (b)

FIG. 2–14

Obviously, the stress in the rope *AB* is 100 lb, but what are the magnitudes of the stresses in the ropes *BC* and *CA*?

The stresses in the ropes *AB*, *BC*, and *CA* constitute three concurrent forces in equilibrium. The magnitude of only one of the forces is known; it is *AB*, 100 lb. Since the three concurrent forces are in equilibrium, we know that their force polygon must close, and this fact enables us to find their magnitudes. Let us construct the force polygon. At a convenient scale, draw the line *ab* [Fig. 2–14(b)] representing the downward force *AB*, 100 lb. The line *ab* is one side of the force polygon. From point *b* draw a line parallel to the force *BC*; point *c* will be at some location on this line. Next, draw a line through point *a* parallel to the force *CA*; point *c* will be at some position on this line. Since point *c* is also on the line through *b* parallel to *BC*, the intersection of the two lines determines point *c*. The force polygon for the three forces is now completed; it is *abc*, and the lengths of the sides of the polygon represent the magnitudes of the forces *BC* and *CA*, 86.6 and 50 lb, respectively.

Particular attention is called to the fact that the lengths of the ropes in Fig. 2–14(*a*) are not an indication of magnitude of the stresses within the ropes; the magnitudes are determined by the lengths of the corresponding sides of the force polygon [Fig. 2–14(*b*)].

2–16. Stresses in Frames. Imagine a hinged frame whose sides are *AO*, *BO*, and *CO*, shown in Fig. 2–15(*a*), attached to the three

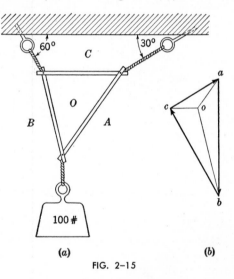

(*a*)   (*b*)

FIG. 2–15

ropes shown in Fig. 2–14(*a*), the ropes maintaining the same angles with the horizontal. The weight *AB*, 100 lb, is again added, and forces are now transferred to the ropes *BC* and *CA* by the members of the frame as shown in Fig. 2–15(*a*).

With respect to the frame, *AB*, *BC*, and *CA* are *external forces*, and, since they are in equilibrium, their force polygon must close. This polygon is *abc*, shown in Fig. 2–15(*b*), exactly the same as Fig. 2–14(*b*).

Now consider the joint *ABO* in Fig. 2–15(*a*). Here we have three concurrent forces in equilibrium; hence their force polygon must close. Of the three forces only one, *AB*, is known, but we do know the lines of action of *BO* and *OA*. Therefore, in Fig. 2–15(*b*) draw a line through point *b* parallel to *BO* and also a line through point *a* parallel to *OA*. The point *o* must be on both of these lines and therefore is at their point of intersection. Thus the polygon *abo* in Fig. 2–15(*b*) is the force polygon for the three forces *AB*, *BO*, and *OA* in Fig. 2–15(*a*).

Next consider the joint *BCO*. Again we have three concurrent forces in equilibrium; hence their force polygon must close. Of these three forces, we now know two, *OB* and *BC*. If in Fig. 2–15(*b*) we draw a line connecting points *c* and *o*, *we find that it is parallel to the member CO* and thus checks the accuracy of the forces previously determined. Figure 2–15(*b*) now contains lines representing the stresses in all the external forces and also in the sides of the frame shown in Fig. 2–15(*a*). We call Fig. 2–15(*b*) a *stress diagram* because it shows the stresses in the members of the frame, *AO*, *BO*, and *CO*. The magnitudes of the stresses in the sides of the frame, *OA*, *OB*, and *OC*, are established by the lengths of the lines *oa*, *ob*, and *oc* in the stress diagram [Fig. 2–15(*b*)].

2–17. Funicular Polygon. The *funicular polygon* is a polygon one of whose uses is to determine whether a system of forces is in equilibrium.

Suppose that we are given the system of three forces, *AB*, *BC*, and *CA*, shown in Fig. 2–16(*a*) and are asked to determine whether

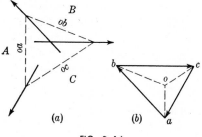

FIG. 2–16

the system is in equilibrium. The test is to construct the funicular polygon; if both the funicular polygon and force polygon close, the system is in equilibrium. First, construct the force polygon *abc*, shown in Fig. 2–16(*b*). The polygon closes. We know that a system of *concurrent* forces is in equilibrium if the force polygon closes, but in this instance let us assume that we do not know whether the lines of action of the forces have a point in common or whether they are nonconcurrent.

In Fig. 2–16(*b*) select *any* point such as point *o* and draw the lines *oa*, *ob*, and *oc*. The point *o* is called the *pole*, and the lines *oa*, *ob*, and *oc* are the *rays*. Note that this diagram somewhat resembles Fig. 2–15(*b*) and that the rays *oa*, *ob*, and *oc* represent the stresses in a frame connecting the forces *AB*, *BC*, and *CA*, *if there were such a frame*. Now, let us construct this imaginary frame, the sides of which are sometimes called *strings*. In Fig. 2–16(*b*) the force *ab* is held in equilibrium by the forces *ao* and *bo*. Therefore, select any point on the line of action of force *AB* in Fig. 2–16(*a*) and draw the lines parallel to *oa* and *ob* in Fig. 2–16(*b*). These lines represent two sides of the imaginary frame. From the point where *ob* intersects the line of action of the force *BC* draw the line *oc* parallel to the ray *oc*. Note that in Fig. 2–16(*b*) *ob* and *oc* hold the force *bc* in equilibrium and therefore have a point in common. The lines *oa* and *oc* are continued in Fig. 2–16(*a*) until they intersect, and, in this example, *they intersect on the line of action of force CA*; we say *this imaginary frame (the funicular polygon) closes*. The lines in Fig. 2–16(*a*), *oa*, *ob*, and *oc*, are sides of an imaginary frame called the *funicular polygon*. This polygon is sometimes called the *string polygon* or *equilibrium polygon*. Since, in this particular instance, both the force polygon and the funicular polygon close, the three given forces are in equilibrium. In this example note that if the line of action of the force *CA* is extended it will pass through the point of intersection of forces *AB* and *BC*. Actually, the system of three forces is concurrent.

Any system of forces is in equilibrium if both the force polygon and the funicular polygon close.

2–18. Mechanical Couple. The system of three forces shown in Fig. 2–17(*a*) is somewhat similar to the given system shown in Fig. 2–16(*a*). The respective forces are equal in magnitude, are parallel, and have the same direction, but their lines of action do not bear the same relation to each other; their lines of action do not have a point in common. Is the system of forces shown in Fig. 2–17(a) in equilibrium? If it is, both the force polygon and the funicular polygon must close. Let us investigate.

First we draw the force polygon, Fig. 2–17(b), and we find that it closes. The next test is the funicular polygon. We select any point, such as o, in the force polygon, and draw the rays oa, ob, and oc. Selecting any point on force AB, we draw the strings oa and ob. At the intersection of string oa with force CA we draw the string oc until it intersects the string ob. In this instance we

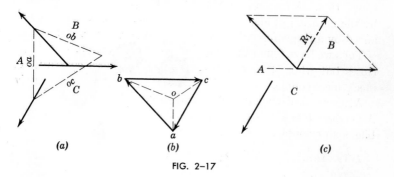

(a)   (b)   (c)

FIG. 2–17

find that the funicular polygon does not close; that is, the strings oc and ob do not intersect on the line of action of the force BC. Consequently, the system is not in equilibrium. The system might be altered to provide equilibrium by moving the force BC to a parallel position in which its line of action passes through the intersection of oc and ob. The system, *thus modified*, would have both the force polygon and the funicular polygon closing. Notice that thus altering the system would result in a system of concurrent forces.

But, if the original three forces shown in Fig. 2–17(a) are not in equilibrium, what is their resultant? These three forces are again drawn in Fig. 2–17(c). Let us find the resultant of the two forces AB and BC. By use of the method explained in Art. 2–13, the force polygon, Fig. 2–17(b), tells us that the resultant of ab and bc is ac, an upward force sloping to the right. Note that this force is equal in magnitude and parallel to CA, the third force of the system, but it acts in the opposite direction. The resultant of AB and BC might also have been found by constructing the parallelogram of forces, the dot-and-dash line marked R_1, shown in Fig. 2–17(c), but, regardless of how it is found, the resultant of two nonparallel forces passes through the point at which their lines of action intersect. Now if, in Fig. 2–17(c), we substitute the force marked R_1 for the two forces AB and BC, we have remaining the two forces R_1 and CA. *These two forces are parallel, equal in magnitude, opposite in direction, and do not have the same lines of action. Such a system constitutes a mechanical couple.* A mechanical couple acting on a body causes motion of rotation rather than motion of translation. A mechanical couple can be held in equilibrium only by the addition of another mechanical couple. It cannot be balanced by a single force.

Thus we have found that a system of forces whose force polygon closes but whose funicular polygon does not close constitutes a mechanical couple.

A mechanical couple is frequently found in daily experiences. A person's two hands operating the steering wheel of an automobile is an example.

2–19. Three Forces in Equilibrium. *The lines of action of any system of three nonparallel forces in equilibrium intersect at a common point.* For such a system the resultant of any two forces must be the equilibrant of the third force.

Figure 2–16(a) shows three nonparallel forces in equilibrium. In accordance with Art. 2–13, the resultant of ab and bc, shown in the force polygon, Fig. 2–16(b), is ac, a force whose direction is upward to the right and whose line of action passes through the intersection of AB and BC. If ac is substituted for ab and bc, we have remaining only ac and ca, two equal parallel forces opposite in direction. Since, by data, these forces are in equilibrium, they must have the same line of action. Therefore, CA must pass through the point common to AB and BC.

2–20. Resultant Found by Funicular Polygon. The construction of the funicular polygon affords a convenient method of determining the resultant of any system of forces.

Example. Let it be required to find the resultant of the four forces, AB, BC, CD, and DE shown in Fig. 2–18(a). This system may or may not be concurrent.

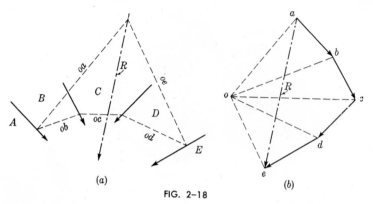

FIG. 2–18

SOLUTION. The polygon of forces is drawn as shown in Fig. 2–18(b), and the resultant is *ae*, as explained in Art. 2–13. Note that this is the resultant in magnitude and direction only; its line of action is found by the funicular polygon. Point *o*, the pole, is selected, and the rays *oa*, *ob*, *oc*, *od*, and *oe* are drawn. From any point on the line of action of force *BC* we next draw the strings *ob* and *oc* [Fig. 2–18(a)]. Care must be exercised in drawing the strings in their proper relation to the various forces. In this particular instance we note that the ray *oc* is common to both *bc* and *cd* in the force polygon and, therefore, the string *oc* must join the forces *BC* and *CD* in the space diagram [Fig. 2–18(a)]. We continue by drawing the strings of the funicular polygon. Now the resultant of the given system of forces is found in the force polygon to be *ae*, shown by the dot-and-dash line. This figure also shows that this force, *ae*, is held in equilibrium by the rays *oa* and *oe*. Therefore, the strings *oa* and *oe* in the funicular polygon are extended until they intersect. This point of intersection is a point on the line of action of the resultant. Therefore, we draw the resultant, whose magnitude and direction are found in the force polygon, through the point of intersection of strings *oa* and *oe* and thus completely determine the resultant.

2–21. Resultant of Parallel Forces.

The resultant of parallel forces may be found by constructing the funicular polygon.

Example. The five forces shown in Fig. 2–19(a) constitute a system of parallel forces. Determine the resultant.

SOLUTION. First draw the force polygon, Fig. 2–19(b). In accordance with the rule given in Art. 2–13, the resultant in magnitude and direction is the vertical downward force *af*. Its position

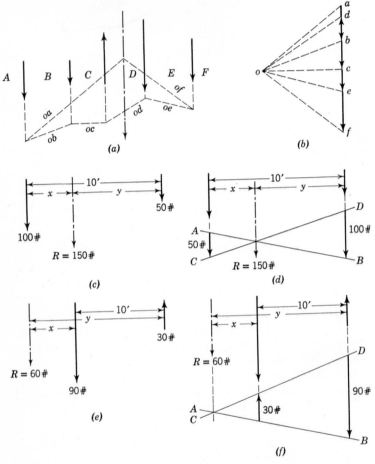

(a) *(b)*

(c) *(d)*

(e) *(f)*

FIG. 2–19

with respect to the five forces in the given system is not yet known. A pole is now selected, the rays are drawn, and the funicular polygon is constructed as indicated in Fig. 2–19(a). The resultant, *af*, in Fig. 2–19(b) is held in equilibrium by the rays *oa* and *of*, and, therefore, the intersection of the strings *oa* and *of* in the funicular polygon lies on the line of action of the resultant. The resultant, indicated by the dot-and-dash line, is drawn through this point of intersection and represents the resultant in magnitude, direction, and line of action.

Another graphical method of finding the position of the resultant of parallel forces is the method of *inverse proportion.* Figure 2–19(c) shows two parallel downward forces of 100 and 50 lb. Their resultant is the downward force of 150 lb at x distance from the 100-lb force and y distance from the 50-lb force. By the principle of moments explained in Art. 4–7, it can be shown that the resultant of the two parallel forces having the same direction divides the distance between them in inverse proportion to the magnitude of the forces; that is, for the forces shown in Fig. 2–19(c), $100:50::y:x$.

To determine the position of the resultant graphically, assume that the two given forces are 10 ft apart, as shown in Fig. 2–19(d), and draw any straight line such as AB that intersects their lines of action. On the line of action of the 100-lb force lay off to a suitable scale a downward force of 50 lb from the intersection of AB with the force of 100 lb. Similarly, from the point where AB intersects the 50-lb force lay off a downward force of 100 lb at the same scale *but on the opposite side of the line AB.* From the extremities of the two lengths just laid off draw the line CD. The point of intersection of AB and CD determines the point through which the resultant of the two forces of 100 and 50 lb will pass because, by similar triangles [Fig. 2–19(d)] $100:50::y:x$. By scaling the lengths of x and y, they are found to be 3.33 and 6.66 ft, respectively. The magnitude of the resultant of two parallel forces having the same direction is equal to their sum, in this instance $50 + 100 = 150$ lb.

Figure 2–19(e) shows two parallel forces of 90 and 30 lb, 10 ft apart and having opposite directions. Their resultant is a downward force of 60 lb at the position shown. By the principle of moments, $90:30::y:x$. The position of the resultant is found graphically in Fig. 2–19(f). The line AB is drawn and it intersects the line of action of the two given forces. We now proceed as before, except that *the forces of 90 and 30 lb are laid off on the same side of line AB.* This is shown in Fig. 2–19(f). From the ends of the two

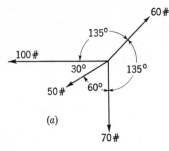

(a)

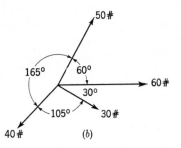

(b)

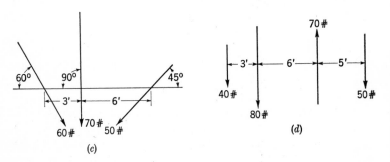

(c)

(d)

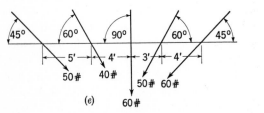

(e)

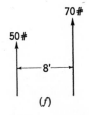

(f)

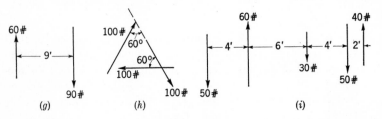

(g)

(h)

(i)

FIG. 2-20

forces just laid off we draw the line CD. The point at which AB and CD intersect is a point through which the resultant of the 90- and 30-lb forces will pass. Note that, by similar triangles, $90:30::y:x$. By scaling the distance y, it is found to be 15 ft 0 in. The resultant of two parallel forces having opposite directions is equal to their difference in magnitude and has the direction of the greater force. In this instance the resultant is $90 - 30$, or a downward force of 60 lb.

The above discussion explains a graphical method of finding the resultant of two parallel forces. Another method, which is possibly shorter, is to construct a funicular polygon. The shortest and most accurate method, however, is to employ the principle of moments as explained in Chapter 4.

Problems 2–21–A–B–C–D–E–F–G–H–I. Find the resultants of the systems of forces shown in Figs. 2–20(a), (b), (c), (d), (e), (f), (g), (h), and (i).

2–22. Reactions Found Graphically. The term given to the upward forces, or supports, that hold a beam in equilibrium is *reactions*. If the loading on a simple beam is symmetrical, the reactions are equal in magnitude. If, however, as frequently happens, the beam is not loaded symmetrically, the magnitudes of the reactions must be computed. The usual and most convenient method of determining the magnitudes of reactions is to use mathematics as explained in Art. 4–6. They may also be determined graphically by employing the force and funicular polygons.

Example. The three loads on a beam are AB, BC, and CD, as shown in Fig. 2–21(a). Determine by graphical methods the magnitudes of the reactions DE and EA.

SOLUTION. So that a numerical answer may be given, the three loads have magnitudes of 1000, 800, and 400 lb, and their positions with respect to each other are shown in Fig. 2–21(a). Since the loads are vertical downward forces due to gravity, the reactions DE and EA are vertical upward forces, and the system, then, is composed of five parallel forces in equilibrium. Three of the five forces (the loads) are determined completely; the lines of action and directions of the reactions are known but their magnitudes are unknown.

To begin, the forces on the beam are laid off at some convenient

scale, in this instance $\frac{1}{8}$ in. = 1 ft 0 in., as shown in the space diagram, Fig. 2–21(*a*). Then the force polygon is begun by drawing
the three known forces, *AB*, *BC*, and *CD*. This is shown in Fig.
2–21(*b*) the scale of which is 1 in. = 1600 lb. Note that point *e* in
the force polygon cannot be located because the magnitudes of *DE*
and *EA* are not yet known. A pole is selected and the rays, *oa*,
ob, *oc*, and *od*, are drawn.

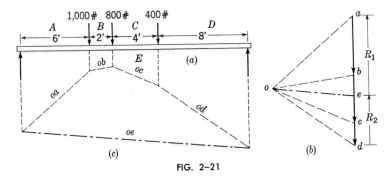

FIG. 2–21

The lines of action of the various forces are continued below the
space diagram, and the sides of the funicular polygon, *oa*, *ob*, *oc*,
and *od*, are drawn [Fig. 2–21(*c*)]. *Since, by data, the five forces are
in equilibrium, we know that the funicular polygon must close, and,
therefore, we draw the closing string oe.* Now we return to the force
polygon, Fig. 2–21(*b*), and draw the ray *oe* parallel to the string *oe*,
thus determining the point *e*. By scaling the lengths of *de* and *ea*,
we find them to be 860 and 1340 lb, the magnitudes of the two
reactions *DE* and *EA*.

Problems 2–22–A–B–C–D. Letter the beams shown in Figs. 2–22(*a*), (*b*), (*c*),
and (*d*) in any convenient manner and determine the magnitudes of the
reactions by graphical methods.

2–23. Parallel Truss Reactions. To determine the stresses in
truss members by graphical methods, the first step, after the
magnitudes of the loads have been established, is to draw a force
polygon of the external forces, the external forces being the loads
and the reactions. For vertical loads placed symmetrically the
reactions are vertical and equal in magnitude, the magnitude of
each being one half the sum of the loads. For wind loads the

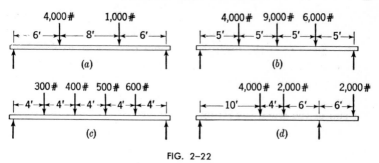

FIG. 2–22

truss is not loaded symmetrically, and the magnitudes of the reactions must be determined.

Example. The upper and lower chords of a truss are shown in Fig. 2–23(a), the web members being omitted to avoid confusion. The wind loads are *AB*, *BC*, *CD*, and *DE* perpendicular to the

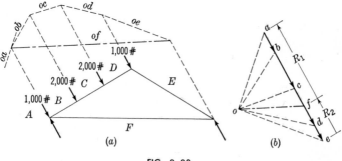

FIG. 2–23

upper chord at the positions shown. Assuming that the reactions are parallel to the wind loads, determine their magnitudes.

SOLUTION. The sides of the force polygon, *ab*, *bc*, *cd*, and *de*, are drawn as shown in Fig. 2–23(b). The pole *o* is selected and the rays *oa*, *ob*, *oc*, *od*, and *oe* are drawn. Next, the lines of action of the loads and reactions are extended above the truss and the funicular polygon is constructed [Fig. 2–23(a)]. Since the six forces are in equilibrium, the funicular polygon must close; therefore, the closing string *of* is drawn. A line from the pole *o* parallel to the closing string determines the point *f* on the force polygon and thus establishes the two reactions EF and FA. Scaling their lengths shows that they are 1860 and 4140 lb, respectively.

The string oa in the funicular polygon requires an explanation. Note that the forces FA and AB in Fig. 2–23(a) have the same line of action and that their resultant is FB. If, in drawing the funicular polygon, only the force FB is considered to be acting at the left end of the truss, the string oa is unnecessary. Another explanation follows: the string ob is extended to the left until it intersects the force AB. From this point of intersection oa is continued until it intersects the next force, FA. But FA and AB have the same line of action, hence the string oa has no length.

2–24. Truss Reactions, Roller at One End.

To provide for expansion and contraction that result from temperature changes, a roller is sometimes used at one support of a truss. If such a bearing were frictionless, a roller support would result in a vertical reaction and the direction of the other reaction would have to be determined.

Example. The upper and lower chords of a truss are shown in Fig. 2–24(a). The resultant of the wind loads on the left side of

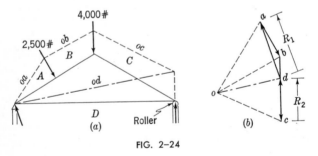

FIG. 2–24

the truss is AB, and BC is the resultant of the vertical loads. A roller is placed at the right-hand support. Let it be required to draw the force polygon of the external forces.

SOLUTION. The force polygon is begun by drawing the two forces ab and bc as shown in Fig. 2–24(b). The pole o is selected and the rays oa, ob, and oc are drawn. Since there is a roller at the right support, the reaction CD is vertical but the direction of DA is not yet known.

The only fact known about the left reaction, *DA*, is that its line of action must pass through the point of support. Therefore, the funicular polygon is started at this point, the string *oa* being continued until it intersects the force *AB*. We continue by drawing the strings *ob* and *oc*, *oc* being extended until it meets the line of action of the reaction *CD*, which we know is vertical. From this point of intersection the closing string *od* is drawn to the left support. Now return to the force polygon and draw the ray *od* parallel to the closing string *od*, thus establishing point *d* on the force polygon. The reactions of the truss are *cd* and *da*, their magnitudes and directions being shown on the force polygon.

Problem 2–24–A. The triangular Howe truss shown in Fig. 2–25(*a*) has a span of 64 ft 0 in., and the upper chord makes an angle of 30° with the horizontal. Assuming that the reactions are parallel to the direction of the wind, draw the force polygon of the external forces, the wind loads, and the reactions and determine the magnitudes of the reactions.

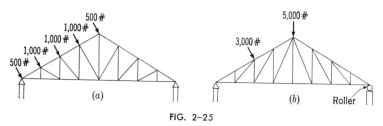

FIG. 2–25

Problem 2–24–B. The truss indicated in Fig. 2–25(*b*) is a triangular Pratt truss having a span of 60 ft 0 in., the angle between the upper and lower chords being 30°. The resultant of the wind loads is 3000 lb, and it acts at the mid-length of the upper chord. The resultant of the vertical loads is 5000 lb at the position shown. Assuming that a roller bearing is used at the right reaction, making its direction vertical, draw the force polygon of all the external forces and scale the magnitudes of the reactions.

2–25. Truss Reactions, Three Forces in Equilibrium. Any three nonparallel forces in equilibrium have lines of action that intersect at a common point; see Art. 2–19. This important fact is frequently used in graphical solutions. The following example is an illustration.

Example. The fan truss shown in Fig. 2–26(*a*) has the wind loads *AB*, *BC*, *CD*, and *DE*. The two reactions are *EF* and *FA*.

Assume that a roller is placed at the right reaction and let it be required to draw the force polygon of the external forces.

SOLUTION. We begin by laying off the forces ab, bc, cd, and de as part of the force polygon, Fig. 2–26(b). The next force in order is ef, a vertical upward force because the roller is at this reaction. Therefore, through point e draw a vertical line; point f will be at some point on this line.

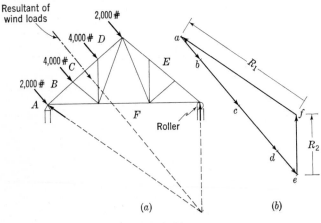

FIG. 2–26

Now return to the truss diagram, Fig. 2–26(a). The three forces acting on the truss are the wind load of 12,000 lb and the two reactions. *These three forces are in equilibrium and are nonparallel; therefore, their lines of action have a point in common.* The wind loads are symmetrically distributed on the left side of the truss; hence their resultant acts at the mid-length of the upper chord as shown in the diagram. The line of action of the resultant is continued until it intersects the line of action of the right reaction, which, we know, is vertical. This point of intersection is the point in common of the three forces; therefore, a line drawn from this point of intersection to the point of support of the left reaction *determines the direction of the left reaction.*

Return now to Fig. 2–26(b). Since the direction of the left reaction, FA, has been established, we can draw a line through point a parallel to the direction of FA found in Fig. 2–26(a). Point f is on this line and is also on the vertical line through point e.

Hence the intersection of these two lines establishes point f and consequently determines the magnitudes and direction of the two reactions.

Problem 2–25–A. The truss indicated in Fig. 2–27 is a triangular Belgian truss having a span of 48 ft 0 in. and a height of 16 ft 0 in. The total wind load on the right side of the truss is 6000 lb, distributed at the panel points as shown. A roller is used at the right reaction. Using the method explained in Art. 2–25, draw the force polygon of the external forces and determine the magnitudes and directions of the two reactions.

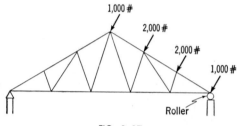

FIG. 2–27

2–26. Stress Diagrams for Trusses. Thus far the discussions relating to trusses have been confined to the loads and the reactions, the construction of the force polygon of the external forces. For the graphic analysis of most of the trusses used in practice the construction of the polygon of external forces requires the greatest attention; after it is completed the remainder of the problem—the construction of the stress diagram—is usually a simple matter.

Figure 2–28(a) represents diagrammatically a triangular fan truss for which the end bearings are simple supports; there is no roller bearing. The total load on the truss is 6000 lb, distributed at the panel points as shown. As the truss is symmetrically loaded, the reactions are vertical and equal in magnitude, each being 3000 lb. Observe that at each panel point there are three or more concurrent forces. At each joint the concurrent forces are in equilibrium, and for this condition we know that their force polygons close. It should be noted that certain forces (the loads and reactions) are known; the remaining forces, the stresses in the truss members, are to be determined. For the unknown forces, note particularly that we do know their lines of action.

Consider first the joint *ABJI*, the left support. Here we have four concurrent forces in equilibrium; the two known forces are *IA* and *AB*, 3000 and 500 lb, respectively, and *BJ* and *JI* are unknown. Begin by drawing, at some convenient scale, the sides of the force polygon *ia* and *ab* as shown in Fig. 2–28(*b*). The next

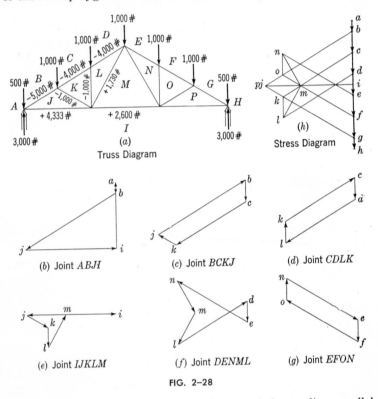

(*a*)
Truss Diagram

(*h*)
Stress Diagram

(*b*) Joint *ABJI*   (*c*) Joint *BCKJ*   (*d*) Joint *CDLK*

(*e*) Joint *IJKLM*   (*f*) Joint *DENML*   (*g*) Joint *EFON*

FIG. 2–28

force in order is *BJ*; therefore, through point *b* draw a line parallel to *BJ*. Point *j* will be somewhere on this line. The next force is *JI*; through point *i* draw a line parallel to *JI*. Since point *j* is on this line, as well as on the line through *b* parallel to *BJ*, it must be at their point of intersection. Thus Fig. 2–28(*b*) is the force polygon for the concurrent forces at joint *ABJI*, and we have established the magnitudes of the stresses in the members *BJ* and *JI*.

The joint *JKLMI* consists of five concurrent forces of which only one, IJ, is known. These data are insufficient for constructing the force polygon. *At any joint we can draw the force polygon provided that there are not more than two unknowns.*

Now consider joint $BCKJ$. We have already determined JB in Fig. 2–28(b), and we know that BC is 1000 lb. Thus we know two of the forces, and only two forces, CK and KJ, are unknown. Therefore, we know that we can draw a force polygon for the forces at this joint. Begin by drawing jb and bc, the two known sides of the force polygon, as shown in Fig. 2–28(c). The next force is CK; therefore, we draw a line through point c parallel to member CK. Point k will be on this line. The next force is KJ; hence through point j we draw a line parallel to KJ. Point k will be on this line, and, consequently, it will be at the point where this line intersects the line through c parallel to CK. The force polygon now completed is $jbck$, and we have determined two more forces, CK and KJ.

In a similar manner the remaining joints are taken in the following sequence: $CDLK$, $IJKLM$, $DENML$, and $EFON$. See Figs. 2–28(d), (e), (f), and (g). The stresses in the members on the right-hand side of the truss are, of course, similar to those on the left.

The construction of separate force polygons for the forces at each joint is a tedious procedure. The method to employ is to construct a single diagram that combines all the separate force polygons. Such a diagram is called a *stress diagram*, for it establishes the stresses (resisting forces) in the members of the truss.

To draw a stress diagram we begin by drawing the force polygon of the external forces. For the truss and loads shown in Fig. 2–28(a) this diagram consists of the known forces, the loads and reactions. The force polygon is shown in Fig. 2–28(h); it is ab, bc, cd, de, ef, fg, gh, hi, and ia. Now we begin at some point at which there are not more than two unknowns and draw the force polygon in conjunction with the force polygon of external forces previously drawn. First take the joint $ABJI$ and construct the polygon $abji$ as shown in Fig. 2–28(h). Note that this is exactly the polygon shown in Fig. 2–28(b). The remaining joints are taken as described, and the complete stress diagram for the truss is shown in Fig. 2–28(h).

The magnitudes of the stresses (resisting forces) in the various members of the truss are found by scaling the lengths of the lines in the stress diagrams; they are shown on the members in Fig. 2–28(*a*). The length of a member of a truss is not an indication of the magnitude of the stress in the member. The lengths of the lines *in the stress diagram*, however, do determine the magnitude of the stresses in the truss members.

2–27. Character of Stresses in Truss Members. The discussion of the construction of a stress diagram in the preceding article explained the method of finding the *magnitude* of stresses in truss members. If we wish to design the truss, it is equally important that the *character* of the stress as well as the magnitude be determined. By character of stress we mean its type, *compression* or *tension.* Having drawn the stress diagram, we may use the following steps to determine the character of stress in the members.

Step 1. In the truss diagram select any joint, called the *reference joint,* and identify a member by its two letters. Care must be taken * to read the member (about the reference joint) in a clockwise or counterclockwise manner, the same manner that was used in drawing the force polygon of external forces in the stress diagram.

Step 2. Now refer to the stress diagram and read the member in the same sequence used in identifying it in Step 1. Note its *direction* in accordance with this sequence, such as downward, upward to the right, to the left, etc.

Step 3. Return now to the truss diagram and consider the member and the *direction* found in Step 2 *with respect to the reference joint selected in Step 1.* If the direction is *toward* the reference joint, the force is *compressive;* if the direction is *away* from the reference joint, the force is a *tensile* force.

To illustrate this procedure, let us determine the character of the stress in the member of the upper chord adjacent to the left support shown in Fig. 2–28(*a*).

---

* The sequence of letters in identifying a member is most important. As an example, consider the vertical truss member that frames into the joint *CDLK* in the truss shown in Fig. 2–28(*a*). (The forces were read in a *clockwise* manner in drawing the stress diagram for this truss.) This vertical member is read *LK* if the reference joint is *CDLK*, but, if the reference joint is *JKLMI*, the same member is read *KL*. Be sure that you understand this before you continue.

Step 1. This member is identified as *BJ* (not *JB*) with respect to the reference joint *ABJI*. Note the sequence, the letter *B* coming before the letter *J*.

Step 2. Turning to the stress diagram, Fig. 2–28(*h*), we find that this force *bj* (read in the same sequence) reads downward to the left.

Step 3. Returning to the truss diagram, Fig. 2–28(*a*), and reading the member *BJ downward to the left* (the direction found in Step 2), we read *toward the reference joint ABJI*, and, therefore, the member is in compression.

Let us try again, testing the same member with respect to another reference joint.

Step 1. Consider the member *JB* with respect to the reference joint *BCKJ*.

Step 2. In the stress diagram this force *jb* reads *upward to the right*.

Step 3. Returning to the stress diagram, we find that, if *JB* has a direction *upward to the right*, we read *toward* the reference joint *BCKJ*, and, therefore, the stress is compressive. This is the same character of stress that was found in the member when the other reference joint was taken.

It is convenient to indicate the character of stress in a truss member by using plus (+) and minus (−) signs before the magnitude of the stress. The system employed in this text is to use the minus sign for compressive stresses and the plus sign for tensile stresses. In some books the plus sign is used for compression members and the minus sign if the stress is tensile. For the truss shown in Fig. 2–28(*a*) the character of stress, as well as the magnitudes, is shown on the truss members.

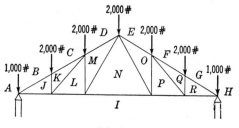

FIG. 2–29

Problem 2–27–A. The triangular Pratt truss shown in Fig. 2–29 has a span of 58 ft 0 in., and the upper chords make angles of 30° with the horizontal. The reactions are vertical. Draw the complete stress diagram for this truss and loading and determine the character and magnitudes of the stresses in the various truss members.

CHAPTER 3

FORCES ACTING ON BODIES

3–1. Free Body Diagram. A convenient way to determine the unknown forces acting on a body is to construct a *free body diagram*. The whole structure or any part of the structure may be taken as the free body. The usual procedure is to select an individual body (ignoring the adjoining parts) and to consider only the external forces acting on this particular body. This isolated

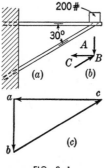

FIG. 3–1

object is known as a *free body*. The problems with which we are concerned deal with forces in equilibrium. Hence the forces are represented as vectors (graphically), and the force polygon of the forces acting on the free body must close; this fact enables us to determine the unknown forces.

Consider Fig. 3–1(*a*), which represents two members framing into a wall, the upper member being horizontal and the angle between them being 30°. A stone block weighing 200 lb is placed over the point at which the two members meet. Figure 3–1(*b*) is a diagram showing the block as a free body, the three forces being the vertical force of 200 lb (the weight of the block), the horizontal force exerted by the horizontal member, and the force acting at an angle of 30° to the horizontal. The system of identifying forces explained in Art. 2–14 is used; thus the forces acting on the free body are AB, the weight due to gravity, and the forces in the frame members, BC and CA.

To determine the stresses in the frame members, we need only to construct the force polygon of the concurrent forces. We begin by drawing the vector (force) ab, a downward vertical force of 200 lb, as shown in Fig. 3–1(c). Any convenient scale of so many pounds to the inch may be used. The next force in order is BC; therefore, through point b we draw a line parallel to the force BC. Point c is at some point on this line. Next is the force CA; hence we draw a line through point a parallel to the force CA. Point c is on this line and therefore is at the point of intersection with the line previously drawn through b parallel to BC. Figure 3–1(c), then, is the force polygon for the three forces acting on the block. By scaling the lengths of the lines in the force polygon, we find that $BC = 400$ lb and $CA = 346$ lb. This is a *graphical solution*, and for such solutions the accuracy in determining the stresses depends on the accuracy employed in constructing the diagram. Minute accuracy is neither necessary nor desirable, and graphical solutions are generally sufficiently accurate for practical purposes. Obviously, a problem similar to this, in which the forces are represented by triangles, may be solved by algebra or trigonometry. Such a solution is called *algebraic*. In this chapter all problems are solved by graphical methods.

The free body diagram shows only the forces acting on the isolated body. Stresses developed within the body do not affect its state of equilibrium. Note also that the stresses in the wall, the compression and tension that result from the forces in the frame members, do not affect the free body.

3–2. Two-Force Members. When a member is acted on by forces at only *two points*, the member is known as a two-force member. The resultant of all the forces at one point must be equal, opposite in direction, and have the same line of action as the resultant of the forces acting at the other point. The stress in a two-force member is either compressive or tensile. A vertical post with a load on its upper end is an illustration. If we ignore the weight of the post, the load on the top (due to gravity) is equal in magnitude to the upward reaction at the base of the post, opposite in direction, and has the same line of action. The stress within the post is *axial*.

In Fig. 3–1(a) each of the two members of the frame is a two-force member. Consider, for example, the horizontal member. The forces acting on the right-hand end are the vertical load of 200 lb and the compressive force from the lower frame member. From Fig. 3–1(c) it is seen that the *resultant* of these two forces is *ac*. The force *ac* is horizontal, and the reaction at the wall (the other force acting on this member) is also horizontal, equal to *ac* in magnitude, and with the same line of action.

A roof truss is a framed structure in which the members are framed together to form triangles. In determining the stresses in the truss members, it is customary to ignore the weights of the members, since they are small in comparison to the loads. Likewise, we assume that the members are not restrained at their ends; theoretically, they are joined together by pins. With these assumptions, the truss members are two-force members and resist either compressive or tensile forces.

3–3. Three-Force Members. When forces act at three points on a body, it is called a three-force member, and the stresses in the member are not axial.

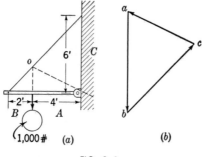

FIG. 3–2

Consider Fig. 3–2(a) in which a horizontal bar 6 ft 0 in. in length is pinned to a wall and its left-hand end is supported by a rod attached to the wall 6 ft 0 in. above the bar. At 4 ft 0 in. from the right end of the bar a load of 1000 lb is suspended.

The rod, which is subjected to tensile stresses, is a two-force member; therefore, its stress is axial, and the wall must offer a resisting tensile force having the same line of action as the force resisted by the rod. The horizontal bar is a three-force member being subjected to a force at each end and to a vertical load of 1000 lb at 2 ft 0 in. from the left end. The stresses in the bar are not axial; this member is subjected to forces that produce bending stresses which are discussed in Art. 11–1.

The frame is subjected to three external forces which are identified as AB, the vertical force of 1000 lb, BC, the force resisting the pull from the rod at the wall, and CA, the resisting thrust from the bar at the pinned end. Thus far the direction of the last resisting force is unknown. However, we know that the three external forces are in equilibrium, and, since they are not parallel, they must be concurrent. To find the point at which the three forces meet, extend upward the line of action of the vertical force of 1000 lb and note where it intersects the tie rod, point o. From this point draw a line to the pinned end of the bar and thus establish the direction of the thrust at the wall. The directions of all three external forces are now known.

To find the magnitudes of the two resisting forces, construct the force polygon. At a convenient scale draw ab, the vertical force of 1000 lb [Fig. 3–2(b)]. The next force is BC; therefore, through point b draw a line parallel to the rod BC. Next draw a line through point a parallel to the direction of the thrust at the pinned end of the bar. The intersection of this line with the line through b parallel to BC establishes point c, thus completing the force polygon. By scaling the length of the lines bc and ca, we find them to be 943 and 745 lb, respectively.

3–4. The Inclined Plane. When a body acts on another body having a perfectly smooth surface, the body having the smooth surface can exert only a perpendicular force to the contacting surfaces. If the surface on which the body acts is not a theoretically smooth surface, the surface may exert forces inclined to the contacting surfaces. *Friction* is the resistance to sliding between two contacting surfaces when the resistance is due to the nature of the surfaces and not to their shape or form.

Figure 3–3(a) represents an inclined plane making an angle of

25° with the horizontal. On the inclined plane is a block of stone weighing 500 lb. Let us assume that the block does not slide, that the friction between the block and the surface of the plane is sufficient to prevent motion. The two forces that hold the vertical force of 500 lb in equilibrium are the resisting pressure from the plane, whose direction is perpendicular to the plane, and the force parallel to the plane that is the result of friction.

A particle of the block is taken as a free body, and the three forces producing equilibrium are drawn as shown in Fig. 3–3(b).

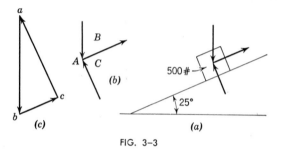

FIG. 3–3

These forces are identified as AB, the vertical force of 500 lb, BC, the frictional component, and CA, the normal component. The forces are concurrent; AB is known, but of BC and CA only the directions are known. As the forces are in equilibrium, their force polygon will close. To construct this polygon, draw, at any convenient scale, a vertical line ab having a length equivalent to 500 lb, as shown in Fig. 3–3(c). The next force is BC; therefore, through point b draw a line parallel to force BC. Next draw a line through point a parallel to force CA. Point c is at the intersection of these two lines, and the force polygon representing equilibrium is completed. By scaling the lengths of lines bc and ca in Fig. 3–3(c), we find BC, the force due to friction, to be 211 lb, and CA, the normal pressure on the inclined plane, to be 453 lb.

3–5. Forces Exerted by Spheres. Figure 3–4(a) indicates a sphere weighing 400 lb which rests in a trough composed of two flat *smooth* surfaces. The surfaces of the trough make angles of 45 and 30° with the horizontal as shown. What forces are exerted on the sides of the trough by the sphere?

Since by data the surfaces of the trough are smooth, the sphere can exert only perpendicular forces to the surfaces of the trough. These resisting forces are shown in Fig. 3–4(a); their lines of action must pass through the center of the sphere. Now that their *directions* are known, their magnitudes are readily found. Figure 3–4(b) is a free body diagram of the forces acting on the sphere. *AB* is 400 lb, the weight of the sphere, and *BC* and *CA* are the resisting forces which hold it in equilibrium. The force polygon

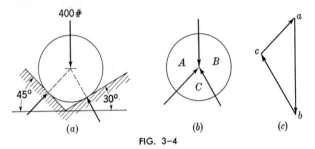

FIG. 3–4

abc, Fig. 3–4(c), is constructed as previously described, and, by scaling the lengths of the lines *BC* and *CA*, the resisting forces exerted by the surfaces of the trough are found to be 295 and 205 lb, respectively.

Example. Two spheres of unequal size, whose radii are 9 and 6 in., rest in a trough having smooth sides as shown in Fig. 3–5(a). If the larger sphere weighs 400 lb and the smaller sphere weighs 250 lb, what pressures are exerted at points *P*, *Q*, *R*, and *S*?

SOLUTION. A free body diagram of the smaller sphere is drawn as indicated in Fig. 3–5(b), the pressure at point *P* having its line of action perpendicular to the side of the trough and passing through the center of the sphere; the line of action of the force exerted on the larger sphere coincides with the line connecting the centers of the two spheres. The three forces are identified as *AB*, *BC*, and *CA*, *AB* being a vertical force of 250 lb; *BC* and *CA* are of unknown magnitudes. These three concurrent forces are in equilibrium; hence their force polygon will close. We begin by drawing force *ab* at a convenient scale as shown in Fig. 3–5(c). The lines *bc* and *ca* are now constructed as previously explained, and, by scaling, their lengths are found to be 273 and 260 lb, respectively.

Figure 3–5(d) is the free body diagram of the larger sphere. The force EA is 400 lb, the weight of the sphere; AC is 260 lb, the thrust from the smaller sphere; CD and DE are the resisting forces at points Q and R. Of these four forces, EA and AC are known; of CD and DE, only their directions are established. To draw the

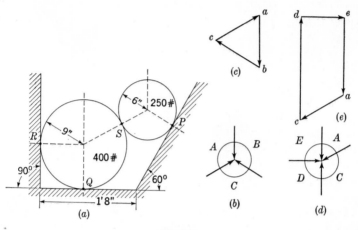

FIG. 3–5

force polygon, we draw ea and ac and finally cd and de [Fig. 3–5(e)]. By scaling the lengths of the sides of the polygon, cd is found to be 515 lb and de, 235 lb. Thus the pressures exerted at points P, Q, R, and S are 273, 515, 235, and 260 lb, respectively.

3–6. Force Required to Produce Motion. A wheel 12 in. in diameter weighs 400 lb. Determine the magnitude of the horizontal force, shown in Fig. 3–6(a), required to start the wheel over the block 3 in. in height.

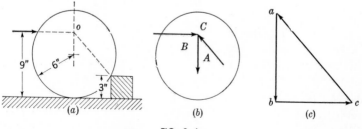

FIG. 3–6

The force necessary to produce motion must be a force slightly greater in magnitude than the force required for equilibrium. The free body diagram is drawn as shown in Fig. 3–6(b), the three forces being the vertical force of 400 lb acting through the center of the wheel, the horizontal force whose line of action intersects the vertical force at point o, and the force whose line of action passes through point o and the point of contact of the wheel and the block. These forces are identified as AB, BC, and CA. The line of action of the last force is established because three non-parallel forces in equilibrium must be concurrent; that is, they must have a point in common. To draw the force polygon, begin by laying off at a suitable scale the vertical force ab, 400 lb, as shown in Fig. 3–6(c). Then draw a line through b parallel to BC and a line through a parallel to CA. Their intersection determines the point c, and, by scaling, we find the horizontal force BC to be 330 lb. A force in excess of 330 lb is required to start the wheel over the block.

Example. The pier of masonry shown in Fig. 3–7(a) weighs 10,000 lb. Determine the magnitude of the horizontal force applied at the upper left side that will be required to turn over the pier.

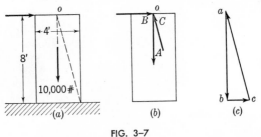

FIG. 3–7

SOLUTION. The free body diagram, Fig. 3–7(b), shows the three forces acting on the pier—AB, the vertical force of 10,000 lb; BC, the horizontal force of unknown magnitude whose line of action intersects the force AB at point o; and CA, the equilibrant of AB and BC, whose line of action passes through point o and the lower right-hand corner of the pier about which the pier will overturn. The line of action of CA is determined by the knowledge that three forces that are in equilibrium and not parallel must have a point in common. Since the lines of action of the three forces are known, and also the magnitude of one of the forces, the force polygon is constructed [Fig. 3–7(c)]. By scaling, the horizontal force is found to be 2500 lb. Since these three forces are in equilibrium, a horizontal force exceeding 2500 lb in magnitude will disturb equilibrium and cause the pier to turn over.

Problem 3–6–A. In the structure shown in Fig. 3–8(a) a weight of 350 lb is suspended from the end of the horizontal strut. Determine the magnitudes of the stresses in the strut and the tie rod.

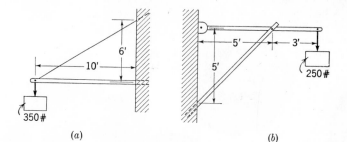

(a)   (b)

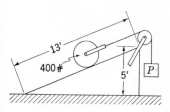

(c)   (d)

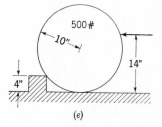

(e)

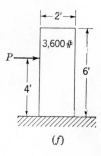

(f)

FIG. 3–8

Problem 3–6–B. A horizontal bar is hinged at the wall and braced by the diagonal strut as shown in Fig. 3–8(b). For a load of 250 lb hung from the end of the bar determine the magnitudes of the stress in the strut and the reaction at the hinged joint of the bar.

Problem 3–6–C. A roller weighing 400 lb rests on a smooth inclined plane having the dimensions shown in Fig. 3–8(c). Determine the magnitude of the load P required to prevent the roller from moving.

Problem 3–6–D. Two cylinders of equal size, weighing 350 and 150 lb, respectively, rest in the trough shown in Fig. 3–8(d). Determine the pressures at points A, B, C, and D.

Problem 3–6–E. A cylinder with a diameter of 20 in. weighs 500 lb. What horizontal force P will be required to start the cylinder over the block shown in Fig. 3–8(e)?

Problem 3–6–F. The pier of masonry indicated in Fig. 3–8(f) weighs 3600 lb. If the horizontal force P is 800 lb, will the pier turn over? What magnitude of force would be required to cause overturning?

MOMENTS OF FORCES

4–1. Moment of a Force. The term *moment of a force* is commonly used in engineering problems. *A moment is the tendency of a force to cause rotation about a given point or axis.* The magnitude of the moment of a force about a given point or axis is the magnitude of the force (pounds, tons, etc.) multiplied by the perpendicular distance (inches, feet, etc.) between the line of action of the force and the given point or axis. The product of multiplying pounds by feet is neither pounds nor feet, it is their combination, foot-pounds. The point or axis about which the force tends to cause turning is called the *center of moments.* The perpendicular distance between the line of action of the force and the center of moments is called the *lever arm* or *moment arm.* Thus

moment of force = magnitude of force × moment arm

Consider the horizontal force of 100 lb shown in Fig. 4–1. If point *A* is the center of moments, the lever arm of the force is

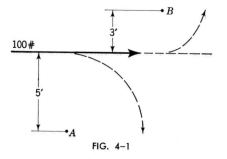

FIG. 4–1

5 ft 0 in. Then the moment of the 100-lb force with respect to point *A* is 100 × 5, or 500 ft-lb. In this illustration the force tends to cause a *clockwise* rotation (shown by the dotted arrow) about

point A and is called a positive moment. Since 1 ft 0 in. = 12 in., we may multiply 500 ft-lb by 12; the product is 6000 in-lb, a moment of the same magnitude.

In the same figure the 100-lb force has a lever arm of 3 ft 0 in. with respect to point B. Therefore, the moment of the 100-lb force about point B is 100 × 3, or 300 ft-lb, which equals 3600 in-lb. With respect to point B, the force tends to cause *counterclockwise* rotation; we call it a negative moment.

It is important to remember that in considering the moment of a force we must have definitely in mind the specific point or axis about which the force tends to cause rotation. Later in this book we shall write *equations of moments* in which more than one moment is considered. In such an equation we must be certain that *the same center of moments* is taken for all the various moments.

4–2. Increasing Moments. A moment may be increased by increasing the magnitude of the force or by increasing the length of the lever arm.

Figure 4–2 represents a wrench used to turn nuts on bolts. Assume that a nut is screwed up tight. A vertical force of 50 lb is

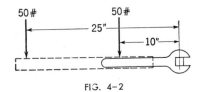

FIG. 4–2

exerted 10 in. from the center of the bolt, thus producing a moment of 50 × 10, or 500 in-lb. It is found that this moment is insufficient to produce motion. A length of pipe is fitted over the handle of the wrench so that the lever arm is increased to 25 in. With the same force of 50 lb, the moment is now 50 × 25, or 1250 in-lb, and motion results. Thus the moment has been increased by increasing the length of the lever arm.

Suppose that we are asked to determine the magnitude of the force necessary to produce motion if the lever arm remains 10 in. Let us call the unknown force P pounds. It was found that the moment required to produce motion was 1250 in-lb. Then

$$P \times 10 = 1250 \quad \text{and} \quad P = 125 \text{ lb}$$

the force required to produce motion if the lever arm is 10 in. in length.

4–3. Moment of a Mechanical Couple. In Art. 2–18 we learned that a *mechanical couple* consists of two parallel forces equal in magnitude, opposite in direction, and not having the same line of action. A mechanical couple is shown in Fig. 4–3; the two equal forces are P_1 and P_2, and the perpendicular distance between their lines of action is x feet.

If we take point a, any point on the line of action of P_2, as the center of moments, the sum of the moments of the two forces

FIG. 4–3

about this point is $(P_1 \times x) + (P_2 \times 0)$, which, of course, equals $P_1 \times x$. The moment of P_2 about point a is $(P_2 \times 0)$ because the lever arm is zero. Therefore, the *moment of a couple* is the product of one of the forces and the perpendicular distance between their lines of action.

A mechanical couple produces motion of rotation; it can be held in equilibrium only by the addition of another mechanical couple. The direction of rotation for the couple shown in Fig. 4–3 is counterclockwise.

4–4. Moments of Forces on a Beam. *If a body acted upon by a number of forces in one plane is in equilibrium, the sum of the moments of all the forces about any point in the plane equals zero.* This law of equilibrium may be stated thus:

$$\Sigma M = 0$$

in which Σ is the Greek letter *sigma* and represents the "algebraic sum of." This law may also be stated thus: the sum of the moments of all the forces that tend to produce clockwise rotation minus the sum of the moments of all the forces that tend to produce counterclockwise rotation is zero. Or, briefly,

sum of positive moments = sum of negative moments

This law of equilibrium is of great importance, and it finds frequent practical application.

Figure 4–4(*a*) indicates a beam 20 ft 0 in. in length acted upon by four vertical forces whose magnitudes, directions, and lines of action are shown. These four forces are in equilibrium, and, in

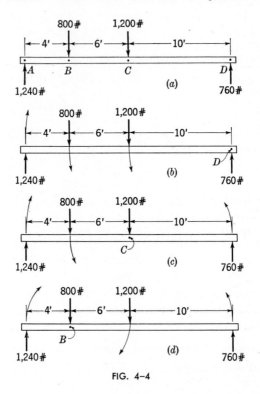

FIG. 4–4

accordance with the above law, the sum of the positive moments, with respect to any point or axis, is equal to the sum of the negative moments with respect to the same point or axis. Let us begin by selecting the point *D* as the center of moments. The only force tending to cause clockwise rotation about point *D* is 1240 lb, and its moment is (1240 × 20). Refer to Fig. 4–4(*b*) and note the directions of the arrows. The moments of the forces that tend to produce counterclockwise rotation *about the same point D* are (800 × 16) and (1200 × 10). Therefore,

$(1240 \times 20) = (800 \times 16) + (1200 \times 10)$ See Fig. 4–4(b).

24,800 ft-lb = 24,800 ft-lb

If, in writing the equation of moments, we say $\Sigma M = 0$, then $(1240 \times 20) - [(800 \times 16) + (1200 \times 10)] = 0$; but this, in effect, is exactly what is written above.

Perhaps you may wonder why the 760-lb force is not considered in the above equation of moments. The force of 760 lb has a lever arm of 0 ft with respect to point D. We know that $(760 \times 0) = 0$; hence it is omitted in writing the equation of moments. Therefore, in the future, when writing an equation of moments, any force or forces whose lines of action pass through the center of moments will have a lever arm of zero and will need no further consideration since they will have a zero moment.

Again, let us write an equation of moments with point C as the center of moments. Then

$(1240 \times 10) = (800 \times 6) + (760 \times 10)$ See Fig. 4–4(c).

12,400 ft-lb = 12,400 ft-lb

With point B as the center of moments,

$(1240 \times 4) + (1200 \times 6) = (760 \times 16)$ See Fig. 4–4(d).

12,160 ft-lb = 12,160 ft-lb

Problems 4–4–A–B–C–D–E. The five vertical forces on the beam shown in Fig. 4–5 are in equilibrium. Write the equations of moments with the center of moments at points A, B, C, D, and E.

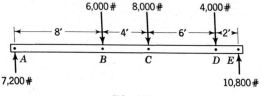

FIG. 4–5

4–5. Basic Laws of Equilibrium. *If a body acted upon by a number of forces in one plane is in equilibrium, the sum of all the horizontal components of all the forces equals zero, the sum of all the vertical components of all the forces equals zero, and the sum of the moments*

of all the forces about any axis equals zero. The three fundamental equations are

$$\Sigma H = 0$$

$$\Sigma V = 0$$

$$\Sigma M = 0$$

The law of moments, $\Sigma M = 0$, was discussed in Art. 4–4.

If the horizontal forces acting toward the right are considered positive and those to the left are considered negative, their algebraic sum equals zero, $\Sigma H = 0$, or *the sum of the horizontal forces acting to the right equals the sum of the horizontal forces acting to the left.*

Similarly, $\Sigma V = 0$, another way of saying that *the sum of the downward forces equals the sum of the upward forces.* For beam problems, in which both the loads and reactions are vertical, the sum of the loads equals the sum of the reactions.

Most of the preceding problems in this text have been solved graphically by the construction of diagrams. The accuracy of the results obtained by such methods depends on the accuracy employed in constructing the diagrams and reading the scales. These problems may be solved by mathematics also, trigonometry frequently being of great assistance but not always necessary.

Figure 4–6 represents a body acted upon by six forces, some being vertical and some horizontal. This system of forces is in equilib-

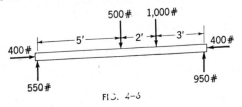

FIG. 4–6

rium, and therefore the three laws of equilibrium must apply. Let us see.

$\Sigma H = 0$ or $400 - 400 = 0$ or $400 \text{ lb} = 400 \text{ lb}$

$\Sigma V = 0$ or $(500 + 1000) - (550 + 950) = 0$ or $1500 \text{ lb} = 1500 \text{ lb}$

To test the third law, $\Sigma M = 0$, take for the center of moments the point at which the 950- and 400-lb forces intersect. Then

$$(550 \times 10) - [(500 \times 5) + (1000 \times 3)] = 0$$

$$(550 \times 10) = (500 \times 5) + (1000 \times 3)$$

$$5500 \text{ ft-lb} = 5500 \text{ ft-lb}$$

In writing the foregoing equation of moments, the horizontal forces of 400 lb each are ignored because their lever arms, about the center of moments selected, are zero, hence their moments are also zero.

For problems of this type, in which certain forces are not vertical or horizontal, it is frequently advantageous to represent the forces by their vertical and horizontal components. The first of the following examples is an illustration.

Example. Figure 4–7(a) shows a bar 10 ft 0 in. in length hinged at the wall at the left support with a roller bearing at the right

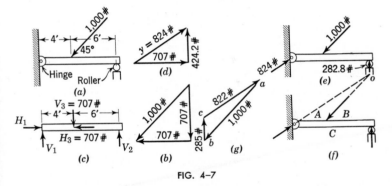

FIG. 4–7

support. A force of 1000 lb at an angle of 45° acts on the bar at 4 ft 0 in. from the left support. Let it be required to determine, by the use of mathematics, the magnitudes of the two reactions (supports).

SOLUTION. If we assume that the roller is frictionless, the right support must be a vertical force. The direction of the left support is not yet known.

First let us find the horizontal and vertical components of the 1000-lb force. Since this force makes an angle of 45° with the horizontal, the two components will be equal; let us call them x pounds each. We know that, for a right triangle, the square of the hypotenuse is equal to the sum of the squares of the other two sides. Thus we may write

$$1000^2 = x^2 + x^2$$

$$2x^2 = 1000^2$$

$$x^2 = 500,000$$

$$x = 707 \text{ lb} \qquad \text{See Fig. 4–7}(b).$$

Now we can draw the free body diagram, Fig. 4–7(c), representing the 1000-lb force by H_3 and V_3, its horizontal and vertical components, the left support by H_1 and V_1, its horizontal and vertical components; the right support is simply V_2, a vertical force.

Applying the law of equilibrium, $\Sigma M = 0$, and writing an equation of moments about the left support as the center of moments,

$$(V_3 \times 4) - (V_2 \times 10) = 0$$

$$4 \times V_3 = 10 \times V_2 \quad \text{or} \quad 4 \times 707 = 10 \times V_2$$

and

$$V_2 = 282.8 \text{ lb, the magnitude of the right reaction}$$

Next

$$\Sigma V = 0$$

$$V_1 + V_2 = V_3$$

$$V_1 + 282.8 = 707$$

$$V_1 = 424.2 \text{ lb, the vertical component of the left support}$$

The magnitude of V_1 might have been found by writing an equation about V_2 as the center of moments; thus

$$V_1 \times 10 = 707 \times 6$$

$$V_1 = 424.2 \text{ lb}$$

Again,

$$\Sigma H = 0$$

$$H_1 - H_3 = 0$$

$$H_1 - 707 = 0$$

$$H_1 = 707 \text{ lb}$$

We have found the horizontal and vertical components of the left support to be 707 and 424.2 lb, respectively. Again applying the theorem of squares, see Fig. 4–7(d), as we did in solving V_3 and H_3, and calling the hypotenuse y,

$$424.2^2 + 707^2 = y^2$$

$$679,794 = y^2$$

$$y = 824 \text{ lb, approximately}$$

the magnitude of the left reaction. Use of a protractor shows that this support makes an angle of about 31° with the horizontal. See Fig. 4–7(e).

Example. For the bar and load shown in Fig. 4–7(a) determine the two reactions by graphical methods.

SOLUTION. The bar is again drawn as shown in Fig. 4–7(f). The three forces consist of the load and the two reactions. Since they are not parallel and are in equilibrium, their lines of action must intersect at a common point. Therefore, the lines of action of the 1000-lb load and right support are extended until they meet at point o. From this point of intersection a line is drawn to the left support, thus determining the *direction* of the left support.

To draw the force polygon, first draw to scale ab, the 1000-lb load [Fig. 4–7(g)]. From point b draw a line parallel to BC, and from point a draw a line parallel to CA. Point c will be at the intersection of these two lines; thus the force polygon is completed. By scaling, bc is 285 lb and ca is 822 lb.

Although the results obtained by the graphical method are not so accurate as the results obtained by mathematics, they are generally sufficiently accurate for practical purposes and frequently require less time.

4–6. Reactions Found by Moments. For beams that are not symmetrically loaded, beams for which the reactions are of unequal magnitudes, the design of the beam requires that the magnitudes of the reactions be determined. Article 2–22 explained how the reactions may be determined graphically, and now it will be shown how readily (and accurately) they may be computed by mathematics. The key to this method of computing reactions is that law of equilibrium, given in Art. 4–5, which states that the sum of the moments of the forces that tend to produce clockwise rotation about any axis is equal to the sum of the moments of the forces that tend to produce counterclockwise rotation about the same axis.

Example. Figure 4–8 shows a simple beam on which there are two concentrated loads of unequal magnitudes. Compute the reactions, R_1 and R_2, by mathematics.

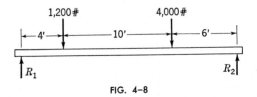

FIG. 4–8

SOLUTION. We begin by selecting a point on the line of action of R_2 as the center of moments and write an equation of moments of all the forces acting on the beam, positive moments on one side of the equation and negative moments on the other.

The force tending to produce clockwise rotation about R_2 is the force R_1. Since it has a lever arm of 20 ft 0 in., its moment is $20 \times R_1$. The two concentrated loads, 1200 and 4000 lb, tend to produce counterclockwise rotation about R_2, and their lever arms are 16 ft 0 in. and 6 ft 0 in., respectively; hence their moments are (1200×16) and (4000×6). We may write

$$20 \times R_1 = (1200 \times 16) + (4000 \times 6)$$

$$20 \times R_1 = 43,200$$

$$R_1 = 2160 \text{ lb}$$

But why is the force R_2 not shown in the above equations? Remember that the center of moments was a point on the line of action of the force R_2. Therefore, the force R_2 has a lever arm of zero and $R_2 \times 0 = 0$. Thus we see that the moment of R_2 is zero, and it may be omitted in writing this equation of moments.

In writing an equation of moments *be particular to see that the moments of the forces are all taken about the same center of moments.*

Carelessness in this respect will result in errors. In the above equation the center of moments was R_2.

To find the magnitude of R_2 we select a point on the line of action of R_1 as the center of moments. Thus we write

$$20 \times R_2 = (1200 \times 4) + (4000 \times 14)$$

$$20 \times R_2 = 60{,}800$$

$$R_2 = 3040 \text{ lb}$$

In the design of beams it is important that no error be made in determining the magnitudes of the reactions. To check their accuracy is a simple matter. One of the laws of equilibrium states, in effect, that the sum of the downward vertical forces equals the sum of the upward vertical forces. In other words, the sum of the loads equals the sum of the reactions. In this example the loads are 1200 and 4000 lb and the reactions, just found, are 2160 and 3040 lb. Thus we write

$$1200 + 4000 = 2160 + 3040$$

$$5200 \text{ lb} = 5200 \text{ lb}$$

showing that the magnitudes of R_1 and R_2 were computed correctly.

Example. Compute the magnitudes of the reactions of the simple beam shown in Fig. 4–9(a), the loads consisting of a concentrated load of 4000 lb and a uniformly distributed load of 1000 lb per lin ft extending over a length of 12 ft 0 in.

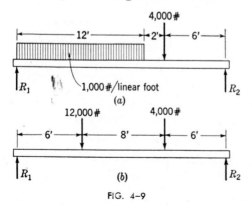

FIG. 4–9

SOLUTION. The reactions of a beam subjected to a uniformly distributed load are similar to the reactions of a beam having a concentrated load of the same magnitude which acts at the center of gravity of the distributed load. See Fig. 4–9(b).

First let us take R_2 as the center of moments. The distributed load of (12×1000) lb has its center of gravity at 14 ft 0 in. from R_2. Then

$$20 \times R_1 = (1000 \times 12 \times 14) + (4000 \times 6)$$
$$20 \times R_1 = 192,000$$
$$R_1 = 9600 \text{ lb}$$

Next take R_1 as the center of moments, noting that the center of gravity of the distributed load is 6 ft 0 in. from R_1. Then

$$20 \times R_2 = (1000 \times 12 \times 6) + (4000 \times 14)$$
$$20 \times R_2 = 128,000$$
$$R_2 = 6400 \text{ lb}$$

Check:

$$(1000 \times 12) + 4000 = 9600 + 6400$$
$$16,000 \text{ lb} = 16,000 \text{ lb}$$

Note that the reactions for the beams and loadings shown in Figs. 4–9(a) and (b) are identical.

Example. Compute the reactions for the overhanging beam shown in Fig. 4–10(a).

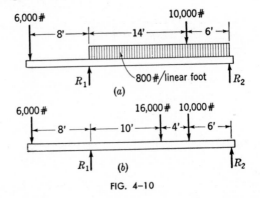

FIG. 4–10

SOLUTION. We first write an equation of moments, taking R_2 as the center of moments. Note that the distributed load of 16,000 lb has its center of gravity at 10 ft 0 in. from R_2 and 10 ft 0 in. from R_1.

$$20R_1 = (6000 \times 28) + (20 \times 800 \times 10) + (10,000 \times 6)$$

$$20R_1 = 388,000$$

$$R_1 = 19,400 \text{ lb}$$

With R_1 as the center of moments, the forces R_2 and the 6000-lb load tend to produce counterclockwise rotation, whereas the distributed load and the 10,000-lb load tend to cause clockwise rotation. Then

$$(20 \times R_2) + (6000 \times 8) = (20 \times 800 \times 10) + (10,000 \times 14)$$

$$20R_2 = 160,000 + 140,000 - 48,000$$

$$20R_2 = 252,000$$

$$R_2 = 12,600 \text{ lb}$$

Check:

$$19,400 + 12,600 = 6000 + 16,000 + 10,000$$

$$32,000 \text{ lb} = 32,000 \text{ lb}$$

The *reactions* for the beams and loads shown in Figs. 4–10(a) and (b) are identical, but, as we explain later, the two types of loadings shown in the figures do not produce bending stresses of the same magnitudes. As an example, consider a simple beam 16 ft 0 in. between supports with a uniformly distributed load of 6400 lb. The reactions for this beam are each 3200 lb. A beam having the same span with a concentrated load of 6400 lb at the center of the span also has reactions of 3200 lb each, but the bending stresses resulting from the concentrated load are greater than for a load of the same magnitude uniformly distributed.

Problem 4–6–A–B–C–D. Compute, by the principle of moments, the magnitudes of the reactions for the beams and loads as shown in Figs. 2–22(a), (b), (c), and (d).

Problem 4–6–E–F–G–H. Compute the magnitudes of the reactions for the beams and loads as shown in Figs. 4–11(a), (b), (c), and (d).

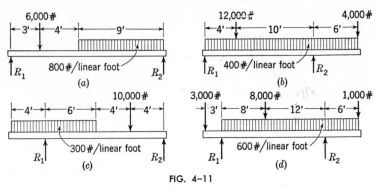

FIG. 4–11

4–7. Relation of Reactions to Loads. A simple beam with a single concentrated load is a condition that occurs very frequently. The magnitudes of the reactions may be computed by moments, of course, but there is a certain relation between the load and the reactions that permits us to determine their magnitudes even more quickly.

Consider Fig. 4–12, in which we have a simple beam with a concentrated load P at a distance from R_1 and b distance from R_2;

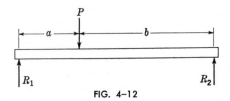

FIG. 4–12

that is, the span is divided into two segments, a and b. Obviously, since P is closer to R_1 than to R_2, R_1 will be greater than R_2. For such a beam *the greater reaction equals the load multiplied by the greater segment divided by the span length.* For the letters shown in Fig. 4–12, $R_1 = P \times \dfrac{b}{a+b}$. This is readily shown by writing an equation of moments about R_2. Thus

$$R_1 \times (a + b) = P \times b \quad \text{and} \quad R_1 = P \times \frac{b}{a+b}$$

Suppose that the load is 800 lb and that it is placed at 4 ft 0 in. from R_1 and 6 ft 0 in. from R_2. Then, applying the rule,

$$R_1 = 800 \times \frac{6}{10} \quad \text{and} \quad R_1 = 480 \text{ lb}$$

It is equally true that the smaller reaction equals the load multiplied by the smaller segment divided by the span. Thus

$$R_2 = 800 \times \frac{4}{10} \quad \text{and} \quad R_2 = 320 \text{ lb}$$

Example. A simple beam having a span of 20 ft 0 in. has a concentrated load of 1000 lb at 12 ft 0 in. from R_1. What are the magnitudes of the reactions?

SOLUTION.

$$R_2 = 1000 \times \frac{12}{20} = 600 \text{ lb}$$

$$R_1 = 1000 \times \frac{8}{20} = 400 \text{ lb}$$

The relation between the reactions and the segments may be stated in several different ways, but the rule given above is as convenient as any and affords a quick method of determining reactions.

4–8. Forces Found by Moments. The principle of moments is employed constantly in everyday problems, and its use enables us to determine the magnitude of unknown forces. For many of the illustrative beam problems previously given the weight of the beam has been ignored; this was done purposely to simplify the explanations. Actually, the weight of the beam constitutes a uniformly distributed load and, with respect to the reactions, is considered to act at its center of gravity. In the following examples the weights of the members as well as the resistance due to friction is purposely omitted.

Example. A safety valve and lever are indicated in Fig. 4–13(a). What pressure would be required to open the valve if the suspended weight were 60 lb?

SOLUTION. Taking the hinge as the center of moments, we may write

$$60 \times 30 = \text{pressure} \times 4$$

$$\text{pressure} = 450 \text{ lb}$$

If the weight of the lever arm and friction were ignored, a valve pressure of 450 lb would balance the 60-lb weight. Theoretically, any pressure in excess of 450 lb would cause the valve to open.

Example. An I-beam 20 ft in length and weighing 80 lb per lin ft rests on rollers placed in the positions shown in Fig. 4–13(b). Compute the pressures of the rollers on the supporting soil.

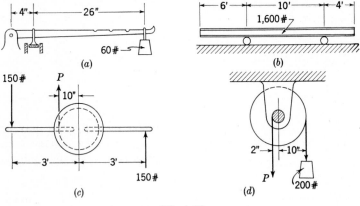

FIG. 4–13

SOLUTION. Calling the left roller R_1 and the right roller R_2, we may write an equation of moments, taking the right roller as the center of moments. Note that the center of gravity of the beam lies 6 ft from R_2 and 4 ft from R_1. Thus

$$R_1 \times 10 = 20 \times 80 \times 6$$

$$R_1 = 960 \text{ lb}$$

$$R_1 + R_2 = 20 \times 80$$

Since $R_1 = 960$,

$$960 + R_2 = 1600$$

$$R_2 = 640 \text{ lb}$$

Example. Figure 4–13(c) indicates a capstan in plan. If two men exert forces of 150 lb each at the positions shown, what tensile force, P, will be exerted in the rope?

SOLUTION. Note that in the diagram the dimensions are given in both feet and inches. *In writing an equation of moments, be careful to have all the moments of the same denomination.* Taking the center of the capstan as the center of moments, we write

$$(150 \times 36) + (150 \times 36) = P \times 10$$

$$P = 1080 \text{ lb}$$

The two forces of 150 lb each constitute a mechanical couple. In Art. 4–3 we found that the moment of a couple is the magnitude of one of the forces multiplied by the normal distance between their lines of action. In this instance the moment of the couple is 72×150, or 10,800 in-lb, and the moment of the force P is $(10 \times P)$ in-lb. Thus we might have said

$$72 \times 150 = 10 \times P \quad \text{and} \quad P = 1080 \text{ lb}$$

Example. A wheel and axle are indicated in Fig. 4–13(d). Compute the magnitude of the force P that will balance the force of 200 lb.

SOLUTION. With the center of the axle as the center of moments, we may write

$$P \times 2 = 200 \times 10$$

$$P = 1000 \text{ lb}$$

Theoretically, the force of 200 lb will hold the 1000-lb force in equilibrium and will raise any force of a smaller magnitude.

Problem 4–8–A. A lever bar is 5 ft 0 in. in length and has a fulcrum (support) 6 in. to the right from a weight to be lifted. The weight is at the left end of the bar. If the weight is 1000 lb, what is the magnitude of the downward force at the right end of the lever that will be required to lift the weight?

Problem 4–8–B. A steel beam 16 ft 0 in. in length and weighing 230 lb per lin ft is suspended by two cables. One cable is 2 ft 0 in. from one end of the beam and the other cable is 4 ft 6 in. from the other end. Compute the magnitude of the stresses in the cables.

Problem 4–8–C. A beam 10 ft 0 in. in length has a concentrated load of 600 lb at 2 ft 0 in. from one end. Compute, by mental arithmetic, the magnitude of the reactions. See Art. 4–7.

Problem 4–8–D. A beam 12 ft 0 in. in length and weighing 200 lb per lin ft has a vertical concentrated load of 100 lb at one end. Compute the distance from the concentrated load at which a single support can be placed to balance the beam and load.

Problem 4–8–E. Assume that the 60-lb weight in Fig. 4–13(a) is 2 ft 8 in. from the valve instead of 26 in. What pressure would be required to open the valve?

Problem 4–8–F. For the beam shown in Fig. 4–13(b) compute the magnitude of the reactions if the left roller is moved to the left end of the beam.

Problem 4–8–G. For the beam shown in Fig. 4–13(b) compute the magnitude of the reactions if the right roller is placed at 10 ft 0 in. from the right end of the beam.

Problem 4–8–H. Figure 4–13(c) indicates a capstan; what should the magnitudes be of the two equal forces to hold the force P, 1800 lb, in equilibrium?

Problem 4–8–I. For the wheel and axle shown in Fig. 4–13(d) what weight should be applied to raise a 1200-lb load at P if the diameter of the wheel is 25 in. instead of 20 in.?

Problem 4–8–J. A beam is 8 ft in length and weighs 120 lb per lin ft. There are three concentrated loads of 100, 200, and 300 lb placed at 2 ft 0 in., 5 ft 0 in., and 8 ft 0 in., respectively, from the left support. What is the distance of the center of gravity of the weight of the beam and the concentrated loads from the left end of the beam?

CHAPTER 5

STRESSES AND DEFORMATIONS

5–1. Mechanical Properties of Materials. Thus far this text has dealt principally with forces. When a force acts on a body, resisting forces are set up in the fibers of the body. We call these resisting forces stresses, a *stress* being an internal resistance in a body to an external force. When we use the term *unit stress*, we mean the magnitude of the stress for each unit of area. In Fig. 2–1, indicating a 6400-lb weight on a wood block having an 8 x 8 in. cross-sectional area, the 6400-lb weight is the external force, the *total stress* in the block directly under the weight is 6400 lb, and the *unit stress* is 6400 ÷ (8 × 8), or 100 psi (100 pounds per square inch).

This is an example of *direct stress*. Direct stresses are uniform in magnitude over the entire cross section of the member. For direct stresses

$$P = f \times A \quad \text{or} \quad f = \frac{P}{A} \quad \text{or} \quad A = \frac{P}{f}$$

in which P = axial load in pounds

f = unit stress in pounds per square inch

A = area of loaded cross section in square inches.

For the above illustration P = 6400 lb and A = 8 × 8, or 64 sq in. Thus

$$f = \frac{P}{A} \quad \text{or} \quad f = \frac{6400}{64} = 100 \text{ psi, the unit stress}$$

The architect or engineer, in designing a member, must first compute the force or forces that the member will be required to resist and then determine the material, size, and shape of the member that will properly resist the applied forces. The member must be sufficiently large, but an excess of material will result in smaller unit stresses and possibly a waste of material. Immediately, the designer is confronted with the question, "What is the proper allowable unit stress to use in the computations?" The materials used vary in quality and physical and mechanical characteristics; hence it is important that the designer have a knowledge of the properties of the materials he will use. Among others, outstanding properties are strength, stiffness, elasticity, ductility, malleability, and brittleness.

5–2. Strength. The *strength* of a material is its ability to resist forces. The three basic stresses are compression, tension, and shear; hence, in speaking of the strength of a material, we must know the type of stress to which the material is to be subjected. As an example, the compressive and tensile strengths of structural steel are about equal, whereas cast iron is strong in compression and relatively weak in tension. The *ultimate strength* of a material is the unit stress that causes failure or rupture. The term *elastic strength* is sometimes applied to the greatest unit stress a material can resist without a permanent change in shape.

5–3. Stiffness. *Stiffness* of a material is that property that enables it to resist deformation. If, for instance, blocks of steel and wood of equal size are subjected to equal compressive loads, the wood block will become shorter than the steel block. The deformation (shortening) of the wood will probably be 30 times that of the steel, and, we say, steel is *stiffer* than wood.

5–4. Elasticity. *Elasticity* is that property of a material that enables it to return to its original size and shape when the load to which it has been subjected is removed. This property varies greatly in different materials. For certain materials there is a unit stress beyond which the material does not regain its original dimensions when the load is removed. This unit stress is called the *elastic limit;* the allowable (desirable) unit stresses for such materials should be well below the elastic limit. Every material changes its size and shape when subjected to loads. For the materials used in building construction the actual unit stresses should be such that these deformations for direct stresses are in direct proportion to the applied loads.

Plasticity is the opposite quality to elasticity. A perfectly plastic material is a material that does not return to its original dimensions when the load causing deformation is removed. There are probably no perfectly plastic materials. Modeling clay and lead are examples of plastic materials.

5–5. Ductility. *Ductility* is that property of a material that permits it to undergo plastic deformation when subjected to a tensile force. A material that may be drawn into wires is a ductile material. A chain made of ductile material is preferable to a chain in which the material is brittle.

5–6. Malleability. A material having the property that permits plastic deformation when subjected to a compressive force is a *malleable* material. Materials that may be hammered into sheets are examples of malleable materials. Ductile materials are generally malleable. A material, such as cast iron, for instance, that is neither malleable nor ductile is called *brittle*.

5–7. Materials Used in Construction. Owing to the limited scope of this book it is neither possible nor necessary to enter into a detailed discussion of the many and varied materials used in building construction. Such information may be found in the numerous volumes devoted to the subject.

Steel varies greatly in its physical properties. These properties are controlled by the method of manufacture and the chemical composition. The percentage of carbon in steel affects both its strength and hardness. In addition to the carbon steels, there are many steel alloys. These alloys are made by the addition of certain other metals, such as nickel and chromium, in various proportions. Steel alloys are employed when certain mechanical properties which are not afforded by the usual carbon steels are desired. In specifying the structural steel to be used in building construction, the specification writer needs only to state that it shall conform to the "Standard Specifications for Structural Steel for Bridges and Buildings" of the American Society for Testing Materials and give the appropriate serial designation number.

Another metal that is being used in greater quantities each year is structural aluminum. Some of its advantages are that it saves weight, it is fabricated economically, and it resists corrosion. See Art. 6–8.

TABLE 5–1. PHYSICAL PROPERTIES OF VARIOUS BUILDING MATERIALS

Material	Elastic Limit in Pounds per Square Inch		Ultimate Strength in Pounds per Square Inch			Allowable Working Unit Stress in Pounds per Square Inch				Modulus of Elasticity in Pounds per Square Inch	Weight in Pounds per Cubic Foot
	Tension	Compression	Tension	Compression	Shear	Tension	Compression	Shear	Extreme Fiber in Bending		
Concrete *				2,500			625	75		2,500,000	150
Brick masonry				2,000			100–250				120
Stone masonry, rubble							200–400				160
Timber †											
Forces parallel to grain	3,000	3,000	10,000	8,000	500	1,200	1,000	100	1,200	1,200,000	40
Forces perpendicular to grain					3,000		300	400			
Aluminum alloy 6061-T-6	35,000		38,000	35,000	24,000	15,000	9,000	3,000		10,000,000	170
Cast iron			25,000	75,000	20,000					12,000,000	450
Wrought iron	25,000	25,000	50,000	50,000	40,000	12,000	12,000	9,000	12,000	28,000,000	485
Steel, structural ‡	33,000	33,000	65,000	65,000	50,000	20,000		13,000	20,000	29,000,000	490

* For allowable stresses in concrete see Table 17–1.

† For allowable stresses in timber see Table 5–4.

‡ For allowable stresses in structural steel see Table 5–5.

68

The ingredients of concrete are so varied in kind and proportions that concrete of various strengths and properties may be produced. In general, the concrete is referred to as 2500-lb (3000-lb, etc.) concrete, by which is meant concrete that has an ultimate compressive stress of 2500 psi at the end of a 28-day curing period.

The many species and grades of timber, direction of grain, size of the member, degree of moisture, and other factors require special attention in assigning allowable working stresses to this material.

The strength of masonry walls and piers depends not only on the strength of the masonry units, such as stones, bricks, and blocks, but also on the kind of mortar that is used.

The designer of structures need not be confused by the complexity of the many kinds and grades of materials in determining the proper unit stresses to employ in his computations. He needs only to consult the building regulations having jurisdiction in his city; his design is based on the allowable unit stresses that are prescribed. Building codes are not uniform in their requirements, and the building regulations of one city may be quite different from those of another city nearby.

The working stresses used in the illustrative problems in this book are not intended to conform to any specific code. The designer must accustom himself to using whatever formula or unit stress that may be required in his locality. For the purpose of solving problems Table 5–1 is presented. The values in this table are merely approximations. The reader should consult his local building regulations and tabulate the stresses that will govern his designs.

5–8. Deformation. Whenever a body is subjected to a force, there is a change in the shape or size of the body. These changes in dimensions are called *deformations*. A block subjected to a compressive force *shortens* in length, and the decrease in length is its deformation. When a tensile force is applied to a rod, the original length of the rod is increased and the *lengthening* or *elongation* is its deformation. A loaded beam resting on two supports at its ends tends to become concave on its upper surface; we say the beam *bends*. The deformation that accompanies bending is called *deflection*.

When stresses occur in a body, there is always an accompanying deformation. The deformation often is so small that it is not apparent to the naked eye; nevertheless, it is always present. In building construction the deformations in most of the structural members are generally so small that they require no special attention. However, the deflection of beams does demand consideration. A beam should be large enough to resist properly the stresses set up in its fibers, and, what is equally important, the beam should be large enough to prevent the deflection from exceeding certain allowable limits.

The term *strain* is sometimes used as a synonym for deformation. We use the phrase "stress and strain," for which we may substitute "stress and deformation."

Consider a wrought iron rod 20 ft 0 in. in length that is subjected to a tensile force. We find that the rod is 0.15 in. longer than it was before the load was applied. The 0.15 in. is the *total elongation*. Since the rod had an original length of 20 ft 0 in., or 240 in., the *unit elongation*, that is, the elongation *per unit of length*, is 0.15 ÷ 240, or 0.00062 in. per in.

5–9. Elastic Limit, Yield Point, and Ultimate Strength. The *elastic limit* is a unit stress that pertains to certain building materials. The following discussion of a test made on a specimen shows why particular attention must be given to this unit stress.

Laboratories devoted to the testing of materials have machines in which tensile tests are made. Such a machine contains screws operated by motors. When the specimen to be tested is secured in gripping devices, the motors are set in motion and tensile forces are thus applied to the specimen. The stresses in the specimen are read by means of a counterpoise and scale, and the accompanying elongations of the specimen are read by an instrument called an extensometer. This instrument permits the reading of minute changes in the length of the specimen. During the testing of a specimen a constant record is kept of the applied loads and the resulting deformations.

For the purpose of illustration, let us imagine that a tensile test is made on a rod of structural steel 1 sq in. in cross section. Two marks, exactly 8 in. apart, are made on the specimen, and the elongations of this marked length are recorded as the test proceeds.

When a load of 5000 psi has been attained, the extensometer reading shows that the total elongation is 0.00139 in. When the next unit of 5000 psi is reached (making a total of 10,000 psi), the total elongation is 2 × 0.00139 in. For an additional 5000-lb load (making a total of 15,000 psi) the total deformation is 3 × 0.00139 in. These stresses and deformations are recorded as shown in Table 5–2. For a unit stress of 35,000 lb the total deformation is

TABLE 5–2. TENSILE TEST

Stress, in Pounds per Square Inch	Total Deformation, in Inches
5,000	0.00139 = 0.00139
10,000	2 × 0.00139 = 0.00278
15,000	3 × 0.00139 = 0.00417
20,000	4 × 0.00139 = 0.00556
25,000	5 × 0.00139 = 0.00695
30,000	6 × 0.00139 = 0.00834
35,000	7 × 0.00139 = 0.00973
40,000	= 0.09950

7 × 0.00139 in., or 0.00973 in. The test is continued, and for the next 5000-lb additional load we would expect to see a deformation of 8 × 0.00139 in., or 0.01112 in. However, we find that the deformation for this stress of 40,000 psi is 0.0995 in.

Note that up to and including the unit stress of 35,000 psi the deformations have been directly proportional to the applied loads. The unit stress beyond which the deformations increase in a faster ratio than the applied loads is called the *elastic limit*. The elastic limit is sometimes called the *proportional limit*. For structural steel it is approximately 36,000 psi.

If during the test, up to the elastic limit, the loads had been removed from the specimen, the bar would have returned to its original length. Sometimes the elastic limit is defined as that unit stress beyond which the stressed member will not return to its original length when the load is removed. If it does not return to its original length, there is a permanent deformation, called a *permanent set.*

In testing certain materials we find that at a stress slightly above the elastic limit a deformation occurs without any increase in stress. The stress at which this deformation occurs is called the *yield point.*

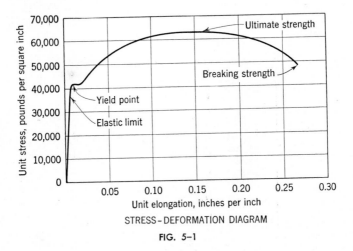

STRESS-DEFORMATION DIAGRAM

FIG. 5–1

When the stresses and their accompanying deformations during a test have been recorded, it is convenient to plot them on a sheet of graph paper. In Fig. 5–1 the vertical distances (ordinates) are the unit stresses and the horizontal distances (abscissas) show the deformations. Since up to a stress of about 36,000 psi (the elastic limit) the deformations were directly proportional to the stresses, the stress-deformation curve is a straight line. At a stress slightly beyond the elastic limit there is a deformation without an additional stress. This stress, the yield point, is shown graphically by the curve extending a slight distance horizontally.

As increased loads are applied, the curve tends to flatten, and the maximum stress recorded is the *ultimate strength* of the material. For a steel specimen there is then a decrease in diameter (necking) at one section of a bar and finally rupture or the *breaking strength.* The *ultimate strength* of a material is defined as the unit stress that occurs just at or before rupture. For structural steel the ultimate strength varies from 60,000 to 74,000 psi.

All materials do not behave in the manner noted above. Cast iron, concrete and wood, as examples, have no yield points, and their elastic limits are difficult to determine. They do not neck, and their ultimate and breaking strengths are identical.

5-10. Modulus of Elasticity. In the preceding article, in which a tensile test on a steel specimen is discussed, it is stated that the elongation for each additional 5000-psi unit there is an additional elongation of 0.00139 in. This is an approximation used for the purpose of illustration. There are always slight deviations in the deformations that result from inaccuracies in the instruments as well as from observation. However, accepting these figures, note that 0.00139 in. is the *total deformation*, the deformation for an 8-in. length. Thus the *unit deformation* is 0.00139 ÷ 8, or 0.000173 in. *per inch of length*.

The *modulus of elasticity* of a material is the ratio of the unit stress to the unit deformation. It is represented by the letter E and is an indication of the *stiffness* of a material. For instance, in the test previously described the unit deformation for a unit stress of 5000 psi is 0.000173 in. Thus the modulus of elasticity of the material is

$$E = \frac{\text{unit stress}}{\text{unit deformation}} = \frac{5{,}000}{0.000173} = 28{,}900{,}000 \text{ psi}$$

The modulus of elasticity is the unit stress divided by the unit deformation, and, since the unit stress is in units of pounds per square inch and the unit deformation is an abstract number (inches divided by inches), the modulus of elasticity is in units of pounds per square inch.

In computations in connection with structural steel E, the modulus of elasticity, is taken to be 29,000,000 psi. As a convenience, E for reinforcing steel in reinforced concrete computations is considered to be 30,000,000 psi. For wood used in building construction, depending on the species, E varies from 1,100,000 to 1,760,000 psi. Let

E = modulus of elasticity of a material in pounds per square inch

P = applied force in pounds

f = unit stress in the member in pounds per square inch

A = area of cross section of the member in square inches

l = length of member in inches

e = total deformation in inches

s = unit deformation in inches per inch

$$E = \frac{\text{unit stress}}{\text{unit deformation}} = \frac{f}{s} = \frac{P/A}{e/l} = \frac{Pl}{Ae}$$

or

$$e = \frac{Pl}{AE}$$

By the use of this formula, we are able to determine the deformation of a member subjected to direct stresses, provided that we know the modulus of elasticity of the material and that *the unit stress does not exceed the elastic limit of the material*. There are five terms in this equation, and if any four are known the remaining term may be computed. In using this formula, be particular to see that l, the length of the member, is in units of inches.

Example. A steel rod 1 in. in diameter and 10 in. in length elongates 0.0069 in. when subjected to a tensile load of 16,000 lb. Compute the modulus of elasticity.

SOLUTION. The cross-sectional area of a rod whose diameter is 1 in. is 0.7854 sq in. Then $f = \dfrac{P}{A} = \dfrac{16,000}{0.7854} = 20,370$ psi. Since the actual unit stress is within the elastic limit of the material, the formula for finding the modulus of elasticity is applicable. Thus

$$E = \frac{Pl}{Ae} = \frac{16,000 \times 10}{0.7854 \times 0.0069}$$

$$= 29,520,000 \text{ psi, the modulus of elasticity}$$

Example. A $\frac{1}{2}$-in. square structural steel rod 10 ft 0 in. in length is subjected to a tensile load of 4800 lb. Compute the total elongation.

SOLUTION. To begin, let us see whether or not the foregoing formula is valid. The area of a $\frac{1}{2}$-in. square rod is 0.5 × 0.5, or 0.25 sq in. Then $f = \dfrac{P}{A} = \dfrac{4800}{0.25} = 19{,}200$ psi, the actual unit stress. Since this stress is below the elastic limit of the material, about 36,000 psi, the formula may be employed. The length of the rod is 10 ft 0 in., or 120 in., and E for steel is 29,000,000 psi (Table 5–1). Thus

$$e = \frac{Pl}{AE} = \frac{4800 \times 120}{0.25 \times 29{,}000{,}000} = 0.079 \text{ in., the total elongation}$$

Problem 5–10–A. A steel bar $\frac{1}{2}$ in. in diameter and 8 in. in length elongates 0.0042 in. under a tensile load of 3000 lb. Compute the modulus of elasticity.

Problem 5–10–B. A steel bar has a length of 16 ft 0 in. and a cross-sectional area of $\frac{1}{2}$ x 1 in. What will be its total length under a tensile load of 9000 lb?

Problem 5–10–C. A timber block 2 x 2 in. in cross section and 6 in. in length is subjected to a compressive force of 5000 lb. The block shortens 0.005 in. Compute the modulus of elasticity of the material.

Problem 5–10–D. If the block given in Problem 5–10–C is of cast iron and the compressive load is 40,000 lb, how much will it shorten? See Table 5–1.

Problem 5–10–E. A wrought iron rod 1 in. in diameter and 12 ft 0 in. in length is subjected to a tensile load of 9,000 lb. Compute its deformation. See Table 5–1.

5–11. Factor of Safety. Suppose that we are asked to design (determine the size of) a wrought iron rod to support a tensile load of 7000 lb. We find in the building code that the allowable tensile unit stress for this material is 12,500 psi, and in Table 5–1 we see that the ultimate tensile strength of wrought iron is 50,000 psi. The term *factor of safety* is given to the quotient that results from dividing the ultimate strength of a material by the unit stress. In this instance

$$\text{factor of safety} = \frac{\text{ultimate strength}}{\text{unit stress}} = \frac{50{,}000}{12{,}500} = 4$$

If the allowable unit stress is 12,500 psi, $P = f \times A$, or $A = P/f$, and $A = 7000/12{,}500$, or 0.56 sq in., the required minimum area of the rod. A rod whose diameter is $\frac{7}{8}$ in. has a cross-sectional area of 0.6 sq in. and, therefore, is acceptable.

The term factor of safety is not used so frequently today as it was in the past. It is frequently misunderstood. In the above example the factor of safety is 4, but the rod would not support safely a load 4 times 7000 lb, for $(7000 \times 4)/0.6 = 46,666$ psi, a tensile unit stress that exceeds the elastic limit of the material. In specifying the allowable unit stresses to be used by designers, building codes generally give the unit stress with no reference to the factor of safety. Table 5–3 lists some average factors of safety

TABLE 5–3. FACTORS OF SAFETY

Material	Factor of Safety When Used in Buildings
Brick and stone	15–20
Timber	8–10
Cast iron	4– 6
Aluminum	2.5– 4
Wrought iron	3.5– 4
Structural steel	3.5– 4

for materials used in building construction. They are presented for the purpose of comparison and are, necessarily, only approximations.

Again, a short piece of cast iron is to be designed to support a compressive load. We are told that the factor of safety is to be 5. What is the allowable compressive unit stress? In Table 5–1 we see that the ultimate compressive strength of cast iron is 75,000 psi; hence

$$\frac{75,000}{\text{unit stress}} = 5$$

$$\text{unit stress} = \frac{75,000}{5} \quad \text{or} \quad 15,000 \text{ psi}$$

Example. A short block of wood having a nominal 6 x 8 in. cross section stands upright and resists a compressive load of 40,000 lb. What is the factor of safety?

SOLUTION. The actual dimensions of a nominal 6 x 8 in. cross section are 5.5 x 7.5 in. (see Table 6–7); hence the cross-sectional area is 5.5 × 7.5, or 41.25 sq in.

The load supported is 40,000 lb; therefore, $f = \dfrac{P}{A} = \dfrac{40,000}{41.25} =$ 970 psi, the actual compressive unit stress.

Since the timber block stands upright, the load is parallel to the grain and Table 5–1 gives 8000 psi as the ultimate compressive stress. The factor of safety is the ultimate strength divided by the unit stress, or $\dfrac{8000}{970} = 8.2$, the factor of safety.

Example. A $1\frac{1}{2}$-in. diameter wrought iron bolt resists a shearing force of 17,000 lb. What is the factor of safety?

SOLUTION. The area of a circle is the radius squared multiplied by 3.1416; hence the cross-sectional area of the $1\frac{1}{2}$-in. diameter bolt is 0.75 × 0.75 × 3.1416, or 1.767 sq in.

$$f = \frac{P}{A} = \frac{17,000}{1.767} = 9620 \text{ psi, the actual shearing unit stress}$$

From Table 5–1 we find that the ultimate shearing strength of wrought iron is 40,000 psi; therefore

$$\frac{40,000}{9620} = 4.1, \text{ the factor of safety}$$

In the following three problems use the values for ultimate strength given in Table 5–1.

Problem 5–11–A. A wrought iron rod $\frac{1}{2}$ in. in diameter supports a tensile load of 2000 lb. Compute the factor of safety.

Problem 5–11–B. A short block of structural steel supports a compressive load of 24,375 lb. If the factor of safety is 4, what is the cross-sectional area of the block?

Problem 5–11–C. A short hollow cast iron post has an outside diameter of 10 in. The thickness of the shell is 1 in. For a factor of safety of 6, compute the maximum allowable load the post will support.

5–12. Allowable Unit Stresses. An *allowable unit stress* is the maximum unit stress considered desirable in a structural member

TABLE 5-4.   ALLOWABLE UNIT STRESSES FOR STRUCTURAL LUMBER

Species	Grade	Classification	Extreme Fiber in Bending f and Tension Parallel to Grain t	Horizontal Shear H	Compression Perpendicular to Grain $c\perp$	Compression Parallel to Grain c	Modulus of Elasticity, E
				Allowable Stresses in Pounds per Square Inch			
Southern cypress	1700 f grade	J.&P.—B.&S.	1700	145	360	1425	1,320,000
	1300 f grade	J.&P.—B.&S.	1300	120	360	1125	1,320,000
	1450 c grade	P.&T.	—	—	360	1450	1,320,000
	1200 c grade	P.&T.	—	—	360	1200	1,320,000
Douglas fir, Coast region	Dense select structural	J.&P.	2050	120	455	1650	1,760,000
	Select structural	J.&P.	1900	120	415	1500	1,760,000
	Construction	J.&P.	1500	120	390	1200	1,760,000
	Standard	J.&P.	1200	95	390	1000	1,760,000
	Dense select structural	B.&S.	2050	120	455	1500	1,760,000
	Select structural	B.&S.	1900	120	415	1400	1,760,000
	Dense construction	B.&S.	1750	120	455	1200	1,760,000
	Construction	B.&S	1500	120	390	1000	1,760,000
	Dense select structural	P.&T.	1900	120	455	1650	1,760,000
	Select structural	P.&T.	1750	120	415	1500	1,760,000
	Dense construction	P.&T.	1500	120	455	1400	1,760,000
	Construction	P.&T.	1200	120	390	1200	1,760,000

Species	Grade	Classification						E
Eastern hemlock	Select structural	J.&P.—B.&S.	1300	85	360	850		1,210,000
	Prime structural	J.&P.	1200	60	360	775		1,210,000
	Common structural	J.&P.	1100	60	360	650		1,210,000
	Utility structural	J.&P.	950	—	360	600		1,210,000
	Select structural	P.&T.			360	850		1,210,000
Southern pine	Dense structural 86	2", 3" & 4" thick	2900	150	455	2200		1,760,000
	Dense structural 58	"	1750	105	455	1450		1,760,000
	No. 1 dense SR	"	1750	120	455	1550		1,760,000
	No. 1 SR	"	1500	120	390	1500		1,760,000
	No. 2 dense SR	"	1400	105	455	1050		1,760,000
	No. 2 SR	"	1200	105	390	900		1,760,000
	Dense structural 86	5" thick & up	2400	150	455	1800		1,760,000
	Dense structural 58	"	1600	105	455	1300		1,760,000
	No. 1 SR	"	1400	120	390	1300		1,760,000
	No. 2 SR	"	1200	105	390	900		1,760,000
Redwood	Dense structural	J.&P.—B.&S.	1700	110	320	1450		1,320,000
	Heart structural	J.&P.—B.&S.	1300	95	320	1100		1,320,000
	Dense structural	P.&T.			320	1450		1,320,000
	Heart structural	P.&T.			320	1100		1,320,000
Eastern spruce	1450 f structural grade	J.&P.	1450	110	300	1050		1,320,000
	1300 f structural grade	J.&P.	1300	95	300	975		1,320,000
	1200 f structural grade	J.&P.	1200	95	300	900		1,320,000

Abbreviations: J.&P.: Joists and Planks, 2" to, but not including 5" thick, and 4" or more wide.
B.&S.: Beams and Stringers, 5" or more thick, and 8" or more wide.
P.&T.: Posts and Timbers, 5" by 5" or larger, primarily carrying longitudinal loads.
SR: Stress Rated.

Compiled by permission from data published by the National Lumber Manufacturers Association.

All parts of the structure shall be so proportioned that the unit stress in pounds per square inch shall not exceed the following values:

TENSION
Structural steel, net section.................................... 20,000
Rivets, on area based on nominal diameter.................. 20,000
Bolts and other threaded parts, on nominal area at root of thread 20,000

COMPRESSION
Columns, gross section
For axially loaded columns with values of l/r not greater than 120............................ $17,000 - 0.485 \dfrac{l^2}{r^2}$

For axially loaded columns (bracing and other secondary members) with values of l/r greater than 120.. $\dfrac{18,000}{1 + \dfrac{l^2}{18,000 r^2}}$

in which l is the unbraced length of the column and r is the corresponding radius of gyration of the section, both in inches.
Plate girder stiffeners, gross section.......................... 20,000
Webs of rolled sections at toe of fillet....................... 24,000

BENDING
Tension on extreme fibers of rolled sections, plate girders, and built-up members................................ 20,000
Compression on extreme fibers of rolled sections, plate girders, and built-up members
With ld/bt not in excess of 600........................ 20,000
With ld/bt in excess of 600............................ $\dfrac{12,000,000}{\dfrac{ld}{bt}}$

in which l is the unsupported length and d the depth of the member; b is the width and t the thickness of its compression flange; all in inches; except that l shall be taken as twice the length of the compression flange of a cantilever beam not fully stayed at its outer end against translation or rotation.
Stress on extreme fibers of pins.............................. 30,000

SHEARING
Rivets... 15,000
Pins, and turned bolts in reamed or drilled holes............. 15,000
Unfinished bolts... 10,000
Webs of beams and plate girders, gross section............... 13,000

BEARING	Double Shear	Single Shear
Rivets...............................	40,000	32,000
Turned bolts in reamed or drilled holes.........	40,000	32,000
Unfinished bolts.............................	25,000	20,000
Pins..		32,000
Contact area		
Milled stiffeners and other milled surfaces.................		30,000
Fitted stiffeners...........................		27,000
Expansion rollers and rockers (pounds per linear inch)........		600d
in which d is diameter of roller or rocker in inches.		

Compiled from data in "Manual of Steel Construction," by permission of the American Institute of Steel Construction.

subjected to loads. Other terms for allowable unit stress are *working unit stress* and *safe working unit stress*.

Formerly, the allowable unit stress was established by dividing the ultimate strength by an arbitrary factor of safety. This method, however, has been discontinued because the term "factor of safety" is misleading. Allowable unit stresses are generally given directly. They should be well below the elastic limit, possibly one half or one third of its value.

Currently, allowable unit stresses for various materials are assigned by different authorities on the basis of tests and experience. To determine the allowable unit stresses to employ, the designer simply consults his local building code and notes the stresses specified therein. Tables 5–4, 5–5, and 5–6 are given as convenient references; they are to be used in the solution of the problems that accompany this text.

Table 5–4 gives the allowable unit stresses for certain species of lumber recommended by the National Lumber Manufacturers Association. In addition to the various grades for the different species, the allowable stresses vary in accordance with the size of the member. In the table J.&P. indicate joists and planks (2 in. to, but not including, 5 in. thick and 4 in. and over wide); B.&S.

TABLE 5–6. ALLOWABLE UNIT STRESSES FOR MASONRY IN POUNDS PER SQUARE INCH

Type of Masonry	Cement-Lime Mortar	Cement Mortar
Granite	640	800
Limestone	400	500
Marble	400	500
Sandstone	320	400
Bluestone	300	400
Rubble	140	250
Brick, solid wall	200	250
Brick, hollow wall	125	150
Structural clay tile	70	80
Concrete block	70	80
Solid concrete units	125	150
Plain concrete, $f_c' = 2500$	625	

indicate beams and stringers (5 in. and over thick and 8 in. and over wide); P.&T. refer to posts and timbers (5 x 5 in. and larger). SR indicates stress rated.

Table 5–5 gives allowable unit stresses for structural steel recommended by the American Institute of Steel Construction.

The allowable unit stresses for masonry, given in Table 5–6, are merely average values, since the strength of masonry depends not only on the quality of the masonry units but also on the strength of the mortar and the workmanship employed in the construction of walls and piers.

Example. Two steel bars are held together by a $\frac{7}{8}$-in. rivet as indicated in Fig. 14–3. What is the maximum allowable load the rivet will resist with respect to shear?

SOLUTION. If loads are applied to the bars, either tensile or compressive, there is a tendency for the rivet to fail by shearing at the plane of contact between the two bars. We say that the rivet is in *single shear*. The area of a circle is the square of the radius multiplied by 3.1416; thus the cross-sectional area of the shank of a rivet $\frac{7}{8}$ in. in diameter is $\left(\dfrac{0.875}{2}\right)^2 \times 3.1416$, or 0.6013 sq in. Table 5–5 gives for the allowable shearing unit stress of rivets 15,000 psi. Then, since this is a direct stress (Art. 5–1),

$$P = f \times A$$

$$P = 15,000 \times 0.6013$$

$$P = 9019 \text{ lb, the maximum allowable load on the rivet}$$

Example. Figure 14–4 shows three bars held together by a rivet. Compute the maximum allowable load that a $\frac{7}{8}$-in. rivet can resist with respect to shear.

SOLUTION. If this rivet fails by shear, there are two planes (at the faces of the enclosed plate) at which the rivet must fail. This rivet is in *double shear*. Since, from the foregoing example, we found that the allowable shearing value for a $\frac{7}{8}$-in. rivet in single shear is 9019 lb, the maximum allowable shearing load for the rivet in double shear is 2 × 9019, or 18,038 lb.

Example. Two steel angle sections are used as a tension member in a truss; their *net* cross-sectional area (gross area minus the area to be deducted for rivet holes) is 6.12 sq in. What is the maximum allowable tensile load the member will resist?

SOLUTION. Reference to Table 5–5 shows that 20,000 psi is the allowable tensile unit stress of structural steel. Then $f = 20,000$ psi and $A = 6.12$ sq in.

$$P = f \times A$$

$$P = 20,000 \times 6.12$$

$P = 122,400$ lb, the allowable tensile load the member will resist

Example. A 10 x 10 in. short post of No. 1 SR grade of southern pine is used to resist a compressive load. Compute the magnitude of the allowable load, assuming that the direction of the load is parallel to the grain of the wood.

SOLUTION. A timber having a nominal size of 10 x 10 in. has actual dimensions of 9.5 x 9.5 in., or 90.25 sq in. See Table 6–7. In Table 5–4 we find that the allowable compressive unit stress for this timber, whose cross-sectional area is larger than 5 x 5 in., is 1300 psi. Thus

$$P = f \times A$$

$$P = 1300 \times 90.25$$

$P = 117,320$ lb, the maximum allowable compressive load

Example. A short brick pier has a 13 x 17 in. cross-sectional area. The brickwork is laid up with cement-lime mortar, and the compressive load on the pier is 40,000 lb. Is the pier safe?

SOLUTION. For problems of this kind the procedure is to compute the *actual* unit stress and to compare it with the allowable. This pier has a cross-sectional area of 13 x 17 in., or 221 sq in. Then $P = 40,000$ lb and $A = 221$ sq in. Thus

$$f = \frac{P}{A}$$

$$f = \frac{40,000}{221} = 180 \text{ psi, the } \textit{actual} \text{ compressive unit stress}$$

On referring to Table 5–6 we find that the *allowable* compressive unit stress for a solid brick pier laid up with cement-lime mortar is 200 psi. Since the actual stress is less than the allowable, the pier is safe.

Problem 5–12–A. A wrought iron rod has a diameter of $1\frac{1}{2}$ in. and is used as a tension member of a truss. The load on the member is 20,000 lb. Is the member safe? (*Note:* For allowable stress of wrought iron, see Table 5–1.)

Problem 5–12–B. Will a structural steel rod $1\frac{1}{4}$ in. in diameter safely support a tensile load of 24,000 lb?

Problem 5–12–C. A steel rod 1 in. in diameter is suspended from a ceiling. If its length is 20 ft, compute the stress in the rod at the ceiling that results from the weight of the rod. (*Note:* For the weight of steel, see Table 5–1.)

Problem 5–12–D. Compute the theoretical length of the rod in Problem 5–12–C that would rupture because of its weight.

Problem 5–12–E. A short post of Douglas fir, select structural grade, has a nominal cross-sectional area of 8 x 8 in. Compute the maximum allowable compressive load the post will support.

Problem 5–12–F. A steel bolt 1 in. in diameter is subjected to a tensile load of 12,000 lb. What is the tensile unit stress?

Problem 5–12–G. The head of the bolt in Problem 5–12–F is 1 in. in length. What is the shearing unit stress that tends to shear off the head? (The area resisting shear is the surface of a cylinder whose diameter and length are each 1 in.)

Problem 5–12–H. If the weight of brickwork is 120 lb per cu ft, what should be the height of a brick pier to result in a stress of 150 psi at the base?

Problem 5–12–I. A square steel bearing plate under a column rests on a concrete footing. If the load on the footing is 90,000 lb, what should be the area of the bearing plate? (*Note:* See Table 5–1.)

Problem 5–12–J. Two aluminum alloy 6061-T6 angle sections, 4 x 3 x $\frac{1}{2}$ in., are used as a tension member. The gross area of the two angles is 6.5 sq in. and the rivets are $\frac{3}{4}$ in. in diameter. Hence the area to be deducted for the rivet hole in each angle is 0.4375 sq in. What is the allowable load this member will support. (*Note:* See Table 5–1 and Art. 14–6.)

CHAPTER 6

PROPERTIES OF SECTIONS

6–1. Centroids. The *center of gravity* of a solid is an imaginary point at which all its weight may be considered to be concentrated or the point through which the resultant weight passes. Since an area has no weight, it has no center of gravity. *The point of a plane area that corresponds to the center of gravity of a very thin homogeneous plate of the same area and shape is called the centroid of the area.*

When a simple beam is subjected to forces that tend to cause it to bend, the fibers above a certain plane in the beam are in compression and those below the plane are in tension. This plane is called the *neutral surface.* For a cross section of the beam the line corresponding to the neutral surface is called the *neutral axis.* The neutral axis passes through the centroid of the section; thus it is important that we know the exact position of the centroid.

The position of the centroid for symmetrical shapes is readily determined. If an area possesses a line of symmetry, the centroid will obviously be on that line; if there are two lines of symmetry, the centroid will be at their point of intersection. For instance, a rectangular area as shown in Fig. 6–1(a) has its centroid at its geometrical center, the point of intersection of the diagonals. The centroid of a circular area is its center [Fig. 6–1(b)]. With respect to a triangular area [Figs. 6–1(c) and (d)], it is convenient to remember that the centroid is at a distance equal to one third of the perpendicular distance measured from any side to the opposite vertex. The intersection of the lines drawn from the vertices to the mid-points of the opposite sides is another method of locating the centroid of a triangle. This is shown in Fig. 6–1(c).

For symmetrical structural steel shapes, such as I-beams, the centroid is on the vertical axis through the web at a point midway between the upper and lower surfaces of the flanges. A 12-in. Standard I-beam has its centroid 6 in. from the uppermost or lowermost fibers of the cross section. For unsymmetrical steel shapes the position of the centroid is given in the tables of properties published by the steel companies. As an example, Table 6–4 gives the properties of channel sections. Consider a 10-in. channel having a weight of 15.3 lb per lin ft, 10 ⌴ 15.3. In this table we find that the vertical axis is 0.64 in. from the back of the web. The centroid is on this axis at a point 5 in. between the top and bottom surfaces of the flanges. The position of the centroid of angle sections is given in Tables 6–5 and 6–6.

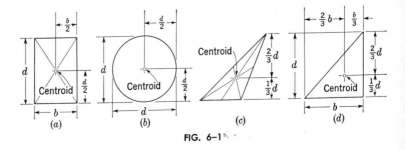

FIG. 6–1

It frequently happens, however, that we must determine the position of the centroid, and this is accomplished most readily by mathematics. The *statical moment* of a plane area with respect to a given axis is the area multiplied by the normal distance of the centroid of the area to the axis. *If an area is divided into a number of parts, the sum of the statical moments of the parts is equal to the statical moment of the entire area.* This is the principle by means of which the position of the centroid is found; its application is remarkably simple.

Example. The T-section shown in Fig. 6–2(a) is symmetrical with respect to the vertical axis. Compute the position of the centroid.

SOLUTION. Since the section is symmetrical about the vertical axis, the centroid will lie at some point on this axis; thus our problem is to find its distance from the upper or lower surface of the section. For convenience divide the area into the two rectangles shown by the diagonals, the horizontal area being the flange and the vertical area the web. The positions of the centroids of the rectangles are at the intersections of the diagonals. The area of the flange is 6 × 2, or 12 sq in., and its centroid is 6 in. *from the bottom of the section.* (Note that this 6 in. is the lever arm of the 12-sq in. area.) Similarly, the area of the web is 5 × 2, or 10 sq in., and its centroid is 2.5 in. *from the bottom of the section.* The

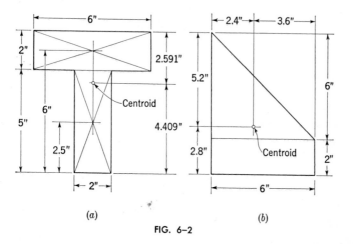

(a)   (b)

FIG. 6–2

area of the entire section is 12 + 10, or 22 sq in., and the position of its centroid is not yet known; let us call its distance from the bottom of the section c inches. Now we can apply the principle given above. Thus

sum of moments of the parts = moment of entire area

$$(12 \times 6) + (10 \times 2.5) = 22 \times c$$

$$97 = 22 \times c$$

$$c = 4.409 \text{ in.}$$

This is the distance from the centroid to the base of the section, and, since the section is 7 in. in depth, $7 - 4.409 = 2.591$ in., the distance of the centroid from the top of the section.

To verify the distance 2.591 in., let us write an equation of moments about an axis through the uppermost edge of the section.

Then

$$(12 \times 1) + (10 \times 4.5) = 22 \times c'$$

$$57 = 22 \times c'$$

$$c' = 2.591 \text{ in.}$$

In writing an equation of moments, be certain that all moments are taken about the same point or axis.

Later in this text we shall wish to know "the distance of the fiber most remote from the neutral surface." Since the neutral surface passes through the centroid of the cross section, what we wish to know is the distance of the centroid from the top or bottom of the section, *whichever is greater*. We generally call this distance c, the shorter distance being called c'.

Example. Determine the position of the centroid of the quadrilateral shown in Fig. 6-2(*b*).

SOLUTION. Because this figure is unsymmetrical, it will be necessary to locate the position of the centroid both vertically and horizontally. To begin, let us divide the area into two parts, the triangle and rectangle indicated in the figure.

Consider first an equation of moments about a horizontal axis through the *top* of the figure. The triangle has an area of $\dfrac{6 \times 6}{2}$, or 18 sq in., and, since its centroid is $\dfrac{2}{3}$, its height from its upper apex, Fig. 6-1(*d*), its centroid is $\dfrac{2}{3} \times 6$, or 4 in. from the axis about which the moments will be taken. The area of the rectangle is 6×2, or 12 sq in., and its centroid is 7 in. from the same axis. Then, letting c be the distance of the centroid of the entire area from the selected axis,

$$(18 \times 4) + (12 \times 7) = 30 \times c$$

$$156 = 30 \times c$$

$$c = 5.2 \text{ in.}$$

Thus we have established the position of the centroid vertically, and now we shall determine its position horizontally, writing an equation of moments about a vertical axis taken through the right-hand edge of the area.

$$\left(\frac{6 \times 6}{2} \times 4\right) + [(6 \times 2) \times 3] = 30 \times c$$

$$108 = 30 \times c$$

$$c = 3.6 \text{ in.}$$

We have now found the position of the centroid both vertically and horizontally. The dimensions just found can be verified by solving two equations of moments, one about an axis through the bottom of the area and the other about a vertical axis through the left-hand side.

Problems 6–1–A–B–C–D–E–F. For the areas shown in Figs. 6–3(*a*), (*b*), (*c*), (*d*), (*e*), and (*f*) compute *c*, the distance of the centroids from the uppermost edge of the areas.

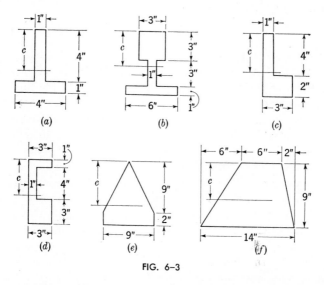

FIG. 6–3

6–2. Moment of Inertia. Consider the area enclosed by the irregular line in Fig. 6–4(*a*), area *A*. In this area an infinitely small area *a* is indicated at *z* distance from an axis marked *X–X*. If we multiply this tiny area by the square of its distance to the axis, we have the quantity $(a \times z^2)$. The entire area is made up of an infinite number of these small elementary areas at various distances from the X–X axis. Now, if we use the Greek letter Σ to represent the sum of an infinite number, we may write Σaz^2, which indicates the sum of all the infinitely small areas (of which the area A is composed) multiplied by the square of their distances from the X–X axis. This quantity is called the *moment of inertia* of the area and is represented by the letter I. Then $I_{X-X} = \Sigma az^2$, meaning that Σaz^2 is the moment of inertia of the area with respect to the axis marked X–X.

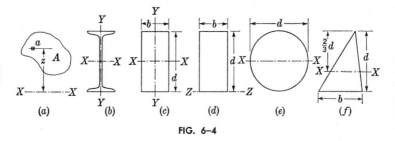

FIG. 6–4

We may define the moment of inertia of an area as *the sum of the products of all the elementary areas multiplied by the square of their distances from an axis*. In the United States the linear dimensions of cross sections of structural members are invariably in units of inches, and, since the moment of inertia involves an area multiplied by the square of a distance, the moment of inertia is expressed in inches to the fourth power and is written in.[4], sometimes called biquadratic inches. We cannot conceive such units as, for example, a linear dimension; it is a mathematical concept, expressed as Σaz^2. Thus the moment of inertia of a cross section depends not only on the number of units in its area but also on the arrangement of the area with respect to the axis under consideration. The moment of inertia of cross sections is of particular importance in the design of beams and columns. It is important to realize that the moment of inertia of cross sections of beams is taken about an axis that passes through the centroid of the area; very often such a moment of inertia is represented as I_0. Figure 6–4(*b*) shows the section of 12-in. Standard I-beam weighing 31.8 lb per lin ft, 12 I 31.8. The horizontal axis is X–X, and the vertical axis is Y–Y. Referring to Table 6–1, we find that $I_{X-X} =$

215.8 in.^{4} and $I_{Y-Y} = 9.5$ in.^{4} Obviously, the farther the component parts of an area are from the axis, the greater is the value of the moment of inertia.

6–3. Moment of Inertia of Rectangles, Circles, and Triangles.

The moment of inertia of rolled steel sections used in building construction is given in tables of properties of sections published by the American Institute of Steel Construction. See Tables 6–1 to 6–6, inclusive. For built-up sections or for sections not given in tables the value of the moment of inertia must be computed. In engineering problems the areas involved most commonly are the rectangle, the circle, and the triangle. The derivations of the formulas to be used for computing moments of inertia are most readily accomplished by the use of calculus. It is beyond the scope of this book to derive such formulas, but their values are given here and the computations involved in computing I for the sections most frequently used present no difficulties.

Consider the rectangle shown in Fig. 6–4(c). Its width is b and its depth is d. The two major axes are X–X and Y–Y, both passing through the centroid of the area. *The value of the moment of inertia of a rectangular area about an axis passing through the centroid parallel to the base is* $I_{X-X} = \dfrac{bd^3}{12}$. With respect to the vertical axis, $I_{Y-Y} = \dfrac{db^3}{12}$. This value for the moment of inertia of a rectangle is developed in Art. 11–4.

Example. Compute the moment of inertia of an 8 x 10 in. rectangular area with respect to a horizontal axis passing through the centroid parallel to the 8-in. side.

SOLUTION. For such a rectangle $b = 8$ in. and $d = 10$ in. Then, since $I_{X-X} = \dfrac{bd^3}{12}$, $I_{X-X} = \dfrac{8 \times 10 \times 10 \times 10}{12} = 666.67$ in.^{4} For timber beams an 8 x 10 in. nominal size has actual dimensions (dressed size) of 7.5 x 9.5 in. Using the dressed size, $I_{X-X} = \dfrac{7.5 \times 9.5 \times 9.5 \times 9.5}{12} = 535.86$ in.^{4} Note that this is the value of the moment of inertia given in Table 6–7.

In computing the moment of inertia of certain sections, it is often convenient to consider an axis passing through the base of a rectangle. Referring to Fig. 6–4(d), consider I about the axis Z–Z. *The moment of inertia of a rectangular area about an axis taken through its base is* $\dfrac{bd^3}{3}$: $I_{Z-Z} = \dfrac{bd^3}{3}$.

Example. Compute the moment of inertia of a 6 x 8 in. rectangular area about an axis taken through its base, the 6-in. side.

SOLUTION. For this rectangle $b = 6$ in. and $d = 8$ in. Then, since $I_{Z-Z} = \dfrac{bd^3}{3}$, $I_{Z-Z} = \dfrac{6 \times 8 \times 8 \times 8}{3} = 1024$ in.^{4}

The moment of inertia of a circular cross section, whose diameter is d, *about an axis passing through its centroid is* $\dfrac{\pi d^4}{64}$: $I_{X-X} = \dfrac{\pi d^4}{64}$. See Fig. 6–4(e).

Example. Compute the moment of inertia of a circular cross section, 10 in. in diameter, about an axis through its centroid.

SOLUTION. Since $d = 10$ and $I_0 = \dfrac{\pi d^4}{64}$, $I_0 = \dfrac{3.1416 \times 10^4}{64} = $ 490.9 in.^{4}, the moment of inertia with respect to an axis through the centroid.

Figure 6–4(f) indicates a triangular cross section having a height d and a base b. The axis X–X passes through the centroid of the area. *The moment of inertia of a triangular cross section about an axis taken through the centroid parallel to the base is* $\dfrac{bd^3}{36}$: $I_{X-X} = \dfrac{bd^3}{36}$.

Example. Compute the moment of inertia of a triangular cross section, whose base is 12 in. and whose height is 10 in., about an axis taken through the centroid parallel to the 12-in. base.

SOLUTION. For this triangle $b = 12$ in. and $d = 10$ in. Since $I_0 = \dfrac{bd^3}{36}$, $I_0 = \dfrac{12 \times 10^3}{36} = 333.33$ in.^{4}, the moment of inertia.

If the moments of inertia of the component parts of an area are taken about the same axis, they may be added or subtracted to find the moment of inertia of the area.

Example. Compute the moment of inertia of the hollow rectangular cross section shown in Fig. 6–5(a) about a horizontal axis through the centroid parallel to the 6-in. base.

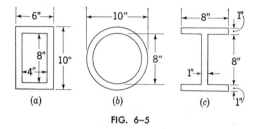

(a)   (b)   (c)

FIG. 6–5

SOLUTION. The moment of inertia of the rectangle of width 6 in. and depth 10 in. is $I = \dfrac{bd^3}{12} = \dfrac{6 \times 10^3}{12} = 500$ in.^{4} For the rectangle whose width and depth are 4 and 8 in., respectively, the moment of inertia is $I = \dfrac{bd^3}{12} = \dfrac{4 \times 8^3}{12} = 170.6$ in.^{4} Since both of these moments of inertia are taken *about the same axis*, we may subtract that of the smaller rectangle from that of the larger and the difference will be the moment of inertia of the hollow rectangle. Thus $500 - 170.6 = 329.4$ in.^{4}

Example. Compute the moment of inertia about an axis through the centroid of the cross-sectional area of the pipe 10 in. in diameter shown in Fig. 6–5(b), the thickness of the shell being 1 in.

SOLUTION. The moment of inertia of the outer circle is $I = \dfrac{\pi d^4}{64} = \dfrac{3.1416 \times 10^4}{64} = 490.87$ in.^{4} For the inner circle $I = \dfrac{\pi d^4}{64} = \dfrac{3.1416 \times 8^4}{64} = 201.06$. Hence $490.87 - 201.06 = 289.81$ in.^{4}, the moment of inertia of the pipe section.

Example. Compute the moment of inertia of the I-section, shown in Fig. 6–5(*c*), about a horizontal axis taken through the centroid of the section parallel to the flange.

SOLUTION. The *I* for the rectangle whose width is 8 in. and whose depth is 10 in. is $I = \dfrac{bd^3}{12} = \dfrac{8 \times 10^3}{12} = 666.67$ in.⁴ This moment of inertia includes the two open spaces at the sides of the web, the vertical area. Taken together, these open spaces are equivalent to a rectangle having a width of 7 in. and a depth of 8 in. For this area $I = \dfrac{bd^3}{12} = \dfrac{7 \times 8^3}{12} = 298.67$ in.⁴ Subtracting *I* for the open paces from that of the large rectangle, $666.67 - 298.67 = 368$ in.⁴, the moment of inertia of the I-section.

Attention is called to Fig. 6–9. Note that the moments of inertia of rectangles, triangles, and circles are given as well as other properties of sections.

Problem 6–3–A. Compute *I* for the rectangle shown in Fig. 6–6(*a*) about a horizontal axis through the centroid parallel to the 10-in. side.

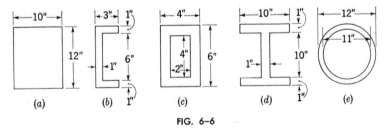

FIG. 6–6

Problem 6–3–B. Compute *I* for the rectangle shown in Fig. 6–6(*a*) about a vertical axis taken through the centroid parallel to the 12-in. side.

Problem 6–3–C. Compute *I* for the rectangle shown in Fig. 6–6(*a*) about an axis taken through its base, a 10-in. side.

Problems 6–3–D–E–F–G. Compute the moments of inertia for the areas shown in Figs. 6–6(*b*), (*c*), (*d*), and (*e*) about a horizontal axis taken through the centroids of the areas.

6–4. Transferring Moments of Inertia.
For unsymmetrical cross sections the moment of inertia is found by transferring moments of inertia from one axis to another. Figure 6–7(*a*) shows an angle section in which the axis marked *X*–*X* passes through its centroid.

A = the area of the section in square inches

I_0 = the moment of inertia of the section about an axis passing through its centroid in inches to the fourth power

I_1 = the moment of inertia of the section with respect to any parallel axis (marked Z–Z) in inches to the fourth power

h = the normal distance between the two axes in inches

Then

$$I_{Z-Z} = I_{X-X} + Ah^2 \quad \text{or} \quad I_1 = I_0 + Ah^2$$

This is sometimes called the *transfer formula;* it may be stated thus: *the moment of inertia of a plane area with respect to any axis*

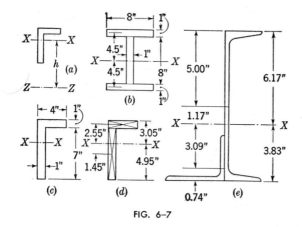

FIG. 6–7

is equal to the moment of inertia of the area with respect to a parallel axis passing through its centroid plus the area multiplied by the square of the normal distance between the two axes. When using this formula, be certain that I_0 is the moment of inertia about an axis passing through the centroid of the section.

Example. Compute, by use of the transfer formula, the moment of inertia of the I-section shown in Fig. 6–7(b) about a horizontal axis passing through its centroid, axis X–X.

SOLUTION. This is the same section shown in Fig. 6–5(c) for which I was found to be 368 in.[4] We shall now compute it again to illustrate the use of the transfer formula.

To begin, the area is divided into three rectangles, the two flanges and the web, as shown in the figure. The web is a 1 x 8 in. rectangle whose centroid is on the X–X axis. For this area

$$I = \frac{bd^3}{12} = \frac{1 \times 8^3}{12} = 42.67 \text{ in.}^4$$

Now consider the upper flange, an 8 x 1 in. rectangle. I_0, the moment of inertia *about an axis passing through its centroid*, is

$$\frac{bd^3}{12} \quad \text{or} \quad \frac{8 \times 1^3}{12} = 0.667 \text{ in.}^4$$

Note that the area of the flange is 8×1, or 8 sq in., and that its centroid is 4.5 in. from the centroidal axis of the entire cross section. Thus 4.5 in. is h in the transfer formula, and 8 sq in. is A. I_1, the moment of inertia of the upper flange about the centroidal axis of the entire cross section, therefore, is

$$I_1 = I_0 + Ah^2 \quad \text{or} \quad I_1 = 0.667 + (8 \times 4.5^2) = 162.667 \text{ in.}^4$$

Of course, the moment of inertia of the lower flange about the centroidal axis of the entire section is of the same magnitude; hence I_{X-X} for the two flanges is 2×162.667, or 325.33 in.^{4} Adding the moments of inertia of the web and flanges, we have 42.67 + 325.33, or 368 in.^{4}, the moment of inertia of the entire I-section with respect to the horizontal axis passing through its centroid.

Example. A 4 x 8 x 1 in. angle section is shown in Fig. 6–7(c). Compute its moment of inertia about an axis passing through its centroid parallel to the short leg, axis X–X.

SOLUTION. Since the angle is an unsymmetrical section, the position of the centroid must be found, as explained in Art. 6–1. Taking an axis through the bottom of the long leg, we shall write an equation of moments of the component parts. The section is divided into the two rectangles shown by the diagonals in Fig. 6–7(d). Note that the 7- and 4-sq in. areas have moment arms of 3.5 and 7.5 in., respectively, about the selected axis. Thus

$$(7 \times 3.5) + (4 \times 7.5) = 11 \times c$$

$$c = 4.95 \text{ in.}$$

the distance of the centroidal axis from the bottom of the section, $c' = 8 - 4.95 = 3.05$ in. The two dimensions just found are shown in Fig. 6–7(d), as also are 2.55 and 1.45 in., the distances of the centroids of the 4- and 7-sq in. areas from X–X, the centroidal axis of the entire section.

The I_0 for the 4-sq in. area is

$$\frac{bd^3}{12} = \frac{4 \times 1^3}{12} \quad \text{or} \quad 0.33 \text{ in.}^4$$

Hence for this area $I_1 = I_0 + Ah^2$ or $I_1 = 0.33 + (4 \times 2.55^2) =$ 26.3 in.^{4}

For the 7-sq in. area

$$I_0 = \frac{bd^3}{12} = \frac{1 \times 7^3}{12} = 28.58 \text{ in.}^4$$

Thus for this area $I_1 = I_0 + Ah^2$ and $I_1 = 28.58 + (7 \times 1.45^2) =$ 43.3 in.^{4}

Now, adding the moments of inertia of the two component areas, we have 26.3 + 43.3, or 69.6 in.^{4}, the moment of inertia of the entire section with respect to a horizontal axis passing through its centroid. Refer to Table 6–6 and check this moment of inertia just found.

Example. Figure 6–7(e) shows a built-up section composed of a 10 ⌣ 15.3 and an ∟ 4 x 3 x $\frac{1}{4}$ with the short leg against the channel. Compute the moment of inertia of this built-up section about a horizontal axis passing through its centroid, axis X–X.

SOLUTION. Let us make use of the properties of sections given by the manufacturers. In Table 6–4, which gives the properties of channels, we find, for a 10 ⌣ 15.3, $I_{X-X} = 66.9$ in.^{4}, $A = 4.47$ sq in., and, since the channel is 10 in. in depth, its centroid is 5.0 in. from the top and bottom surfaces of the channel section.

For the angle section Table 6–6 gives, for an axis parallel to the long leg, $I_{Y-Y} = 1.4$ in.^{4}, $A = 1.69$ sq in., and 0.74 in. as the distance of its centroid from the back of the long leg. The two dimensions, 5.0 and 0.74 in., are shown on Fig. 6–7(e).

Writing an equation of moments with respect to an axis through the top of the built-up section,

$$(4.47 \times 5) + (1.69 \times 9.26) = (6.16 \times c)$$

$$c = 6.17 \text{ in.}$$

the distance of the X–X axis from the top of the section. To find c', $10 - 6.17 = 3.83$ in. Note these dimensions on Fig. 6–7(e).

The two dimensions just found enable us to determine 1.17 and 3.09 in., the distances of the centroids of the channel and angle, respectively, from the X–X axis of the entire section. See Fig. 6–7(e). These two dimensions will be the h's in the transfer formula.

To compute I for the channel about the X–X axis,

$$I_1 = I_0 + Ah^2$$
$$I_1 = 66.9 + (4.47 \times 1.17^2)$$
$$I_1 = 73.0 \text{ in.}^4$$

I for the angle about the X–X axis is

$$I_1 = I_0 + Ah^2$$
$$I_1 = 1.4 + (1.69 \times 3.09^2)$$
$$I_1 = 17.5 \text{ in.}^4$$

Adding the moments of inertia of the channel and angle with respect to the X–X axis of the built-up section gives $73.0 + 17.5 = 90.5$ in.^{4}, the moment of inertia of the built-up section.

Problem 6–4–A. If I for a rectangle about an axis through the centroid parallel to base is $\dfrac{bd^3}{12}$, compute I for an axis through the base, using the transfer formula. *Note:* $h = \dfrac{d}{2}$.

Problem 6–4–B. Compute I for the T-section shown in Fig. 6–3(a) about a horizontal axis through the centroid.

Problem 6–4–C. Compute I for the angle section shown in Fig. 6–7(c) about an axis through the centroid parallel to the long leg.

Problem 6–4–D. Compute I for the built-up section shown in Fig. 6–7(e) about an axis through the centroid parallel to the back of the channel.

6–5. Section Modulus. One of the properties of sections constantly used by the designer is a quantity called the *section modulus*. Its use in the design of beams is explained later; for the present it is only necessary to know that if I is the moment of inertia of a cross section about an axis passing through the centroid and if c is the distance of the most remote fiber of the cross section from the neutral axis the section modulus equals $\dfrac{I}{c}$. We use the letter S to represent the section modulus. Note that if I is in units of inches to the fourth power (in.^{4}) and c is a linear dimension in inches, $\dfrac{I}{c}$, the section modulus is in units of inches to the third power (in.^{3}). Thus, referring to Table 6–1, we find that S, the section modulus, of a 12 I 31.8 for an axis through the centroid parallel to the flange is 36.0 in.^{3}; we write $S_{X-X} = 36$ in.^{3} For the vertical centroidal axis, $S_{Y-Y} = 3.8$ in.^{3}

The rectangular cross section of a beam shown in Fig. 6–1(a) has a width b and depth d. The centroidal moment of inertia about an axis parallel to the side b is $\dfrac{bd^3}{12}$. The distance of the most remote fiber of the cross section from the neutral axis is one half the depth, that is, $c = \dfrac{d}{2}$. Then, if $S = \dfrac{I}{c}$,

$$S = \frac{bd^3}{12} \div \frac{d}{2} = \frac{bd^3}{12} \times \frac{2}{d} \quad \text{or} \quad S = \frac{bd^2}{6}$$

the section modulus of the rectangle.

For commonly used cross sections this important property is found in tables. Thus, consider S for a 6 x 4 x $\frac{1}{2}$ in. angle section (∟ 6 x 4 x $\frac{1}{2}$) about the centroidal axis parallel to the short leg. Table 6–6 shows I_{X-X} to be 17.4 in.^{4} The table also shows that the distance from the back of the short leg to the centroid is distance y, 1.99 in. Since the depth of the long leg is 6 in., $c = 6 - 1.99$, or 4.01 in. The distance 1.99 in. given in the table is the distance we have used for the term c'. Now, if $S = \dfrac{I}{c}$,

$$S_{X-X} = \frac{17.4}{4.01} \quad \text{or} \quad 4.3 \text{ in.}^3$$

It need not be computed as we have just done; note that this quantity is given in the table.

Example. Compute the section modulus of an 8 x 10 in. timber section about an axis through the centroid parallel to the shorter side.

SOLUTION. The actual dimensions of an 8 x 10 in. timber beam are 7.5 and 9.5 in. See Table 6–7. If 9.5 is its depth, $c = \dfrac{9.5}{2}$, or 4.75 in. Then

$$I = \frac{bd^3}{12} = \frac{7.5 \times 9.5^3}{12} = 535.86 \text{ in.}^4$$

Therefore,

$$S = \frac{I}{c} = \frac{535.86}{4.75} = 112.81 \text{ in.}^3$$

Note that this quantity is given in Table 6–7. Since we found that $S = \dfrac{bd^2}{6}$, we might have said

$$S = \frac{bd^2}{6} = \frac{7.5 \times 9.5^2}{6} = 112.81 \text{ in.}^3$$

Problem 6–5–A. Compute S for the T-section shown in Fig. 6–3(a) about a horizontal axis through the centroid.

Problem 6–5–B. Compute S_{X-X} for a 6 x 12 in. timber beam, using dressed size dimensions.

Problem 6–5–C. Table 6–4 shows that, for a 12 ⌐ 20.7, $S_{X-X} = 21.4$ in.^{3} By use of other properties given in the table, show that this quantity is correct.

Problem 6–5–D. Compute S_{X-X} for the angle section shown in Fig. 6–7(c).

Problem 6–5–E. Compute S_{X-X} for the built-up section shown in Fig. 6–7(e).

6–6. Radius of Gyration. In formulas used for the design of steel columns we find the term r, *the radius of gyration.* In Art. 6–2 we found the equation expressing the value of the moment of inertia of a cross section, $I = \Sigma az^2$. If we substitute A, the area of the cross section, for Σa and r^2 for z^2, we have $I = Ar^2$. In the original equation for I we remember that z is a variable; that is, it has various magnitudes with certain limitations. In the equation $I = Ar^2$, r is the distance from the neutral axis of a plane area to a point at which the entire area might be considered to be concentrated, so that A multiplied by the square of this distance gives the moment of inertia of the distributed area. The radius of gyration, r, of commonly used sections may be found in tables. If required, it is readily computed, for, if $I = Ar^2$,

$$r^2 = \frac{I}{A} \quad \text{and} \quad r = \sqrt{\frac{I}{A}}$$

In the design of steel columns we use the term *slenderness ratio*. It is the ratio $\frac{l}{r}$, the unsupported length of the column divided by the radius of gyration. As a cross-sectional area may have more than one value for r, depending on the axis considered, r, the radius of gyration, in column design is generally its smallest value; we use the term "least radius of gyration." Attention is called to Tables 6–5 and 6–6. Note that the least radius of gyration of these angle sections occurs with respect to the oblique axis $Z–Z$.

Example. A 10-in. wide-flange section weighing 49 lb per lin ft (10 **WF** 49) is to be used as a column. By use of other properties given in Table 6–2, compute the least radius of gyration of the section.

SOLUTION. By referring to Table 6–2 we find that this section has a 10-in. depth and a 10-in. width of flange. Obviously I for the two major axes, $X–X$ and $Y–Y$, will have unequal magnitudes. Since $r = \frac{I}{A}$, the smaller value of I will give the smaller value for the radius of gyration. In the table we find $I_{X-X} = 272.9$ in.[4] and $I_{Y-Y} = 93.0$ in.[4]; therefore we shall use the value for the $Y–Y$ axis, 93 in.[4] From the table we find $A = 14.40$ sq in. Then

$$r = \sqrt{\frac{I}{A}}$$

$$r = \sqrt{\frac{93}{14.4}}$$

$r = 2.54$ in., the least radius of gyration of the section

Note that this value is given in the table.

Example. A section is built up of a 14 x $\frac{1}{4}$ in. web plate and four 4 x 3 x $\frac{1}{4}$ in. angles as shown in Fig. 6–8. The angles have their short legs against the web plate. Compute the least radius of gyration of the built-up section.

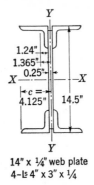

14" x ¼" web plate
4-l̲s̲ 4" x 3" x ¼

FIG. 6–8

solution. By inspection, the smaller moment of inertia occurs with respect to the vertical or Y–Y axis. Consequently, this is the axis to be considered in determining the least radius of gyration of the section. If there is doubt concerning this, I is computed for both of the major axes.

First we compute I for the web with respect to the Y–Y axis of the section:

$$I = \frac{bd^3}{12} = \frac{14 \times 0.25^3}{12} = 0.018 \text{ in.}^4$$

Now refer to Table 6–6, which gives the properties of angles. For an $\llcorner$ 4 x 3 x $\frac{1}{4}$ with respect to a centroidal axis parallel to the short leg (axis X–X in Table 6–6) we find $I_{X-X} = 2.8$ in.^{4}, $A = 1.69$ sq in., and the distance of the centroid to the back of the short leg is 1.24 in. This distance is shown on Fig. 6–8, and, since one half the thickness of the web is 0.125 in., $1.24 + 0.125 = 1.365$ in., the h distance to be used in the transfer formula.

To transfer the moment of inertia of *one angle* from its centroidal axis, parallel to its short leg, to the Y–Y axis of the built-up section,

$$I_1 = I_0 + Ah^2 = 2.8 + (1.69 \times 1.365^2) = 5.96 \text{ in.}^4$$

Since there are four angles, $4 \times 5.96 = 23.84$ in.^{4}, the moment of inertia of the four angles with respect to the Y–Y axis of the built-up section. To this we add the moment of inertia of the web plate, $23.84 + 0.018$, or 23.858 in.^{4}, the I_{Y-Y} for the built-up section. Since $c = 4 + 0.125$, or 4.125 in.,

$$S_{Y-Y} = \frac{I}{c} = \frac{23.858}{4.125} = 5.8 \text{ in.}^3$$

The area of the entire cross section is the sum of the areas of the angles and web plate $(4 \times 1.69) + 3.5 = 10.26$ sq in. $= A$.

$$r_{Y-Y} = \sqrt{\frac{I}{A}} = \sqrt{\frac{23.858}{10.26}}$$

$= 1.54$ in., the least radius of gyration of the built-up section

Problem 6–6–A. A $6 \times 4 \times \frac{7}{8}$ in. angle is to be used as a column. What is the least radius of gyration? See Table 6–6.

Problem 6–6–B. Compute the radius of gyration for the built-up section shown in Fig. 6–7(e) with respect to the X–X axis.

Problem 6–6–C. Compute the radius of gyration for the angle section shown in Fig. 6–7(c) with respect to the X–X axis.

Problem 6–6–D. Compute the radius of gyration for the built-up section shown in Fig. 6–8 with respect to the X–X axis.

Problem 6–6–E. A 10 W^F 33 has $12 \times \frac{1}{2}$ in. cover plates riveted to the flanges. Compute the radius of gyration of the section with respect to the Y–Y axis.

6–7. Properties of Sections. The preceding articles in this chapter have pertained to the computation of the properties of sections used in the design of structural members. Since the rectangle, circle, and triangle are the areas most commonly involved in engineering problems, the properties of these shapes are given in Fig. 6–9. This figure will serve as a reference. Although the properties of commonly used structural sections may be found directly in tables, a thorough knowledge of their significance will be of great value to the designer. Thus far nothing has been said concerning the use of these properties or their application in the design of members that resist forces. This is explained later, particularly in connection with members in bending and in the design of columns.

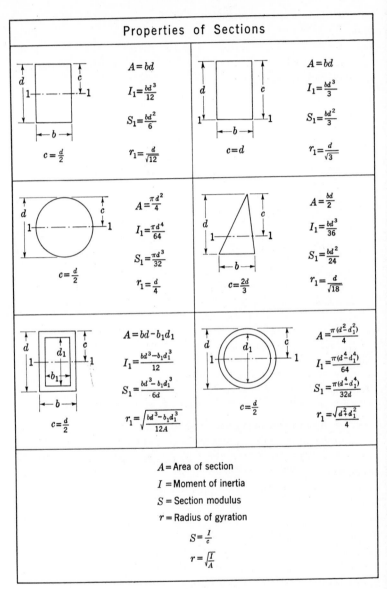

FIG. 6-9

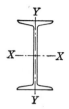

TABLE 6-1.   PROPERTIES OF AMERICAN STANDARD I-BEAMS

Nominal Size	Weight per Foot	Area	Depth	Flange		Web Thickness	Axis $X-X$			Axis $Y-Y$		
				Width	Thickness		I	S	r	I	S	r
In	Lb	In^2	In	In	In	In	In^4	In^3	In	In^4	In^3	In
24 x 7⅞	120.0	35.13	24.00	8.048	1.102	.798	3010.8	250.9	9.26	84.9	21.1	1.56
	105.9	30.98	24.00	7.875	1.102	.625	2811.5	234.3	9.53	78.9	20.0	1.60
24 x 7	100.0	29.25	24.00	7.247	.871	.747	2371.8	197.6	9.05	48.4	13.4	1.29
	90.0	26.30	24.00	7.124	.871	.624	2230.1	185.8	9.21	45.5	12.8	1.32
	79.9	23.33	24.00	7.000	.871	.500	2087.2	173.9	9.46	42.9	12.2	1.36
20 x 7	95.0	27.74	20.00	7.200	.916	.800	1599.7	160.0	7.59	50.5	14.0	1.35
	85.0	24.80	20.00	7.053	.916	.653	1501.7	150.2	7.78	47.0	13.3	1.38
20 x 6¼	75.0	21.90	20.00	6.391	.789	.641	1263.5	126.3	7.60	30.1	9.4	1.17
	65.4	19.08	20.00	6.250	.789	.500	1169.5	116.9	7.83	27.9	8.9	1.21
18 x 6	70.0	20.46	18.00	6.251	.691	.711	917.5	101.9	6.70	24.5	7.8	1.09
	54.7	15.94	18.00	6.000	.691	.460	795.5	88.4	7.07	21.2	7.1	1.15
15 x 5½	50.0	14.59	15.00	5.640	.622	.550	481.1	64.2	5.74	16.0	5.7	1.05
	42.9	12.49	15.00	5.500	.622	.410	441.8	58.9	5.95	14.6	5.3	1.08
12 x 5¼	50.0	14.57	12.00	5.477	.659	.687	301.6	50.3	4.55	16.0	5.8	1.05
	40.8	11.84	12.00	5.250	.659	.460	268.9	44.8	4.77	13.8	5.3	1.08
12 x 5	35.0	10.20	12.00	5.078	.544	.428	227.0	37.8	4.72	10.0	3.9	.99
	31.8	9.26	12.00	5.000	.544	.350	215.8	36.0	4.83	9.5	3.8	1.01
10 x 4⅝	35.0	10.22	10.00	4.944	.491	.594	145.8	29.2	3.78	8.5	3.4	.91
	25.4	7.38	10.00	4.660	.491	.310	122.1	24.4	4.07	6.9	3.0	.97
8 x 4	23.0	6.71	8.00	4.171	.425	.441	64.2	16.0	3.09	4.4	2.1	.81
	18.4	5.34	8.00	4.000	.425	.270	56.9	14.2	3.26	3.8	1.9	.84
7 x 3⅝	20.0	5.83	7.00	3.860	.392	.450	41.9	12.0	2.68	3.1	1.6	.74
	15.3	4.43	7.00	3.660	.392	.250	36.2	10.4	2.86	2.7	1.5	.78
6 x 3⅜	17.25	5.02	6.00	3.565	.359	.465	26.0	8.7	2.28	2.3	1.3	.68
	12.5	3.61	6.00	3.330	.359	.230	21.8	7.3	2.46	1.8	1.1	.72
5 x 3	14.75	4.29	5.00	3.284	.326	.494	15.0	6.0	1.87	1.7	1.0	.63
	10.0	2.87	5.00	3.000	.326	.210	12.1	4.8	2.05	1.2	.82	.65
4 x 2⅝	9.5	2.76	4.00	2.796	.293	.326	6.7	3.3	1.56	.91	.65	.58
	7.7	2.21	4.00	2.660	.293	.190	6.0	3.0	1.64	.77	.58	.59
3 x 2⅜	7.5	2.17	3.00	2.509	.260	.349	2.9	1.9	1.15	.59	.47	.52
	5.7	1.64	3.00	2.330	.260	.170	2.5	1.7	1.23	.46	.40	.53

TABLE 6-2.   PROPERTIES OF WIDE-FLANGE SHAPES

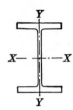

Nominal Size	Weight per Foot	Area	Depth	Flange Width	Flange Thickness	Web Thickness	Axis X–X I	Axis X–X S	Axis X–X r	Axis Y–Y I	Axis Y–Y S	Axis Y–Y r
In	Lb	In²	In	In	In	In	In⁴	In³	In	In⁴	In³	In
36 x 16½	230	67.73	35.88	16.475	1.260	.765	14988.4	835.5	14.88	870.9	105.7	3.59
36 x 12	150	44.16	35.84	11.972	.940	.625	9012.1	502.9	14.29	250.4	41.8	2.38
33 x 15¾	200	58.79	33.00	15.750	1.150	.715	11048.2	669.6	13.71	691.7	87.8	3.43
33 x 11½	130	38.26	33.10	11.510	.855	.580	6699.0	404.8	13.23	201.4	35.0	2.29
30 x 15	172	50.65	29.88	14.985	1.065	.655	7891.5	528.2	12.48	550.1	73.4	3.30
30 x 10½	108	31.77	29.82	10.484	.760	.548	4461.0	299.2	11.85	135.1	25.8	2.06
27 x 14	145	42.68	26.88	13.965	.975	.600	5414.3	402.9	11.26	406.9	58.3	3.09
27 x 10	94	27.65	26.91	9.990	.747	.490	3266.7	242.8	10.87	115.1	23.0	2.04
24 x 14	130	38.21	24.25	14.000	.900	.565	4009.5	330.7	10.24	375.2	53.6	3.13
24 x 12	100	29.43	24.00	12.000	.775	.468	2987.3	248.9	10.08	203.5	33.9	2.63
24 x 9	76	22.37	23.91	8.985	.682	.440	2096.4	175.4	9.68	76.5	17.0	1.85
21 x 13	112	32.93	21.00	13.000	.865	.527	2620.6	249.6	8.92	289.7	44.6	2.96
21 x 9	96	28.21	21.14	9.038	.935	.575	2088.9	197.6	8.60	109.3	24.2	1.97
	82	24.10	20.86	8.962	.795	.499	1752.4	168.0	8.53	89.6	20.0	1.93
21 x 8¼	68	20.02	21.13	8.270	.685	.430	1478.3	139.9	8.59	60.4	14.6	1.74
	62	18.23	20.99	8.240	.615	.400	1326.8	126.4	8.53	53.1	12.9	1.71
18 x 11¾	105	30.86	18.32	11.792	.911	.554	1852.5	202.2	7.75	231.0	39.2	2.73
	96	28.22	18.16	11.750	.831	.512	1674.7	184.4	7.70	206.8	35.2	2.71
18 x 8¾	70	20.56	18.00	8.750	.751	.438	1153.9	128.2	7.49	78.5	17.9	1.95
	64	18.80	17.87	8.715	.686	.403	1045.8	117.0	7.46	70.3	16.1	1.93
18 x 7½	55	16.19	18.12	7.532	.630	.390	889.9	98.2	7.41	42.0	11.1	1.61
	50	14.71	18.00	7.500	.570	.358	800.6	89.0	7.38	37.2	9.9	1.59
16 x 11½	96	28.22	16.32	11.533	.875	.535	1355.1	166.1	6.93	207.2	35.9	2.71
	88	25.87	16.16	11.502	.795	.504	1222.6	151.3	6.87	185.2	32.2	2.67
16 x 8½	64	18.80	16.00	8.500	.715	.443	833.8	104.2	6.66	68.4	16.1	1.91
	58	17.04	15.86	8.464	.645	.407	746.4	94.1	6.62	60.5	14.3	1.88
16 x 7	40	11.77	16.00	7.000	.503	.307	515.5	64.4	6.62	26.5	7.6	1.50
	36	10.59	15.85	6.992	.428	.299	446.3	56.3	6.49	22.1	6.3	1.45

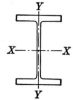

TABLE 6–2. PROPERTIES OF WIDE-FLANGE SHAPES (CONTINUED)

Nominal Size	Weight per Foot	Area	Depth	Flange		Web Thickness	Axis X–X			Axis Y–Y		
				Width	Thickness		I	S	r	I	S	r
In	Lb	In^2	In	In	In	In	In^4	In^3	In	In^4	In^3	In
14 x 16	150	44.08	14.88	15.515	1.128	.695	1786.9	240.2	6.37	702.5	90.6	3.99
	142	41.85	14.75	15.500	1.063	.680	1672.2	226.7	6.32	660.1	85.2	3.97
14 x 14½	95	27.94	14.12	14.545	.748	.465	1063.5	150.6	6.17	383.7	52.8	3.71
	87	25.56	14.00	14.500	.688	.420	966.9	138.1	6.15	349.7	48.2	3.70
14 x 12	84	24.71	14.18	12.023	.778	.451	928.4	130.9	6.13	225.5	37.5	3.02
	78	22.94	14.06	12.000	.718	.428	851.2	121.1	6.09	206.9	34.5	3.00
14 x 10	68	20.00	14.06	10.040	.718	.418	724.1	103.0	6.02	121.2	24.1	2.46
	61	17.94	13.91	10.000	.643	.378	641.5	92.2	5.98	107.3	21.5	2.45
14 x 8	48	14.11	13.81	8.031	.593	.339	484.9	70.2	5.86	51.3	12.8	1.91
	43	12.65	13.68	8.000	.528	.308	429.0	62.7	5.82	45.1	11.3	1.89
14 x 6¾	34	10.00	14.00	6.750	.453	.287	339.2	48.5	5.83	21.3	6.3	1.46
	30	8.81	13.86	6.733	.383	.270	289.6	41.8	5.73	17.5	5.2	1.41
12 x 12	72	21.16	12.25	12.040	.671	.430	597.4	97.5	5.31	195.3	32.4	3.04
	65	19.11	12.12	12.000	.606	.390	533.4	88.0	5.28	174.6	29.1	3.02
12 x 10	58	17.06	12.19	10.014	.641	.359	476.1	78.1	5.28	107.4	21.4	2.51
	53	15.59	12.06	10.000	.576	.345	426.2	70.7	5.23	96.1	19.2	2.48
12 x 8	45	13.24	12.06	8.042	.576	.336	350.8	58.2	5.15	50.0	12.4	1.94
	40	11.77	11.94	8.000	.516	.294	310.1	51.9	5.13	44.1	11.0	1.94
12 x 6½	31	9.12	12.09	6.525	.465	.265	238.4	39.4	5.11	19.8	6.1	1.47
	27	7.97	11.95	6.500	.400	.240	204.1	34.1	5.06	16.6	5.1	1.44
10 x 10	54	15.88	10.12	10.028	.618	.368	305.7	60.4	4.39	103.9	20.7	2.56
	49	14.40	10.00	10.000	.558	.340	272.9	54.6	4.35	93.0	18.6	2.54
10 x 8	39	11.48	9.94	7.990	.528	.318	209.7	42.2	4.27	44.9	11.2	1.98
	33	9.71	9.75	7.964	.433	.292	170.9	35.0	4.20	36.5	9.2	1.94
10 x 5¾	25	7.35	10.08	5.762	.430	.252	133.2	26.4	4.26	12.7	4.4	1.31
	21	6.19	9.90	5.750	.340	.240	106.3	21.5	4.14	9.7	3.4	1.25
8 x 8	35	10.30	8.12	8.027	.493	.315	126.5	31.1	3.50	42.5	10.6	2.03
	31	9.12	8.00	8.000	.433	.288	109.7	27.4	3.47	37.0	9.2	2.01
8 x 6½	28	8.23	8.06	6.540	.463	.285	97.8	24.3	3.45	21.6	6.6	1.62
	24	7.06	7.93	6.500	.398	.245	82.5	20.8	3.42	18.2	5.6	1.61
8 x 5¼	20	5.88	8.14	5.268	.378	.248	69.2	17.0	3.43	8.5	3.2	1.20
	17	5.00	8.00	5.250	.308	.230	56.4	14.1	3.36	6.7	2.6	1.16

Reproduced from "Manual of Steel Construction," by permission of the American Institute of Steel Construction.

PROPERTIES OF SECTIONS

TABLE 6–3. PROPERTIES OF WIDE-FLANGE SHAPES, MISCELLANEOUS COLUMNS AND BEAMS

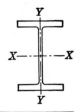

Nominal Size	Weight per Foot	Area	Depth	Flange		Web Thickness	Axis X–X			Axis Y–Y		
				Width	Thickness		I	S	r	I	S	r
In	Lb	In²	In	In	In	In	In⁴	In³	In	In⁴	In³	In
WF SHAPES AND LIGHT COLUMNS												
6 WF	25	7.37	6.37	6.080	.456	.320	53.5	16.8	2.69	17.1	5.6	1.52
6 x 6	20	5.90	6.20	6.018	.367	.258	41.7	13.4	2.66	13.3	4.4	1.50
	15.5	4.62	6.00	6.000	.269	.240	30.3	10.1	2.56	9.69	3.2	1.45
5 WF	18.5	5.45	5.12	5.025	.420	.265	25.4	9.94	2.16	8.89	3.54	1.28
5 x 5	16	4.70	5.00	5.000	.360	.240	21.3	8.53	2.13	7.51	3.00	1.26
4 WF	13	3.82	4.16	4.060	.345	.280	11.3	5.45	1.72	3.76	1.85	.99
LIGHT BEAMS												
12 x 4	22	6.47	12.31	4.030	.424	.260	155.7	25.3	4.91	4.55	2.26	.84
	19	5.62	12.16	4.010	.349	.240	130.1	21.4	4.81	3.67	1.83	.81
	16½	4.86	12.00	4.000	.269	.230	105.3	17.5	4.65	2.79	1.39	.76
10 x 4	19	5.61	10.25	4.020	.394	.250	96.2	18.8	4.14	4.19	2.08	.86
	17	4.98	10.12	4.010	.329	.240	81.8	16.2	4.05	3.45	1.72	.83
	15	4.40	10.00	4.000	.269	.230	68.8	13.8	3.95	2.79	1.39	.80
8 x 4	15	4.43	8.12	4.015	.314	.245	48.0	11.8	3.29	3.30	1.65	.86
	13	3.83	8.00	4.000	.254	.230	39.5	9.88	3.21	2.62	1.31	.83
6 x 4	16	4.72	6.25	4.030	.404	.260	31.7	10.1	2.59	4.32	2.14	.96
	12	3.53	6.00	4.000	.279	.230	21.7	7.24	2.48	2.89	1.44	.90
JOISTS												
12 x 4	14	4.14	11.91	3.970	.224	.200	88.2	14.8	4.61	2.25	1.13	.74
10 x 4	11½	3.39	9.87	3.950	.204	.180	51.9	10.5	3.92	2.01	1.02	.77
8 x 4	10	2.95	7.90	3.940	.204	.170	30.8	7.79	3.23	1.99	1.01	.82
6 x 4	8½	2.50	5.83	3.940	.194	.170	14.8	5.07	2.43	1.89	.96	.87

Reproduced from "Manual of Steel Construction," by permission of the American Institute of Steel Construction.

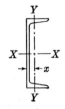

TABLE 6–4. PROPERTIES OF AMERICAN STANDARD CHANNELS

Nominal Size	Weight per Foot	Area	Depth	Flange			Axis X–X			Axis Y–Y			
				Width	Average Thickness	Web Thickness	I	S	r	I	S	r	x
In	Lb	In^2	In	In	In	In	In^4	In^3	In	In^4	In^3	In	In
18 x 4	58.0	16.98	18.00	4.200	.625	.700	670.7	74.5	6.29	18.5	5.6	1.04	.88
	51.9	15.18	18.00	4.100	.625	.600	622.1	69.1	6.40	17.1	5.3	1.06	.87
	45.8	13.38	18.00	4.000	.625	.500	573.5	63.7	6.55	15.8	5.1	1.09	.89
	42.7	12.48	18.00	3.950	.625	.450	549.2	61.0	6.64	15.0	4.9	1.10	.90
15 x 3⅜	50.0	14.64	15.00	3.716	.650	.716	401.4	53.6	5.24	11.2	3.8	.87	.80
	40.0	11.70	15.00	3.520	.650	.520	346.3	46.2	5.44	9.3	3.4	.89	.78
	33.9	9.90	15.00	3.400	.650	.400	312.6	41.7	5.62	8.2	3.2	.91	.79
12 x 3	30.0	8.79	12.00	3.170	.501	.510	161.2	26.9	4.28	5.2	2.1	.77	.68
	25.0	7.32	12.00	3.047	.501	.387	143.5	23.9	4.43	4.5	1.9	.79	.68
	20.7	6.03	12.00	2.940	.501	.280	128.1	21.4	4.61	3.9	1.7	.81	.70
10 x 2⅝	30.0	8.80	10.00	3.033	.436	.673	103.0	20.6	3.42	4.0	1.7	.67	.65
	25.0	7.33	10.00	2.886	.436	.526	90.7	18.1	3.52	3.4	1.5	.68	.62
	20.0	5.86	10.00	2.739	.436	.379	78.5	15.7	3.66	2.8	1.3	.70	.61
	15.3	4.47	10.00	2.600	.436	.240	66.9	13.4	3.87	2.3	1.2	.72	.64
9 x 2½	20.0	5.86	9.00	2.648	.413	.448	60.6	13.5	3.22	2.4	1.2	.65	.59
	15.0	4.39	9.00	2.485	.413	.285	50.7	11.3	3.40	1.9	1.0	.67	.59
	13.4	3.89	9.00	2.430	.413	.230	47.3	10.5	3.49	1.8	.97	.67	.61
8 x 2¼	18.75	5.49	8.00	2.527	.390	.487	43.7	10.9	2.82	2.0	1.0	.60	.57
	13.75	4.02	8.00	2.343	.390	.303	35.8	9.0	2.99	1.5	.86	.62	.56
	11.5	3.36	8.00	2.260	.390	.220	32.3	8.1	3.10	1.3	.79	.63	.58
7 x 2⅛	14.75	4.32	7.00	2.299	.366	.419	27.1	7.7	2.51	1.4	.79	.57	.53
	12.25	3.58	7.00	2.194	.366	.314	24.1	6.9	2.59	1.2	.71	.58	.53
	9.8	2.85	7.00	2.090	.366	.210	21.1	6.0	2.72	.98	.63	.59	.55
6 x 2	13.0	3.81	6.00	2.157	.343	.437	17.3	5.8	2.13	1.1	.65	.53	.52
	10.5	3.07	6.00	2.034	.343	.314	15.1	5.0	2.22	.87	.57	.53	.50
	8.2	2.39	6.00	1.920	.343	.200	13.0	4.3	2.34	.70	.50	.54	.52
5 x 1¾	9.0	2.63	5.00	1.885	.320	.325	8.8	3.5	1.83	.64	.45	.49	.48
	6.7	1.95	5.00	1.750	.320	.190	7.4	3.0	1.95	.48	.38	.50	.49
4 x 1⅝	7.25	2.12	4.00	1.720	.296	.320	4.5	2.3	1.47	.44	.35	.46	.46
	5.4	1.56	4.00	1.580	.296	.180	3.8	1.9	1.56	.32	.29	.45	.46
3 x 1½	6.0	1.75	3.00	1.596	.273	.356	2.1	1.4	1.08	.31	.27	.42	.46
	5.0	1.46	3.00	1.498	.273	.258	1.8	1.2	1.12	.25	.24	.41	.44
	4.1	1.19	3.00	1.410	.273	.170	1.6	1.1	1.17	.20	.21	.41	.44

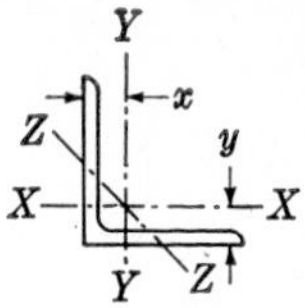

TABLE 6-5. PROPERTIES OF ANGLES WITH EQUAL LEGS

| Size | Thickness | Weight per Foot | Area of Section | Axis X–X and Axis Y–Y | | | | Axis Z–Z |
| | | | | I | S | r | x or y | r |
In	In	Lb	In^2	In^4	In^3	In	In	In
8 x 8	1⅛	56.9	16.73	98.0	17.5	2.42	2.41	1.56
	1	51.0	15.00	89.0	15.8	2.44	2.37	1.56
	⅞	45.0	13.23	79.6	14.0	2.45	2.32	1.57
	¾	38.9	11.44	69.7	12.2	2.47	2.28	1.57
	⅝	32.7	9.61	59.4	10.3	2.49	2.23	1.58
	½	26.4	7.75	48.6	8.4	2.50	2.19	1.59
6 x 6	1	37.4	11.00	35.5	8.6	1.80	1.86	1.17
	⅞	33.1	9.73	31.9	7.6	1.81	1.82	1.17
	¾	28.7	8.44	28.2	6.7	1.83	1.78	1.17
	⅝	24.2	7.11	24.2	5.7	1.84	1.73	1.18
	½	19.6	5.75	19.9	4.6	1.86	1.68	1.18
	7⁄16	17.2	5.06	17.7	4.1	1.87	1.66	1.19
	⅜	14.9	4.36	15.4	3.5	1.88	1.64	1.19
5 x 5	⅞	27.2	7.98	17.8	5.2	1.49	1.57	0.97
	¾	23.6	6.94	15.7	4.5	1.51	1.52	0.97
	⅝	20.0	5.86	13.6	3.9	1.52	1.48	0.98
	½	16.2	4.75	11.3	3.2	1.54	1.43	0.98
	7⁄16	14.3	4.18	10.0	2.8	1.55	1.41	0.98
	⅜	12.3	3.61	8.7	2.4	1.56	1.39	0.99
	5⁄16	10.3	3.03	7.4	2.0	1.57	1.37	0.99
4 x 4	¾	18.5	5.44	7.7	2.8	1.19	1.27	0.78
	⅝	15.7	4.61	6.7	2.4	1.20	1.23	0.78
	½	12.8	3.75	5.6	2.0	1.22	1.18	0.78
	7⁄16	11.3	3.31	5.0	1.8	1.23	1.16	0.78
	⅜	9.8	2.86	4.4	1.5	1.23	1.14	0.79
	5⁄16	8.2	2.40	3.7	1.3	1.24	1.12	0.79
	¼	6.6	1.94	3.0	1.1	1.25	1.09	0.80
3½ x 3½	½	11.1	3.25	3.6	1.5	1.06	1.06	0.68
	7⁄16	9.8	2.87	3.3	1.3	1.07	1.04	0.68
	⅜	8.5	2.48	2.9	1.2	1.07	1.01	0.69
	5⁄16	7.2	2.09	2.5	0.98	1.08	0.99	0.69
	¼	5.8	1.69	2.0	0.79	1.09	0.97	0.69
3 x 3	½	9.4	2.75	2.2	1.1	0.90	0.93	0.58
	7⁄16	8.3	2.43	2.0	0.95	0.91	0.91	0.58
	⅜	7.2	2.11	1.8	0.83	0.91	0.89	0.58
	5⁄16	6.1	1.78	1.5	0.71	0.92	0.87	0.59
	¼	4.9	1.44	1.2	0.58	0.93	0.84	0.59
	3⁄16	3.71	1.09	0.96	0.44	0.94	0.82	0.59
2½ x 2½	½	7.7	2.25	1.2	0.72	0.74	0.81	0.49
	⅜	5.9	1.73	0.98	0.57	0.75	0.76	0.49
	5⁄16	5.0	1.47	0.85	0.48	0.76	0.74	0.49
	¼	4.1	1.19	0.70	0.39	0.77	0.72	0.49
	3⁄16	3.07	0.90	0.55	0.30	0.78	0.69	0.49
2 x 2	⅜	4.7	1.36	0.48	0.35	0.59	0.64	0.39
	5⁄16	3.92	1.15	0.42	0.30	0.60	0.61	0.39
	¼	3.19	0.94	0.35	0.25	0.61	0.59	0.39
	3⁄16	2.44	0.71	0.27	0.19	0.62	0.57	0.39

Reproduced from "Manual of Steel Construction," by permission of the American Institute of Steel Construction.

TABLE 6–6. PROPERTIES OF ANGLES WITH UNEQUAL LEGS

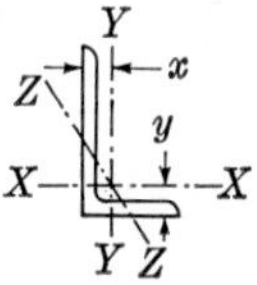

Size	Thickness	Weight per Foot	Area of Section	Axis X–X				Axis Y–Y				Axis Z–Z
				I	S	r	y	I	S	r	x	r
In	In	Lb	In^2	In^4	In^3	In	In	In^4	In^3	In	In	In
8 x 6	¾	33.8	9.94	63.4	11.7	2.53	2.56	30.7	6.9	1.76	1.56	1.29
	½	23.0	6.75	44.3	8.0	2.56	2.47	21.7	4.8	1.79	1.47	1.30
8 x 4	1	37.4	11.00	69.6	14.1	2.52	3.05	11.6	3.9	1.03	1.05	0.85
	¾	28.7	8.44	54.9	10.9	2.55	2.95	9.4	3.1	1.05	0.95	0.85
	⅝	24.2	7.11	46.9	9.2	2.57	2.91	8.1	2.6	1.07	0.91	0.86
	½	19.6	5.75	38.5	7.5	2.59	2.86	6.7	2.2	1.08	0.86	0.86
7 x 4	⅞	30.2	8.86	42.9	9.7	2.20	2.55	10.2	3.5	1.07	1.05	0.86
	¾	26.2	7.69	37.8	8.4	2.22	2.51	9.1	3.0	1.09	1.01	0.86
	⅝	22.1	6.48	32.4	7.1	2.24	2.46	7.8	2.6	1.10	0.96	0.86
	½	17.9	5.25	26.7	5.8	2.25	2.42	6.5	2.1	1.11	0.92	0.87
	⅜	13.6	3.98	20.6	4.4	2.27	2.37	5.1	1.6	1.13	0.87	0.88
6 x 4	⅞	27.2	7.98	27.7	7.2	1.86	2.12	9.8	3.4	1.11	1.12	0.86
	¾	23.6	6.94	24.5	6.3	1.88	2.08	8.7	3.0	1.12	1.08	0.86
	⅝	20.0	5.86	21.1	5.3	1.90	2.03	7.5	2.5	1.13	1.03	0.86
	½	16.2	4.75	17.4	4.3	1.91	1.99	6.3	2.1	1.15	0.99	0.87
	⁷⁄₁₆	14.3	4.18	15.5	3.8	1.92	1.96	5.6	1.9	1.16	0.96	0.87
	⅜	12.3	3.61	13.5	3.3	1.93	1.94	4.9	1.6	1.17	0.94	0.88
6 x 3½	½	15.3	4.50	16.6	4.2	1.92	2.08	4.3	1.6	0.97	0.83	0.76
	⅜	11.7	3.42	12.9	3.3	1.94	2.04	3.3	1.2	0.99	0.79	0.77
	⁵⁄₁₆	9.8	2.87	10.9	2.7	1.95	2.01	2.9	1.0	1.00	0.76	0.77
5 x 3½	¾	19.8	5.81	13.9	4.3	1.55	1.75	5.6	2.2	0.98	1.00	0.75
	⅝	16.8	4.92	12.0	3.7	1.56	1.70	4.8	1.9	0.99	0.95	0.75
	½	13.6	4.00	10.0	3.0	1.58	1.66	4.1	1.6	1.01	0.91	0.75
	⁷⁄₁₆	12.0	3.53	8.9	2.6	1.59	1.63	3.6	1.4	1.01	0.88	0.76
	⅜	10.4	3.05	7.8	2.3	1.60	1.61	3.2	1.2	1.02	0.86	0.76
5 x 3	½	12.8	3.75	9.5	2.9	1.59	1.75	2.6	1.1	0.83	0.75	0.65
	⁷⁄₁₆	11.3	3.31	8.4	2.6	1.60	1.73	2.3	1.0	0.84	0.73	0.65
	⅜	9.8	2.86	7.4	2.2	1.61	1.70	2.0	0.89	0.84	0.70	0.65
	⁵⁄₁₆	8.2	2.40	6.3	1.9	1.61	1.68	1.8	0.75	0.85	0.68	0.66
4 x 3½	⅝	14.7	4.30	6.4	2.4	1.22	1.29	4.5	1.8	1.03	1.04	0.72
	½	11.9	3.50	5.3	1.9	1.23	1.25	3.8	1.5	1.04	1.00	0.72
	⅜	9.1	2.67	4.2	1.5	1.25	1.21	3.0	1.2	1.06	0.96	0.73
	⁵⁄₁₆	7.7	2.25	3.6	1.3	1.26	1.18	2.6	1.0	1.07	0.93	0.73
	¼	6.2	1.81	2.9	1.0	1.27	1.16	2.1	0.81	1.07	0.91	0.73
4 x 3	⅝	13.6	3.98	6.0	2.3	1.23	1.37	2.9	1.4	0.85	0.87	0.64
	½	11.1	3.25	5.1	1.9	1.25	1.33	2.4	1.1	0.86	0.83	0.64
	⅜	8.5	2.48	4.0	1.5	1.26	1.28	1.9	0.87	0.88	0.78	0.64
	⁵⁄₁₆	7.2	2.09	3.4	1.2	1.27	1.26	1.7	0.73	0.89	0.76	0.65
	¼	5.8	1.69	2.8	1.0	1.28	1.24	1.4	0.60	0.90	0.74	0.65
3½ x 3	½	10.2	3.00	3.5	1.5	1.07	1.13	2.3	1.1	0.88	0.88	0.62
	⁷⁄₁₆	9.1	2.65	3.1	1.3	1.08	1.10	2.1	0.98	0.89	0.85	0.62
	⅜	7.9	2.30	2.7	1.1	1.09	1.08	1.9	0.85	0.90	0.83	0.62
	⁵⁄₁₆	6.6	1.93	2.3	0.95	1.10	1.06	1.6	0.72	0.90	0.81	0.63
	¼	5.4	1.56	1.9	0.78	1.11	1.04	1.3	0.59	0.91	0.79	0.63
3 x 2½	½	8.5	2.50	2.1	1.0	0.91	1.00	1.3	0.74	0.72	0.75	0.52
	⅜	6.6	1.92	1.7	0.81	0.93	0.96	1.0	0.58	0.74	0.71	0.52
	⁵⁄₁₆	5.6	1.62	1.4	0.69	0.94	0.93	0.90	0.49	0.74	0.68	0 53
	¼	4.5	1.31	1.2	0.56	0.95	0.91	0.74	0.40	0.75	0.66	0.53

PROPERTIES OF SECTIONS

TABLE 6-7. PROPERTIES OF AMERICAN STANDARD SIZES OF YARD LUMBER AND TIMBERS

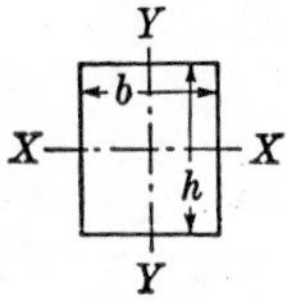

Nominal Size, in Inches		American Standard Dressed Size (S4S), in Inches		Area of Section, in Inches^2	Moment of Inertia, in Inches^4		Section Modulus, in Inches^3	
b	h	b	h	$A = b \times h$	$I_{X-X} = bh^3/12$	$I_{Y-Y} = b^3h/12$	$S_{X-X} = bh^2/6$	$S_{Y-Y} = b^2h/6$
2 x 6		1⅝ x	5⅝	9.14	24.10	2.01	8.57	2.48
2 x 8		1⅝ x	7½	12.19	57.13	2.68	15.23	3.30
2 x 10		1⅝ x	9½	15.44	116.10	3.40	24.44	4.18
2 x 12		1⅝ x 11½		18.69	205.95	4.11	35.82	5.06
2 x 14		1⅝ x 13½		21.94	333.18	4.83	49.36	5.94
3 x 4		2⅝ x	3⅝	9.52	10.42	5.46	5.75	4.16
3 x 6		2⅝ x	5⅝	14.77	38.93	8.48	13.84	6.46
3 x 8		2⅝ x	7½	19.69	92.29	11.30	24.61	8.61
3 x 10		2⅝ x	9½	24.94	187.55	14.32	39.48	10.91
3 x 12		2⅝ x 11½		30.19	332.69	17.33	57.86	13.21
3 x 14		2⅝ x 13½		35.44	538.21	20.35	79.73	15.50
4 x 4		3⅝ x	3⅝	13.14	14.39	14.39	7.94	7.94
4 x 6		3⅝ x	5⅝	20.39	53.76	22.33	19.12	12.32
4 x 8		3⅝ x	7½	27.19	127.44	29.77	33.98	16.43
4 x 10		3⅝ x	9½	34.44	259.00	37.71	54.53	20.81
4 x 12		3⅝ x 11½		41.69	459.43	45.65	79.90	25.19
4 x 14		3⅝ x 13½		48.94	743.24	53.59	110.11	29.57
6 x 6		5½ x	5½	30.25	76.26	76.26	27.73	27.73
6 x 8		5½ x	7½	41.25	193.36	103.98	51.56	37.81
6 x 10		5½ x	9½	52.25	392.96	131.71	82.73	47.90
6 x 12		5½ x 11½		63.25	697.07	159.44	121.23	57.98
6 x 14		5½ x 13½		74.25	1,127.67	187.17	167.06	68.06
8 x 8		7½ x	7½	56.25	263.67	263.67	70.31	70.31
8 x 10		7½ x	9½	71.25	535.86	333.98	112.81	89.06
8 x 12		7½ x 11½		86.25	950.55	404.30	165.31	107.81
8 x 14		7½ x 13½		101.25	1,537.73	474.61	227.81	126.56
8 x 16		7½ x 15½		116.25	2,327.42	544.92	300.31	145.31
10 x 10		9½ x	9½	90.25	678.76	678.76	142.90	142.90
10 x 12		9½ x 11½		109.25	1,204.03	821.65	209.40	172.98
10 x 14		9½ x 13½		128.25	1,947.80	964.55	288.56	203.06
10 x 16		9½ x 15½		147.25	2,948.07	1,107.44	380.40	233.15
12 x 12		11½ x 11½		132.25	1,457.51	1,457.51	253.48	253.48
12 x 14		11½ x 13½		155.25	2,357.86	1,710.98	349.31	297.56
12 x 16		11½ x 15½		178.25	3,568.71	1,964.46	460.48	341.65

Reproduced by permission of the Timber Engineering Company.

For use in the design of structural steel members, certain tables of properties of sections are presented. Tables 6–1 through 6–6, selected from tables in *Manual of Steel Construction,* published by the American Institute of Steel Construction, give properties of certain rolled sections or shapes. Attention is called to the two major axes, X–X and Y–Y. I, S, and r are given for both axes; the values to be used in design depend on the position in which the member is placed. If an I-section is used as a beam, the web is placed in a vertical position, and therefore the X–X or horizontal axis determines the section modulus to be used.

Table 6–7 gives the properties of American Standard sizes of yard lumber and timbers. Note the difference between the nominal and dressed sizes. The properties A, I, and S are based on the dressed or actual sizes.

6–8. Aluminum Sections. Because the use of aluminum results in a considerable reduction of weight and, in ordinary environments, needs no protection, structural aluminum shapes are being used more extensively each year. Aluminum is supplied in hundreds of different alloys and thousands of shapes and forms.

A widely used, heat-treated, wrought aluminum alloy used for structural shapes is 6061-T6. The number 6061 identifies the alloy composition, the letter T shows that the metal has been heat-treated, and the final figure 6 indicates the type of heat treatment. Another alloy used for structural members is 2014-T6, a somewhat stronger material. Structural aluminum may be obtained in angles, channels, I-beams, wide-flange sections, tees, and zees. All "standard" sections are approximations of the American Standard sections employed for structural steel.* Certain physical properties of the 6061-T6 alloy are given in Table 5–1.

* For detailed information relating to aluminum shapes, see *Alcoa Structural Handbook,* published by the Aluminum Company of America.

CHAPTER 7

SHEARING STRESSES IN BEAMS

7–1. Types of Beams. A *beam* is a structural member, resting on supports, usually at its ends, which supports transverse loads. The loads on a beam tend to *bend* rather than to shorten or lengthen the member. The great majority of beams used in building construction are placed in a horizontal position. Generally, the loads on a beam that result from the force of gravity are vertical. The forces a beam is required to resist are the downward loads and the upward supporting forces called *reactions*.

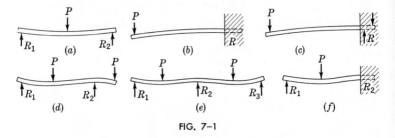

FIG. 7–1

A *simple beam* rests on a support at each end, there being no restraint against bending at the supports; the ends are *simply supported*. Figure 7–1(a) is a conventional representation of a simple beam; it shows the shape the beam tends to take as it deforms under bending stresses.

A *cantilever beam* projects beyond the support or supports and is loaded on the projecting part. Figure 7–1(b) is an illustration of a cantilever beam built into and projecting beyond the face of a wall. For such a beam there are both upward and downward distributed forces exerted on the portion built into the wall; the resultants of these forces are indicated in Fig. 7–1(c).

An *overhanging beam* rests on two or more supports, one or both ends projecting beyond the supports. Figure 7–1(*d*) indicates an overhanging beam; the part of the beam projecting beyond the right support is a cantilever.

A *continuous beam* rests on more than two supports; see Fig. 7–1(*e*).

A *fixed beam* is a beam in which one or both ends are restrained against rotation. Figure 7–1(*f*) shows a beam whose left support is *simply supported*, the right support being *fixed*.

In order to establish the stresses (internal forces) a beam will be required to resist, it is first necessary to determine the magnitudes of the reactions. For the beams indicated in Figs. 7–1(*a*), (*b*), (*c*), and (*d*) the basic laws of equilibrium (Art. 4–5), enable us to compute their reactions.

7–2. Kinds of Loads. The two kinds of loads which commonly occur on beams are *concentrated* and *uniformly distributed* loads.

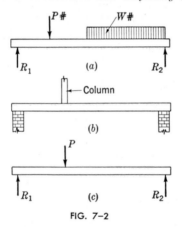

FIG. 7–2

A concentrated load extends over such a short length of the beam that, without appreciable error, it is assumed to act at a point. The end of one beam supported by another beam and a column supported by a beam are illustrations of concentrated loads; we consider that they act at points in the length of the beam, whereas we know that such loads actually extend over relatively short distances. It is usual to represent a concentrated load by the letter *P* as in Fig. 7–2(*a*). A beam supported by brick walls is indicated in Fig. 7–2(*b*). Similarly, we consider that the reactions act at points even though the bearing length in Fig. 7–2(b) is the width of the wall. Theoretically, the line of action of the reaction should be at the mid-point of bearing, as shown in Fig. 7–2(c).

A *distributed* load acts over a considerable length of beam. Most distributed loads are *uniformly distributed;* that is, they exert an equal downward force for each linear unit of beam length. A brick wall of uniform height built on a beam is assumed to exert a uniformly distributed load on the beam. The weight of the beam itself constitutes a uniformly distributed load tending to cause the beam to bend. A uniformly distributed load may extend over a part or the entire length of a beam. It is customary to represent the magnitude of a uniformly distributed load by the letter W, as in Fig. 7–2(a). Frequently the uniformly distributed load is given as so many pounds per linear foot; in this case we use the lower-case w to represent the weight per foot. For instance, suppose that a simple beam has a length of 18 ft 0 in. and a uniformly distributed load of 300 lb per lin ft; that is, $w = 300$ lb. The total load on the beam is $300 \times 18 = 5400$ lb, or $W = 5400$ lb. Unless otherwise noted, this significance of the terms w and W applies to the succeeding problems in this book.

7–3. Vertical Shear. Figure 7–3(a) represents a simple beam supporting a uniformly distributed load W. As indicated in Fig. 7–3(b), there is a tendency for the beam to fail by dropping verti-

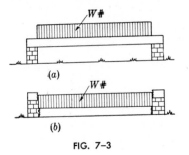

(a)

(b)

FIG. 7–3

cally between the supports, the fibers of the beam failing by *vertical shear*. A shearing stress results when two parallel forces having opposite directions act on a body, tending to cause one part of the body to slide past an adjacent part.

The magnitude of the vertical shear is represented by V; it varies in magnitude at different places in the beam's length. It is readily computed, for *the shear at any section of a beam is equal to the algebraic sum of all the external forces on either the right or left side of the section.* If we call the upward forces (reactions) positive and the downward forces (loads) negative, this may be expressed in the following rule:

The magnitude of the vertical shear at any section of a beam is equal to the reactions minus the loads to the left of the section. If we take the forces to the right instead of the left, the magnitude of the shear will be the same. However, to avoid confusion, we shall consider the forces to the left in the following illustrative examples. It should be noted that since the shear is reactions minus loads it is given in units of pounds.

Example. A simple beam 20 ft 0 in. in length between supports has a concentrated load of 800 lb at 4 ft 0 in. from the left reaction and another concentrated load of 400 lb at 6 ft 0 in. from the right reaction, as shown in Fig. 7–4(a). Ignoring the weight of the beam, compute the magnitude of vertical shear at various sections in the length of the beam.

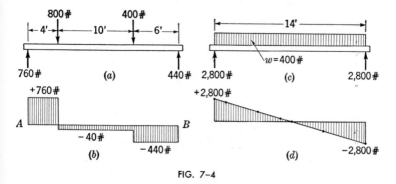

FIG. 7–4

SOLUTION. It is convenient to use subscripts to identify the section at which the shear is taken. Thus $V_{(x=2)}$ indicates that we are writing an equation for the vertical shear at 2 ft 0 in. from the *left* end of the beam.

By the principle of moments explained in Art. 4–6, we find that R_1 and R_2 have magnitudes of 760 and 440 lb, respectively.

First let us determine the shear at a section 1 ft 0 in. from the left support. At this section the reactions to the left are but one, 760 lb. There are no loads to the left of this section. Then, applying the above rule,

$$\text{shear} = \text{reactions minus loads}$$

$$V_{(x=1)} = \quad 760 \quad - \quad 0 \quad = 760 \text{ lb}$$

Since there are no intervening loads between R_1 and the 800-lb load, the shear at any section in this portion of the beam is 760 lb.

Now let us consider a section at 5 ft 0 in. from R_1. The reaction to the left is 760 lb and the load to the left of the section is 800 lb. Then, repeating the rule,

$$V_{(x=5)} = 760 - 800 = -40 \text{ lb.}$$

This is the magnitude of V between the two concentrated loads.

Next consider a section 15 ft 0 in. from R_1. The reaction to the left is 760 lb and the loads are 800 and 400 lb. Repeating the rule, we write

$$V_{(x=15)} = 760 - (800 + 400) = -440 \text{ lb}$$

Since there are no loads between the 400-lb load and R_2, the shear at any section at this portion of the beam has the same magnitude, −440 lb.

7–4. Shear Diagram. We have found that the magnitude of the shear varies at successive sections along the length of the beam. It is of great convenience to represent the various values graphically by constructing a shear diagram. It will be found later that a glance at a shear diagram will disclose important information to be used in the design of a beam.

Let us draw a shear diagram for the beam and loads shown in Fig. 7–4(a), the beam diagram. We construct the shear diagram directly below the beam diagram, beginning by drawing a horizontal line AB, sometimes called the base line [see Fig. 7–4(b)], and plotting the positive shear values above and the negative values below. In the preceding article we found the value of the shear at 1 ft from R_1 to be 760 lb. Therefore, at some convenient scale of so many pounds to the inch, we lay off a point equal to 760 lb *above* the base line AB at 1 ft from R_1. At all sections of the beam between R_1 and the 800-lb load the value of V is 760 lb; thus the upper line of the shear diagram is horizontal. At 5 ft 0 in. from R_1, $V = -40$ lb; consequently we lay off a distance equal to -40 lb *below* the base line because the shear at this section is a negative quantity. This same magnitude of V continues up to the 400-lb load. To the right of the 400-lb load we found V to be -440 lb, and this value is plotted in a similar manner. The vertical lines in the shear diagram show, at the scale selected, the magnitude of the shear at the successive sections of the beam.

For this particular beam the shear diagram shows that the magnitude of the *maximum shear* is 760 lb and that it occurs between R_1 and the 800-lb load. Obviously, for simple beams the maximum vertical shear has the same magnitude as the greater reaction. We observe also, for this beam, that the shear diagram "passes through zero"; that is, it changes from a positive to a negative quantity at a point 4 ft 0 in. from R_1, directly under the 800-lb load. We shall find that *the section at which the shear passes through zero is the section at which the beam is most likely to fail by bending stresses.*

Example. A simple beam has a span length of 14 ft 0 in. and a uniformly distributed load of 400 lb per lin ft, as shown in Fig. 7–4(c). Construct the shear diagram for this beam and note the magnitude of the maximum vertical shear and also the section of the beam at which the shear passes from a positive to a negative quantity.

SOLUTION. Unlike the preceding example, this beam has a uniformly distributed load. Since the load is 400 lb per lin ft and the length of the beam is 14 ft 0 in., W, the total uniformly distributed load, is 400×14, or 5600 lb. The beam is symmetrically loaded; hence $R_1 = R_2 = \frac{1}{2} \times 5600 = 2800$ lb.

At the left reaction the value of V is equal to R_1, 2800 lb.

Now let us write the value of V for various sections in the length of the beam, bearing in mind that the load is 400 lb *per lin ft* and that vertical shear = reaction minus loads (to left of the section)

$$V_{(x=1)} = 2800 - (1 \times 400) = 2400 \text{ lb}$$

$$V_{(x=4)} = 2800 - (4 \times 400) = 1200 \text{ lb}$$

$$V_{(x=6)} = 2800 - (6 \times 400) = 400 \text{ lb}$$

$$V_{(x=7)} = 2800 - (7 \times 400) = 0$$

$$V_{(x=10)} = 2800 - (10 \times 400) = -1200 \text{ lb}$$

$$V_{(x=14)} = 2800 - (14 \times 400) = -2800 \text{ lb}$$

These values are plotted above and below the base line, as previously explained, and we note that they fall on a straight line from $+2800$ lb at R_1 to -2800 lb at R_2, Fig. 7–4(d). Actually the shear decreases uniformly as x increases. The value of the maximum vertical shear is 2800 lb; it occurs at both R_1 and R_2. The shear passes from a positive to a negative quantity at $x = 7$, the center of the span.

Example. Construct the shear diagram for the overhanging beam and loading shown in Fig. 7–5(a). Note the value of the

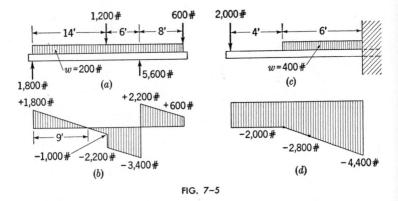

FIG. 7–5

maximum shear and the section or sections at which the shear passes through zero.

SOLUTION. R_1 and R_2 are computed as explained in Art. 4–6.

Thus

$$20 \times R_2 = (28 \times 200 \times 14) + (1200 \times 14)$$
$$+ (600 \times 28)$$
$$R_2 = 5600 \text{ lb}$$
$$20 \times R_1 + (600 \times 8) = (28 \times 200 \times 6) + (1200 \times 6)$$
$$R_1 = 1800 \text{ lb}$$

From the preceding examples it is seen that it is necessary to compute the value of the shear only at certain sections of the beam in order to construct the shear diagram. At R_1 the value of V is 1800 lb. Next, let us find the value of V at an infinitely short distance to the left of the 1200-lb concentrated load; we identify this section as $V_{(x=14-)}$. The reason for this is that we wish to know the value of the shear on *both* sides of and adjacent to the 1200-lb load. Then

$$V_{(x=14-)} = 1800 - (200 \times 14) = -1000 \text{ lb}$$

The next section is a slight distance to the right of the 1200-lb load:

$$V_{(x=14+)} = 1800 - [(200 \times 14) + 1200] = -2200 \text{ lb}$$
$$V_{(x=20-)} = 1800 - [(200 \times 20) + 1200] = -3400 \text{ lb}$$
$$V_{(x=20+)} = (1800 + 5600) - [(200 \times 20) + 1200] = +2200 \text{ lb}$$
$$V_{(x=28-)} = (1800 + 5600) - [(200 \times 28) + 1200] = +600 \text{ lb}$$

The various values of V are plotted, and the shear diagram is shown in Fig. 7–5(b). Inspecting this diagram, we see that the maximum shear is 3400 lb and that it occurs immediately to the left of R_2.

We see also that the shear passes through zero at two points, one at R_2 and the other at some point between R_1 and the 1200-lb load. To find this point, let us call it x feet from R_1. We shall write an expression for the shear at this section (the expression will contain the term x), and, since we know that the value of the shear at this section is zero, we shall equate the expression to zero.

Then, solving for x, the unknown, we shall have found the distance from R_1 at which the shear passes through zero. Thus

$$1800 - (200 \times x) = 0$$

$$200 \times x = 1800$$

$$x = 9 \text{ ft } 0 \text{ in.}$$

Example. Construct the shear diagram for the cantilever beam loaded as shown in Fig. 7–5(c).

SOLUTION. When computing the values of the shear in cantilever beams, it is convenient to draw the beam diagram with the support at the right-hand side. Then, when the rule is applied, the magnitudes of the shear at various sections of the beam are all found to be negative quantities, there being no reactions to the left of the various sections.

$$V_{(x=1)} = -2000 \text{ lb}$$

This is the value of the shear at all sections between the 2000-lb load and the uniformly distributed load.

$$V_{(x=6)} = -[2000 + (400 \times 2)] = -2800 \text{ lb}$$

$$V_{(x=10)} = -[2000 + (400 \times 6)] = -4400 \text{ lb}$$

The shear diagram is shown in Fig. 7–5(d). Note that the maximum shear is −4400 lb, the total load on the beam.

In the design of beams it is necessary that the designer know the magnitude of the maximum vertical shear. Redraw the beam shown in Fig. 7–4(a), placing the 400-lb load 6 ft from R_1 and the 800-lb load 4 ft from R_2. We now find that $R_1 = 440$ lb and $R_2 = 760$ lb. When the shear diagram is constructed, Fig. 7–4(b) is reversed; the value of V at R_1 is +440 lb and at R_2 it is −760 lb. In the design of beams the *magnitude* of the shear is the important consideration; whether it is positive or negative is of no importance. It is of the utmost importance, however, to differentiate the positive and negative values in constructing the shear diagram.

Problem 7–4–A–B–C–D–E–F–G–H–I. For the beams and loadings shown in Fig. 7–6 construct the shear diagrams and note the magnitudes of the maximum vertical shear and the section or sections at which the shear passes through zero.

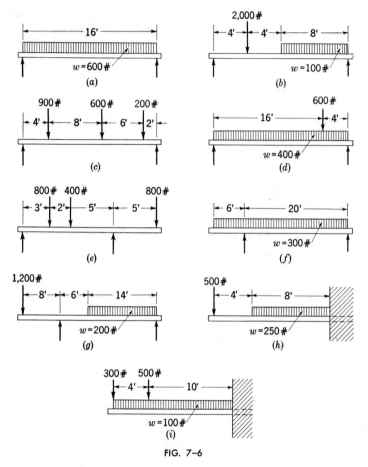

FIG. 7–6

7–5. Horizontal Shear. Figure 7–7(a) represents a number of boards placed one above the other with supports under the ends. A load placed on the boards, or even the weight of the boards alone, tends to cause them to slide horizontally, as indicated in the figure. This tendency to move laterally is called *horizontal shear* or, sometimes, *longitudinal shear*. In solid beams this tendency to slide horizontally is always present; it is resisted by the stresses set up in the fibers of the beam. The magnitude of the total horizontal shear at any section of a beam is equal to the magnitude of the total vertical shear. Note, however, that the horizontal shearing unit stresses are not distributed uniformly over the cross section of the beam. This stress may be found by the formula

$$q = \frac{VQ}{Ib}$$

in which q = the horizontal shearing unit stress at any specific point in the cross section of a beam in pounds per square inch

V = the total vertical shear in the beam at the section selected in pounds

Q = the statical moment with respect to the neutral axis of the area of the cross section above (or below) the point at which q is to be determined (a statical moment is an area multiplied by the distance of its centroid to a given axis) in inches [3]

I = the moment of inertia of the cross section of the beam with respect to its neutral axis in inches [4]

b = the width of the beam at the point at which q is to be computed in inches

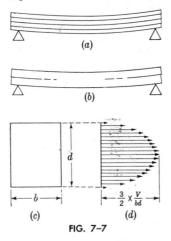

(a)

(b)

(c)   (d)

FIG. 7–7

The maximum horizontal shearing unit stress of a rectangular cross section occurs at the neutral surface and its magnitude is $q = \dfrac{3}{2} \times \dfrac{V}{bd}$, that is, $1\frac{1}{2}$ times the average. Consider the rectangular cross section of width b and depth d, Fig. 7–7(c). Let us determine the horizontal shearing unit stress *at the neutral axis.* The area above the neutral axis is $\left(b \times \dfrac{d}{2} \right)$ and its centroid is $\dfrac{d}{4}$ distance from the neutral axis; thus

$$Q = b \times \frac{d}{2} \times \frac{d}{4} = \frac{bd^2}{8}$$

I, the moment of inertia of the cross section, $= \dfrac{bd^3}{12}$, Art. 6–3. Then

$$q = \frac{VQ}{Ib} = \frac{V \times \dfrac{bd^2}{8}}{\dfrac{bd^3}{12} \times b} \quad \text{and} \quad q = \frac{3}{2} \times \frac{V}{bd}$$

It should be remembered that the total horizontal shear over the cross-sectional area is V; the maximum unit stress occurs at the neutral surface, and this is the stress with which we are principally concerned. The lengths of the arrows shown in Fig. 7–7(d) indicate the distribution of horizontal shearing stresses in a rectangular cross section. Since in solid timber beams there is less resistance to shear parallel to the grain than perpendicular to it, the design of a timber beam should include investigation for horizontal shear. This stress is maximum at the neutral surface; the tendency to fail by shear is indicated in Fig. 7–7(b). This is sometimes called "two-beam action."

From the foregoing discussion it is apparent that a loaded timber beam may fail by horizontal shear as well as by bending. Both of these stresses should be investigated. The horizontal shearing unit stress should always be computed for beams having short spans with large loads.

To find the maximum horizontal shearing unit stress, *we consider the section at which V has its maximum value.*

Example. An 8 x 12 in. Douglas fir timber, dense construction grade, is used for a beam having a span of 16 ft 0 in. There is a uniformly distributed load (including the weight of the beam) of 400 lb per lin ft extending over the entire length of the beam and, in addition, a concentrated load of 4000 lb at 4 ft 0 in. from one end. Compute the maximum horizontal shearing unit stress. Is the beam safe with respect to horizontal shear?

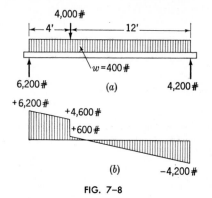

FIG. 7–8

SOLUTION. The beam diagram, Fig. 7–8(a), is drawn and the reactions computed thus:

$$16R_1 = (4000 \times 12) + (400 \times 16 \times 8) \quad \text{and} \quad R_1 = 6200 \text{ lb}$$

$$16R_2 = (4000 \times 4) + (400 \times 16 \times 8) \quad \text{and} \quad R_2 = 4200 \text{ lb}$$

Next, the shear diagram is drawn as shown in Fig. 7–8(b). We note that V, the maximum vertical shear, has a magnitude of 6200 lb immediately to the right of the left reaction. Since the actual dimensions of a timber whose nominal size is 8 x 12 in. are $7\frac{1}{2}$ x $11\frac{1}{2}$ in., Table 6–7,

$$q = \frac{3}{2} \times \frac{V}{bd} = \frac{3}{2} \times \frac{6200}{7.5 \times 11.5}$$

$$= 108 \text{ psi, the maximum horizontal shearing unit stress}$$

Referring to Table 5–4, we find that the allowable horizontal shearing unit stress for this species and grade of timber is 120 psi. Since the actual stress is less than the allowable, the beam is safe with respect to horizontal shear.

Problem 7–5–A. A 6 x 12 in. southern pine simple beam, No. 1 SR grade, has a span of 16 ft 0 in. and a uniformly distributed load of 400 lb per lin ft, including the weight of the beam. Compute the maximum horizontal shearing unit stress. Is the beam safe with respect to shear?

Problem 7–5–B. A simple 10 x 12 in. beam has a span of 10 ft 0 in. with a uniformly distributed load, including its own weight, of 100 lb per lin ft, a concentrated load of 6000 lb at 5 ft 0 in. from the left reaction, and another concentrated load of 4000 lb at 2 ft 0 in. from the right reaction. If the timber is eastern hemlock, Select Structural grade, is the beam safe with respect to horizontal shear?

Problem 7–5–C. A 3 x 10 in. cantilever beam 6 ft 0 in. in length has a uniformly distributed load of 100 lb per lin ft, including its own weight, and a concentrated load of 400 lb at the unsupported end. The timber is the heart structural grade of redwood. Is this beam sufficiently large to resist horizontal shear?

7–6. Shearing Stresses in Steel Beams. In designing steel beams, the designer, in accordance with the current specifications for structural steel (see Table 5–5), is permitted a shearing stress of 13,000 psi *on the gross area of the webs* of beams and plate girders. Although this procedure ignores the material in the flanges and we know that the shearing stresses are distributed unequally, this method of designing errs on the side of safety and results in simple computations. The shearing unit stress in structural steel beams is generally well within the allowable. To determine the shearing unit stress in steel beams, we use the formula

$$f_s = \frac{V}{dt}$$

in which f_s = the shearing unit stress in pounds per square inch

V = the total vertical shear at that section of the beam being investigated in pounds

d = the depth of the beam in inches

t = the thickness of the web in inches

If we are to determine the *maximum* shearing unit stress, we consider that section of the beam at which V has its maximum magnitude.

Example. A 12 I 31.8 (12 in. standard I-beam weighing 31.8 lb per lin ft) has a span of 19 ft 0 in. with a uniformly distributed load, including its own weight, of 25,000 lb. Compute the shearing unit stress. Is it excessive?

SOLUTION. Since the load is uniformly distributed, each reaction is equal to $25,000 \div 2$, or 12,500 lb. Thus, V, the maximum vertical shear, has the same magnitude at each reaction, 12,500 lb.

On referring to Table 6–1, we find the depth of a 12 I 31.8 to be 12 in. and the thickness of the web, 0.35 in. Hence

$$f_s = \frac{V}{dt}$$

$$= \frac{12,500}{12 \times 0.35} = 2980 \text{ psi, the actual shearing unit stress}$$

Since this stress is less than 13,000 psi, the allowable (Table 5–5), the beam is sufficiently large with respect to shear.

Example. What is the maximum shear that is permitted on a 10 WF 21 (10-in. wide flange beam weighing 21 lb per lin ft)?

SOLUTION. From Table 6–2 we find that 9.9 and 0.24 in. are the depth and web thickness, respectively, of this beam. Then, since the allowable shearing unit stress is 13,000 psi,

$$f_s = \frac{V}{dt}$$

$$V = f_s \times d \times t$$

$$= 13,000 \times 9.9 \times 0.24 = 30,900 \text{ lb, the maximum}$$
allowable shear

Problem 7–6–A. An 18 WF 55 is used for a simple beam having a span of 6 ft 0 in. At the center of the span is a concentrated load of 100,000 lb. Investigate the beam for shear.

Problem 7–6–B. A 15 I 42.9 has a span of 20 ft 0 in. with a concentrated load of 20,000 lb 5 ft 0 in. from one of the supports. Compute the shearing unit stress.

Problem 7–6–C. A 14 WF 30 is used for an overhanging beam whose total length is 24 ft 0 in. The distance between supports is 18 ft 0 in., and the overhang at one end is 6 ft 0 in. Over the entire length of the beam there is a uniformly distributed load of 2000 lb per lin ft, including its own weight. Compute the shearing unit stress.

7–7. Shearing Stresses in Built-Up Beams. Built-up timber beams have their component parts secured together by bolts, timber connectors, and sometimes glue. In built-up steel beams riveting and welding are employed. To determine the number of rivets or connecting devices required, the shearing stress at the plane of contact of the parts to be joined is determined by use of the shear formula, $q = \dfrac{VQ}{Ib}$, as explained in Art. 7–5. The following examples illustrate the procedure.

Example. A built-up beam is composed of a 20 I 65.4 with $\frac{1}{2}$ x 10 in. cover plates riveted to the upper and lower flanges by two rows of $\frac{3}{4}$-in. rivets in each flange, as indicated in Fig. 7–9(a).

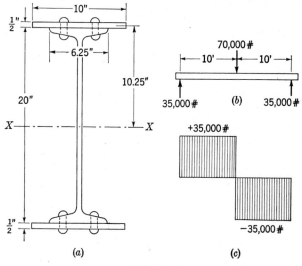

FIG. 7–9

The beam is a simple beam, 20 ft 0 in. in length, with a concentrated load of 70,000 lb at the center of the span, Fig. 7–9(b). Compute the spacing of the rivets in a line parallel to the length of the beam.

SOLUTION. First a shear diagram is constructed as shown in Fig. 7–9(c). The maximum vertical shear, V, is 35,000 lb, the weight of the beam being ignored for the purpose of explanation.

Since the rivets are in shear at the plane of contact between the plates and the flanges of the I-beam, the shearing unit stress must be computed at a point 10 in. above (or below) the neutral axis of the beam. The area of the built-up section (the plate) above the plane of contact is 10×0.5, or 5 sq in., and its lever arm with respect to the neutral axis of the built-up section is 10.25 in., Fig. 7–9(a); hence $Q = (5 \times 10.25)$.

By the method explained in Art. 6–4, I, the moment of inertia of the built-up section, is found by computations to be 2220 in.[4]

From Table 6–1 we find that the width of flange of a 20 I 65.4 is 6.25 in.

Then

$$q = \frac{VQ}{Ib} = \frac{35,000 \times 5 \times 10.25}{2220 \times 6.25} = 129 \text{ psi}$$

the horizontal shearing unit stress at the planes between the I-beam flanges and the cover plates. Hence the total shear per inch of length of beam is 129×6.25, or 806 lb.

The area of a circle is $\dfrac{\pi d^2}{4}$, Fig. 6–9. Therefore, the cross-sectional area of a $\frac{3}{4}$-in. rivet is $\dfrac{3.1416 \times 0.75^2}{4}$, or 0.4418 sq in. The allowable shearing unit stress of rivet steel is 15,000 psi, Table 5–5. Hence $0.4418 \times 15,000 = 6630$ lb, the allowable shearing stress for one $\frac{3}{4}$-in. rivet. As there are two rows of rivets in each flange, $2 \times 6630 = 13,260$ lb, the allowable shearing stress for two rivets.

Now, since the total shear *per inch of length of beam* is 806 lb, $13,260 \div 806 = 16$ in., the theoretical required maximum spacing of the rivets in a line parallel to the length of the beam.

It should be noted that in this example 35,000 lb is the value of the shear at all sections in the length of the beam, and therefore 16 in. will be the maximum allowable spacing over the entire length of the beam. If the load had been uniformly distributed or if the weight of the beam had been considered, the value of V would have been maximum at the supports and diminished in magnitude as we approached the center of the span. For such a beam it would have been necessary to compute the spacing at various sections; the spacing would have increased in magnitude as we approached the center of the span.

Example. A simple beam having a span of 15 ft 0 in. has two concentrated loads of 5800 lb each placed at the third points of the span. The beam is composed of two 6 x 8 in. sections of No. 1 dense SR grade of southern pine placed one above the other and held together with 4-in. split ring connectors. Determine the spacing of the connectors.

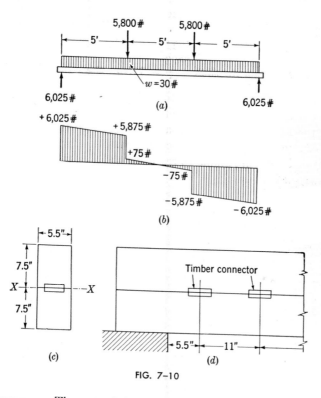

FIG. 7-10

SOLUTION. The actual dimensions of a 6 x 8 in. timber beam cross section are 5.5 x 7.5 in., Table 6–7. Hence the dimensions of the built-up section are 5.5 x 15 in., as shown in Fig. 7–10(c). Assume that the weight of the timber beam is 30 lb per lin ft. The beam diagram, Fig. 7–10(a), is drawn, and the shear diagram, Fig. 7–10(b), shows that the maximum vertical shear is 6025 lb.

Since the timber connectors are placed at the plane of contact of the two individual members, we shall find the maximum horizontal shearing unit stress at this point, which is at the mid-depth of the built-up beam; thus

$$q = \frac{3}{2} \times \frac{V}{bd} = \frac{3 \times 6025}{2 \times 5.5 \times 15}$$

= 110 psi, the maximum horizontal shearing unit stress

Therefore the total shear per inch of length of beam is $110 \times 5.5 =$ 605 lb.

The allowable working value for one 4-in. split ring in this species of timber is 6680 lb; thus $\frac{6680}{605} = 11$ in., the required maximum spacing of the timber connectors. It is customary to place the first connector one half a space from the support [see Fig. 7–10(d)], and the 11-in. spacing will be accepted between the supports and the concentrated loads. Two connectors placed between the concentrated loads are ample to resist the shearing stress in this portion of the beam.

CHAPTER 8

BENDING MOMENTS IN BEAMS

8–1. Moment of a Force. In Chapter 4 we learned that the *moment of a force* is the tendency of a force to cause rotation about a certain point or axis. The point or axis is called the *center of moments*, and the perpendicular distance between the line of action of the force and the point or axis is the *lever arm* or *moment arm* of the moment. The magnitude of the moment is the magnitude of the force (usually pounds) multiplied by the lever arm (usually feet or inches). Hence the moment of a force is in units of foot-pounds or inch-pounds, as, for instance, 30,000 ft-lb or 360,000 in-lb. In computations involving moments be particular to designate the units. This will aid in avoiding errors. If a force tends to produce clockwise rotation, it is customary to designate the moment as *positive*, such as +20,000 ft-lb. Similarly, if the tendency to rotate is counterclockwise, the moment is *negative*, as, for instance, −45,000 ft-lb.

8–2. Bending Moment and Bending Moment Diagram. Figure 8–1(a) represents a simple beam having a length of 16 ft 0 in. with a concentrated load of 20,000 lb at 4 ft 0 in. from the left reaction. As explained in Art. 4–6, the reactions are found by computations to be $R_1 = 15,000$ lb and $R_2 = 5000$ lb. The magnitude of the vertical shear at various sections in the length of the beam is computed as explained in Art. 7–3, and the shear diagram, Fig. 8–1(b), is drawn in accordance with the explanations given in Art. 7–4. Note that the maximum vertical shear is 15,000 lb and that the shear passes through zero at 4 ft 0 in. from R_1.

It should be noted that the weight of a beam constitutes a uniformly distributed load. Frequently this weight is quite small in comparison to the applied loads. In this example, and in many of the succeeding examples, the weight of the beam is neglected to simplify the explanations.

The *bending moment* at any section in the length of a beam is the effect of the various forces acting on the beam that tend to cause it to bend. The bending moment is represented by the letter *M*. This tendency to bend is not uniform over the length of the beam but varies in magnitude.

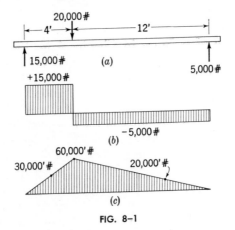

FIG. 8–1

The bending moment at any section of a beam is equal to the algebraic sum of the moments of the forces on either the right or the left of the section. By "algebraic sum" is meant the sum of the positive and negative quantities. For the purpose of simplification, let us consider only the forces to the *left* of the section. Thus we can say: *the bending moment at any section in the length of a beam equals the moments of the reactions minus the moments of the loads to the left of the section.*

Particular attention is called to the similarity between this rule and the rule for determining the shear given in Art. 7–3. The shear is *reactions minus loads*, whereas the bending moment is *moments of reactions minus moments of loads*.

Like the shear variations, the value of the bending moments may be plotted; the resulting diagram is a *bending moment diagram*. Frequently such a diagram is simply called the *moment diagram*. To construct the bending moment diagram, we draw directly below the shear diagram a horizontal line called the base line. Then, at a convenient scale of so many foot-pounds (or inch-pounds) to the inch, we plot the value of the bending moment for the various sections above and below this base line, positive moments above and negative moments below.

To illustrate, let us consider the beam shown in Fig. 8-1(a). Again we shall use subscripts to designate the section at which the bending moment is taken. Thus $M_{(x=3)}$ indicates that we are writing an expression for the bending moment 3 ft 0 in. from the left end of the beam.

Consider first a section 2 ft 0 in. from R_1 and apply the foregoing rule. The reaction to the left of this section is 15,000 lb, and its lever arm *about the section* is 2 ft 0 in.; hence the moment is (15,000 $\times$ 2) ft-lb. There are no loads to the left of this section. Therefore, since bending moment equals moments of reactions minus moments of loads to the left,

$$M_{(x=2)} = (15,000 \times 2) - 0 = +30,000 \text{ ft-lb}$$

This is a positive moment; hence at 2 ft 0 in. from R_1 we plot, at a convenient scale, a point equal to 30,000 ft-lb above the base line, as shown in Fig. 8-1(c). For a section 4 ft 0 in. from R_1 we write

$$M_{(x=4)} = (15,000 \times 4) - (20,000 \times 0) = +60,000 \text{ ft-lb}$$

The 20,000-lb load has a lever arm of zero about the section; (20,000 $\times$ 0) = 0. We might have written (as we do)

$$M_{(x=4)} = (15,000 \times 4) = +60,000 \text{ ft-lb}$$

This value is plotted as shown in Fig. 8-1(c).

Now consider a section 12 ft 0 in. from R_1.

$$M_{(x=12)} = (15,000 \times 12) - (20,000 \times 8) = +20,000 \text{ ft-lb}$$

In this equation (20,000 $\times$ 8) indicates that the load of 20,000 lb is 8 ft 0 in. from the selected section.

$$M_{(x=16)} = (15,000 \times 16) - (20,000 \times 12) = 0$$

Any number of sections might be taken, but in this particular beam the values of the moments fall on the straight lines indicated in the bending moment diagram. For a simple beam the moments at the supports are always zero. *The value of the maximum bending moment occurs at that section of the beam at which the shear passes through zero;* in this beam it is 4 ft 0 in. from R_1; its value is 60,000 ft-lb, or $60,000 \times 12 = 720,000$ in-lb. In designing beams, the value of the *maximum bending moment* is the moment with which we are particularly concerned.

Example. A simple beam 20 ft 0 in. in length has a uniformly distributed load of 1000 lb per lin ft extending over a length of 12 ft 0 in. from the right reaction. Compute the maximum bending moment and draw the bending moment diagram.

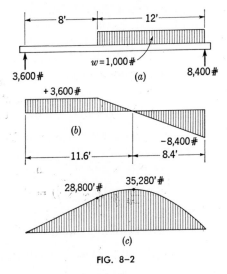

FIG. 8–2

SOLUTION. The beam diagram is drawn as shown in Fig. 8–2(*a*). To compute the reactions,

$$20R_1 = (12 \times 1000 \times 6) \quad \text{and} \quad R_1 = 3600 \text{ lb}$$
$$20R_2 = (12 \times 1000 \times 14) \quad \text{and} \quad R_2 = 8400 \text{ lb}$$

The shear diagram, Fig. 8–2(*b*), is drawn next, and we find that the shear passes through zero somewhere between R_2 and a point 12 ft 0 in. from R_2. This is the section at which the bending moment will have its maximum value. To find this point let us call it x feet from R_1. Then

$$3600 - [(x - 8) \times 1000] = 0 \quad \text{and} \quad x = 11.6 \text{ ft}$$

This method of determining the point of zero shear is explained in the example in Art. 7–4 referring to Fig. 7–5.

$$M_{(x=8)} = 3600 \times 8 = 28{,}800 \text{ ft-lb}$$

$$M_{(x=11.6)} = (3600 \times 11.6) - \left(3.6 \times 1000 \times \frac{3.6}{2}\right)$$

$$= 35{,}280 \text{ ft-lb, the maximum bending moment}$$

Thus far in computing the bending moment we have taken the forces to the *left* of the selected section. If we consider the forces to the right, the result will be the same. Referring to the shear diagram in Fig. 8–2(*b*), consider the forces to the *right* of the point of zero shear and let y feet be the distance from this point to R_2. Then

$$8400 - (1000 \times y) = 0 \quad \text{and} \quad y = 8.4 \text{ ft}$$

$$M_{(y=8.4)} = (8400 \times 8.4) - \left(8.4 \times 1000 \times \frac{8.4}{2}\right)$$

$$= 35{,}280 \text{ ft-lb, the maximum bending moment}$$

the same value found above.

For this beam the value of M should be computed at several sections in order to draw the moment diagram accurately. Note that from R_1 to the distributed load the moment diagram is a straight line and the remainder is a curve having its maximum value 11.6 ft from R_1.

Example. Draw the shear and moment diagrams for the simple beam shown in Fig. 8–3(*a*).

SOLUTION.

$$16R_1 = (6000 \times 14) + (4000 \times 10) + (8000 \times 4)$$

$$R_1 = 9750 \text{ lb}$$

$$R_2 = (6000 + 4000 + 8000) - 9750$$

$$R_2 = 8250 \text{ lb}$$

The shear diagram in Fig. 8–3(*b*) is drawn, and we find that the shear passes through zero under the 4000-lb load. This is the section at which the bending moment will have its maximum value.

$$M_{(x=2)} = 9750 \times 2 = 19{,}500 \text{ ft-lb}$$

$$M_{(x=6)} = (9750 \times 6) - (6000 \times 4) = 34{,}500 \text{ ft-lb}$$

$$M_{(x=12)} = (9750 \times 12) - [(6000 \times 10) + (4000 \times 6)]$$

$$= 33{,}000 \text{ ft-lb}$$

The bending moment diagram is shown in Fig. 8–3(*c*), the maximum bending moment being 34,500 ft-lb.

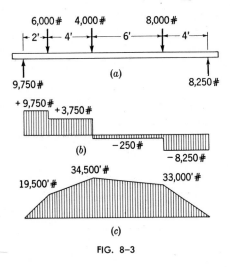

FIG. 8–3

If we ignore the weight of the beam, the bending moment diagram for a beam loaded only with concentrated loads is composed of straight lines. See Figs. 8–1(*c*) and 8–3(*c*). When the load is distributed over a length of beam, the moment diagram under the load is a curved line, as shown in Fig. 8–2(*c*).

Problem 8–2–A–B–C–D. Draw bending moment diagrams for the simple beams shown in Figs. 7–6(*a*), (*b*), (*c*), and (*d*). What is the maximum bending moment for each beam?

Problem 8–2–E. For the beam shown in Fig. 7–8(*a*) compute the maximum bending moment.

8–3. Bending Moments for Typical Loadings. In the construction of buildings, certain types of loadings on beams occur very frequently. It is a simple matter to compute the maximum shear and moments for such beams, and, if these values, particularly

Beam and Loading	Maximum bending moment	Maximum shear	Maximum deflection
Case 1	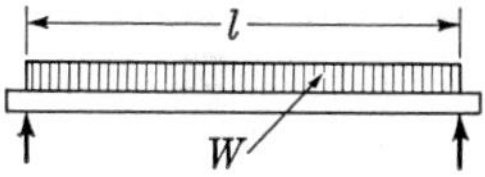 $\frac{Wl}{8}$	$\frac{W}{2}$	$\frac{5}{384} \times \frac{Wl^3}{EI}$
Case 2	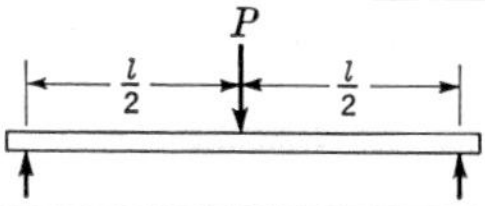 $\frac{Pl}{4}$	$\frac{P}{2}$	$\frac{1}{48} \times \frac{Pl^3}{EI}$
Case 3	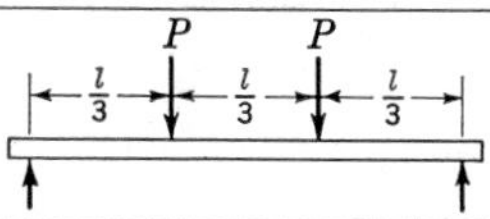 $\frac{Pl}{3}$	P	$\frac{23}{648} \times \frac{Pl^3}{EI}$
Case 4	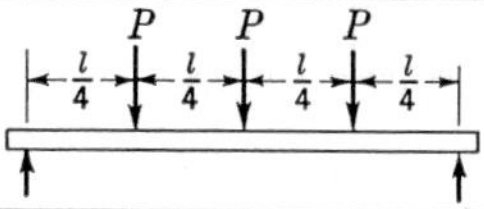 $\frac{Pl}{2}$	$\frac{3P}{2}$	$\frac{19}{384} \times \frac{Pl^3}{EI}$
Case 5	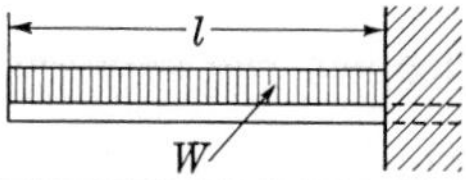 $\frac{Wl}{2}$	W	$\frac{1}{8} \times \frac{Wl^3}{EI}$
Case 6	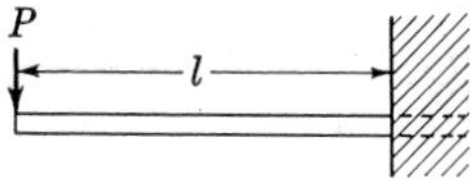 Pl	P	$\frac{1}{3} \times \frac{Pl^3}{EI}$

FIG. 8–4

the moments, are memorized, they will prove to be timesavers in designing beams. Figure 8–4 gives the maximum shear, maximum bending moment, and maximum deflection for loadings that occur frequently in practice. The values of the shear and moments are readily computed as shown in the following articles. The last column in the table gives maximum deflections. These are discussed in Chapter 10. In deriving the values for the bending moment and shear for the following typical loadings, the weight of the beam has been ignored.

8-4. Uniformly Distributed Load on a Simple Beam. Consider a simple beam having a span length of l feet with a uniformly distributed load of W pounds extending over the entire length of the beam as shown in Fig. 8–5(a). This beam occurs more frequently than any other.

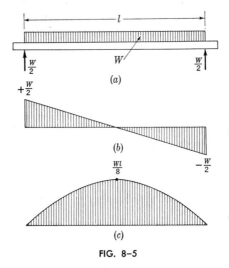

FIG. 8–5

Since the beam is symmetrically loaded, the reactions are each equal to one half the load, or $\dfrac{W}{2}$. The maximum shear is $\dfrac{W}{2}$; the shear diagram is shown in Fig. 8–5(b). The shear passes through zero at the center of the span, at $x = \dfrac{l}{2}$, and at this point the bending moment has its maximum magnitude. Thus

$$M_{(x=l/2)} = \left(\frac{W}{2} \times \frac{l}{2}\right) - \left(\frac{W}{2} \times \frac{l}{4}\right)$$

$$= \frac{Wl}{4} - \frac{Wl}{8} = \frac{Wl}{8}, \text{ the maximum bending moment}$$

Very often the distributed load is given in so many pounds per linear foot. In this text the letter W indicates the total uniformly distributed load and the letter w indicates the uniformly distributed load in *pounds per linear foot.* Suppose that we are given the beam shown in Fig. 8–5(*a*) with w pounds per linear foot instead of W, the total distributed load; that is, $W = wl$. Then the total load is wl, and each reaction is $\dfrac{wl}{2}$. The maximum bending moment occurs at $x = \dfrac{l}{2}$, and

$$M_{(x=l/2)} = \left(\frac{wl}{2} \times \frac{l}{2}\right) - \left(\frac{wl}{2} \times \frac{l}{4}\right) = \frac{wl^2}{4} - \frac{wl^2}{8} = \frac{wl^2}{8}$$

Thus the maximum bending moment is $\dfrac{wl^2}{8}$ or $\dfrac{Wl}{8}$, depending on whether the load is given as W, the total load, or w, the number of pounds per linear foot. If, for a uniformly distributed load, we compute the value of the bending moment at various sections in the length of the beam, the moment diagram takes the curve of a parabola as shown in Fig. 8–5(*c*). If l is given in feet, the bending moment is in units of foot-pounds. The number of foot-pounds multiplied by 12 gives the number of inch-pounds.

Example. A simple beam has a span of 22 ft 0 in. with a total uniformly distributed load of 26,400 lb. What is the maximum bending moment?

SOLUTION. We remember that the value of the maximum bending moment for this loading is $\dfrac{Wl}{8}$. Thus

$$M = \frac{Wl}{8} = \frac{26,400 \times 22}{8} = 72,600 \text{ ft-lb}$$

If the load had been given as 1200 lb per lin ft, the value of w, then

$$M = \frac{wl^2}{8} = \frac{1200 \times 22 \times 22}{8} = 72,600 \text{ ft-lb}$$

If we wish to have the bending moment in inch-pounds, *as we generally do*, $72,600 \times 12 = 871,200$ in-lb.

8–5. Concentrated Load at Center of Span of a Simple Beam.
Figure 8–6(*a*) represents a simple beam with a span length of *l*
feet with a concentrated load of *P* pounds at the center of the span.

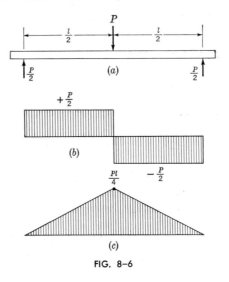

FIG. 8–6

The beam being symmetrically loaded, R_1 and R_2 each equal $\dfrac{P}{2}$.

Hence the maximum shear is $\dfrac{P}{2}$; the shear diagram is shown in
Fig. 8–6(*b*). The shear passes through zero at the center of the
span. Thus

$$M_{(x=l/2)} = \frac{P}{2} \times \frac{l}{2}$$

$$= \frac{Pl}{4}, \text{ the magnitude of the maximum bending moment}$$

Figure 8–6(*c*) shows the moment diagram.

Example. A simple beam has a span of 18 ft 0 in. with a single
concentrated load of 7000 lb at the center of the span. Compute
the maximum bending moment.

SOLUTION. As shown above, for this type of load the maximum bending moment has a magnitude of $\dfrac{Pl}{4}$. Then

$$M = \frac{Pl}{4} = \frac{7000 \times 18}{4} = 31,500 \text{ ft-lb} \quad \text{or} \quad 378,000 \text{ in-lb}$$

8–6. Equal Concentrated Loads at Third Points of Span. A simple beam with equal loads of P pounds at the third points of span is shown in Fig. 8–7(a). The span length is l feet.

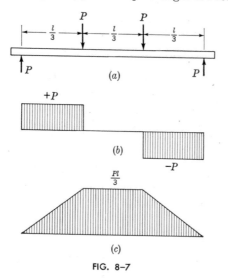

FIG. 8–7

As the beam is symmetrically loaded, each reaction, and consequently the maximum vertical shear, is equal to P pounds. When the shear diagram, Fig. 8–7(b), is constructed, note that the shear has a zero magnitude at all sections of the beam between the two concentrated loads. At any of these sections the bending moment will have its maximum magnitude. It is most readily computed at the concentrated load nearest R_1, at $x = \dfrac{l}{3}$.

$$M_{(x=l/3)} = P \times \frac{l}{3} = \frac{Pl}{3}, \text{ the maximum bending moment}$$

Now let us compute M at $x = \dfrac{l}{2}$, the center of the span.

$$M_{(x=l/2)} = \left(P \times \frac{l}{2}\right) - \left(P \times \frac{l}{6}\right)$$

$$= \frac{Pl}{2} - \frac{Pl}{6} = \frac{2Pl}{6} = \frac{Pl}{3}, \text{ the same magnitude}$$

The moment diagram is shown in Fig. 8–7(c).

Example. A simple beam has a span of 24 ft 0 in. with concentrated loads of 9000 lb each placed at the third points of span. Compute the maximum bending moment.

SOLUTION. We have just found that the maximum bending moment for this loading is $\dfrac{Pl}{3}$. Then

$$M = \frac{Pl}{3} = \frac{9000 \times 24}{3} = 72{,}000 \text{ ft-lb} \quad \text{or} \quad 864{,}000 \text{ in-lb}$$

8–7. Equal Concentrated Loads at Fourth Points of Span. Three concentrated loads of P pounds each are placed at the fourth points of span, as shown in Fig. 8–8(a). Each reaction is equal to one half the sum of the loads, or $\dfrac{3P}{2}$ pounds. Figure 8–8(b) shows the shear diagram, the shear passing through zero at $x = \dfrac{l}{2}$, the center of the span.

$$M_{(x=l/2)} = \left(\frac{3P}{2} \times \frac{l}{2}\right) - \left(P \times \frac{l}{4}\right) = \frac{3Pl}{4} - \frac{Pl}{4} = \frac{2Pl}{4}$$

$$= \frac{Pl}{2}, \text{ the magnitude of the maximum bending moment}$$

$$M_{(x=l/4)} = \frac{3P}{2} \times \frac{l}{4} = \frac{3Pl}{8}$$

The bending moment diagram is shown in Fig. 8–8(c).

Example. A simple beam has a span of 24 ft 0 in. with three concentrated loads of 8000 lb each placed at the fourth points of the
span. Compute the maximum bending moment.

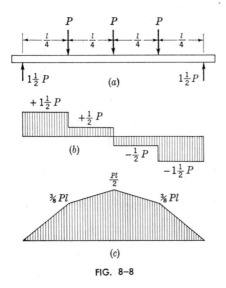

FIG. 8–8

SOLUTION. The maximum bending moment for this loading
has been found to be $\dfrac{Pl}{2}$. Hence

$$M = \frac{Pl}{2} = \frac{8000 \times 24}{2}$$

= 96,000 ft-lb or 1,152,000 in-lb, the maximum bending
moment

8–8. Cantilever Beam with Uniformly Distributed Load. A uniformly distributed load of W pounds extends over the entire length
of a cantilever beam whose length is l feet, as shown in Fig. 8–9(a).
Note in the figure that the unsupported portion of the beam extends to the left side of the support.

From the unsupported end of the beam the magnitude of the
shear increases directly with the length of the span and has a max-

imum value at the face of the support. At this point there are no reactions to the left. Thus

$$V_{(x=l)} = 0 - W = -W$$

as shown in Fig. 8–9(*b*).

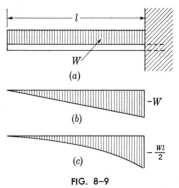

(a)

(b)

(c)

FIG. 8–9

Although the portion of the beam to the right of the face of the support is subjected to unequally distributed forces, these forces are purposely neglected in computations since they have no significance in the computation of the bending moment. If the forces were considered, the shear diagram would pass through zero at the face of the support; this is the section at which the bending moment has its greatest magnitude. There are no reactions to the left of the support; therefore

$$M_{(x=l)} = -\left(W \times \frac{l}{2}\right) = -\frac{Wl}{2}, \text{ the maximum bending moment}$$

The bending moment diagram is shown in Fig. 8–9(*c*).

If the distributed load is *w* pounds per linear foot instead of *W*, the load to the left is *wl* and the lever arm is $\frac{l}{2}$. Hence

$$M_{(x=l)} = -\left(wl \times \frac{l}{2}\right) = -\frac{wl^2}{2}$$

Example. A cantilever beam 7 ft 0 in. in length has a uniformly distributed load of 200 lb per lin ft over its entire length. Compute the maximum bending moment.

SOLUTION. Since the beam is 7 ft 0 in. long and the load is 200 lb per ft, W, the total distributed load, is 7×200, or 1400 lb. Then

$$M = -\frac{Wl}{2} = -\frac{1400 \times 7}{2}$$

  $= -4900$ ft-lb, or $-58{,}800$ in-lb, the maximum bending moment

8–9. Cantilever Beam with Load at Unsupported End. In Fig. 8–10(a) the anchorage of the cantilever beam is again shown on the

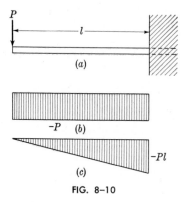

FIG. 8–10

right-hand side. The length of the beam is l, and the concentrated load is P. Therefore the magnitude of the shear at any section in the beam is $-P$, Fig. 8–10(b). At the face of the support

$V_{(x=l)} = 0 - P = -P$, the maximum vertical shear

The bending moment is zero under the load and increases directly as we approach the face of the support, Fig. 8–10(c). At this point

$M_{(x=l)} = 0 - (P \times l) = -Pl$, the maximum bending moment

Example. A cantilever beam has a length of 5 ft 0 in. with a concentrated load of 2000 lb at its unsupported end. What is the maximum bending moment?

  SOLUTION. As the maximum bending moment is $-Pl$,

$$M = -Pl = -(2000 \times 5) = -10{,}000 \text{ ft-lb or } -120{,}000 \text{ in-lb}$$

Problem 8–9–A. A simple beam has a span of 21 ft 0 in. with concentrated loads of 4500 lb each at the third points of span. Compute the maximum bending moment.

Problem 8–9–B. A uniformly distributed load of 850 lb per lin ft extends over the entire length of a simple beam, the span of which is 16 ft 0 in. What is the maximum bending moment in units of inch-pounds?

Problem 8–9–C. Three loads of 4400 lb each are concentrated at the fourth points of span of a simple beam having a length of 22 ft 0 in. Compute the maximum bending moment.

Problem 8–9–D. A cantilever beam has a length of 7 ft 0 in. with a uniformly distributed load of 550 lb per lin ft over its entire length. Compute the maximum bending moment.

Problem 8–9–E. Compute the maximum bending moment for a simple beam having a length of 18 ft 0 in. with a concentrated load of 7500 lb at the center of the span.

Problem 8–9–F. A cantilever beam has a length of 9 ft 0 in. with a concentrated load of 3250 lb at its unsupported end. Compute the maximum bending moment.

Problem 8–9–G. For the beams given in the above six problems, what are the values of the maximum vertical shear?

8–10. Triangular Load on a Simple Beam. The triangular loading shown in Fig. 8–11(a) occurs often in practice. Because of the

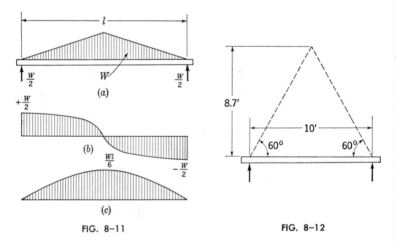

FIG. 8–11   FIG. 8–12

corbeling action in the masonry, a beam over an opening in a masonry wall supports a load of this type. The apex of the triangle is at the center of the span, and, in computing the magnitude of the load, we assume that the sides of the triangle make 60° angles with the horizontal, as indicated in Fig. 8–12.

Since the total distributed triangular load is W and the beam is symmetrically loaded, each reaction is $\dfrac{W}{2}$. The shear diagram is shown in Fig. 8–11(b). The maximum bending moment occurs at the center of the span; thus

$$M_{(x=l/2)} = \left(\frac{W}{2} \times \frac{l}{2}\right) - \left(\frac{W}{2} \times \frac{l}{6}\right)$$

$$= \frac{Wl}{6}, \text{ the maximum bending moment}$$

In the above equation the expression $\left(\dfrac{W}{2} \times \dfrac{l}{6}\right)$ is the moment of the load to the left of the section. The load to the left of the section is $\dfrac{W}{2}$, and, since the centroid of a triangle lies at a point one third the distance from the base to the altitude, the lever arm of this triangular load, $\dfrac{W}{2}$, is $\left(\dfrac{1}{3} \times \dfrac{l}{2}\right)$, or $\dfrac{l}{6}$. See Art. 6–1, and refer to Fig. 6–1(d).

Example. A beam in a stone wall 16-in. thick has a span of 10 ft 0 in. If the only load supported by the beam is the masonry, compute the maximum bending moment in the beam.

SOLUTION. A diagram of the beam and load, Fig. 8–12, is drawn, and, by scaling, the height of the triangular load carried by the beam is found to be 8.7 ft. As the wall is 16 in. thick, 1.33 ft, $\dfrac{10 \times 8.7 \times 1.33}{2} = 58$ cu ft, the volume of masonry supported by the beam. The weight of 1 cu ft of stone masonry is 160 lb (Table 5–1); hence $58 \times 160 = 9280$ lb, the triangular load on the beam.

$$M = \frac{Wl}{6} = \frac{9280 \times 10}{6}$$

$$= 15{,}467 \text{ ft-lb, the maximum bending moment}$$

Problem 8–10–A. A brick wall 17 in. thick contains an opening whose width is 20 ft 0 in. The only load on the beam spanning this opening is the weight of the wall. Compute the maximum bending moment in the beam.

8–11. Overhanging Beam, Negative Bending Moments. An overhanging beam with three concentrated loads is shown in Fig. 8–13(a). When such a beam bends, it tends to take the shape

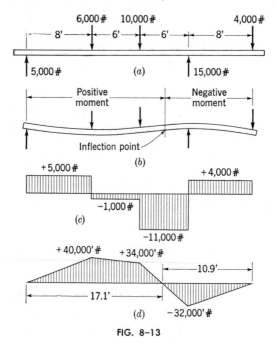

FIG. 8–13

indicated in Fig. 8–13(b). Note that the left-hand end of the beam is concave upward. In this portion of the beam the fibers above the neutral surface are in compression and those below are in tension; the bending moments in all sections of this portion of the beam are *positive*. The right-hand end of the beam presents a reverse condition. Here the beam is concave downward, the fibers above the neutral surface are in tension, and compressive stresses occur in the fibers below. In this portion of the beam the bending moments are *negative*. The section of the beam at which the bending moment changes from positive to negative is the *inflection point*, sometimes called the *point of contraflexure*. The bending moment at the inflection point is zero. It should be noted that the bending moments in all simple beams are positive, whereas negative bending moments occur in cantilever beams.

Example. Figure 8–13(a) represents an overhanging beam with three concentrated loads. Compute the maximum shear, the maximum bending moment, and the position of the inflection point and draw the shear and moment diagrams.

SOLUTION. First compute the reactions.

$$20R_1 = (6000 \times 12) + (10{,}000 \times 6) - (4000 \times 8)$$

$$R_1 = 5000 \text{ lb}$$

$$20R_2 = (6000 \times 8) + (10{,}000 \times 14) + (4000 \times 28)$$

$$R_2 = 15{,}000 \text{ lb}$$

The shear diagram is constructed as shown in Fig. 8–13(c), and we find that the maximum shear is −11,000 lb. From this diagram we see that the shear passes through zero at two different sections, at $x = 8$ ft and at $x = 20$ ft; at one of the sections we shall find the maximum positive bending moment and at the other will be the maximum negative moment.

$$M_{(x=8)} = 5000 \times 8$$

$$= 40{,}000 \text{ ft-lb, the maximum positive bending moment}$$

$$M_{(x=14)} = (5000 \times 14) - (6000 \times 6) = +34{,}000 \text{ ft-lb}$$

$$M_{(x=20)} = (5000 \times 20) - [(6000 \times 12) + (10{,}000 \times 6)]$$

$$= -32{,}000 \text{ ft-lb, the maximum negative bending moment}$$

The values of the bending moments are plotted; the bending moment diagram is shown in Fig. 8–13(d). Note that at some section of the beam between the 10,000-lb load and R_2 the bending moment is zero; this is the inflection point, the section at which the bending moment changes from a plus to a minus quantity. To compute the position of this section, let us call it x feet from R_1, write an expression for the bending moment at this section, and equate it to zero. Solving the equation will give the value of x, thus determining the position of the inflection point. Then

$(5000 \times x) - \{[6000 \times (x - 8)] + [10,000 \times (x - 14)]\} = 0$

$5000x = (6000x - 48,000) + (10,000x - 140,000)$

$11,000x = 188,000$

$x = 17.1$ ft, the distance of the inflection point from R_1

In this beam we have found that the maximum positive and negative bending moments are $+40,000$ ft-lb and $-32,000$ ft-lb, respectively. In the design of a homogeneous beam, a beam composed of but one material such as steel or timber, we are concerned only with the maximum magnitude, regardless of whether it is positive or negative. However, in a beam made up of two materials, such as a reinforced concrete beam, both moments must be given consideration and the inflection point is an important factor.

Example. Figure 8–14(a) shows an overhanging beam with a uniformly distributed load extending over its entire length. Draw the shear and moment diagrams, note the values of the maximum shear and maximum bending moment, and compute the position of the inflection point.

SOLUTION. The curve the beam tends to take is shown in Fig. 8–14(b). This indicates that we shall find both positive and negative bending moments in the bending moment diagram.

$$10R_1 = 800 \times 14 \times 7 \quad \text{and} \quad R_1 = 7840 \text{ lb}$$

$$10R_2 = 800 \times 14 \times 3 \quad \text{and} \quad R_2 = 3360 \text{ lb}$$

$$V_{(x=4-)} = -(800 \times 4) = -3200 \text{ lb}$$

$$V_{(x=4+)} = 7840 - (800 \times 4) = 4640 \text{ lb}$$

$$V_{(x=14)} = 7840 - (800 \times 14) = -3360 \text{ lb}$$

The shear diagram is shown in Fig. 8–14(c). The value of the maximum shear is 4640 lb. There are two sections at which the shear passes through zero. At one the maximum negative moment is found, and the maximum positive moment occurs at the other.

$$M_{(x=4)} = -(800 \times 4 \times 2)$$

$$= -6400 \text{ ft-lb, the maximum negative bending moment}$$

Let x feet be the distance from the left end of the beam to the section between R_1 and R_2 at which the shear passes through zero. Then

$$7840 - (800 \times x) = 0 \quad \text{and} \quad x = 9.8 \text{ ft}$$

$$M_{(x=9.8)} = (7840 \times 5.8) - (800 \times 9.8 \times 4.9)$$

$$= 7056 \text{ ft-lb, the maximum positive bending moment}$$

The curve shown in Fig. 8–14(d) represents the bending moment diagram. In this example we have computed the value of the

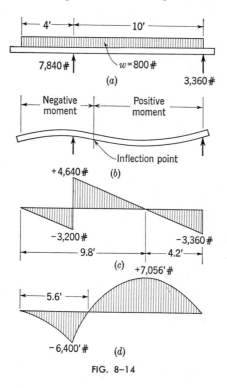

FIG. 8–14

bending moment at only two points. To draw this moment diagram accurately, the values of the bending moment should be computed for a number of points. The value of the bending moment is zero at some section (the inflection point) to the right of R_1. To find this point, call it x feet from the left end of the beam.

Then

$$[7840 \times (x - 4)] - \left(800 \times x \times \frac{x}{2}\right) = 0$$

$$7840x - 31{,}360 - 400x^2 = 0$$

$$x^2 - 19.6x = -78.4$$

Completing the square,

$$x^2 - 19.6x + 96.04 = -78.4 + 96.04$$

$$x - 9.8 = \pm 4.2$$

$$x = 14 \text{ ft or } 5.6 \text{ ft}$$

We know that the bending moment is zero at R_2 ($x = 14$); therefore, the inflection point lies at a distance of 5.6 ft from the left end of the beam.

Problem 8–11–A–B–C. Draw bending moment diagrams for the beams shown in Figs. 7–6(e), (f), and (g). What are the magnitudes of the maximum positive and negative bending moments? Compute the position of the inflection points.

Problem 8–11–D. A beam whose total length is 36 ft 0 in. overhangs both supports a distance of 8 ft 0 in. at each end. The beam has a uniformly distributed load of 1000 lb per lin ft over its entire length. Compute the maximum shear, the maximum positive and negative bending moments, and the positions of the inflection points and draw the shear and moment diagrams.

8–12. Moving Loads. Thus far in our discussion of beams the loads have been in fixed positions, but another condition encountered is a *moving load*. A traveling crane is an example. Here we have two loads, of equal magnitude and at a fixed distance from each other, moving over the length of a supporting beam. Consider Fig. 8–15(a), in which we have two loads of 5000 lb each, 8 ft apart, moving in unison over a simple beam whose length is 20 ft 0 in. One might think that the maximum bending moment in the beam would occur when the moving loads were equidistant from the center of the span. This, however, is not true. *The maximum bending moment occurs under one of the loads when that load and the resultant of all the loads (two or more) are at equal distances from the center of the span.*

Consider first the position of the two equal loads as shown in

Fig. 8–15(*a*). R_1 and R_2 each equal 5000 lb; hence the maximum bending moment in the beam is 5000 × 6, or 30,000 ft-lb.

Now let us apply the above rule. The resultant of the two loads of 5000 lb each has its line of action at a point 4 ft from each load. The two loads are moved to the position shown in Fig.

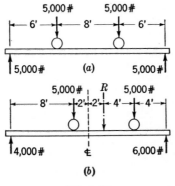

FIG. 8–15

8–15(*b*) where the left load is 2 ft to the left of the center of the span and the resultant of the loads is 2 ft to the right.

When the loads are in this position,

$$20R_1 = (5000 \times 12) + (5000 \times 4) \quad \text{and} \quad R_1 = 4000 \text{ lb}$$

$$20R_2 = (5000 \times 8) + (5000 \times 16) \quad \text{and} \quad R_2 = 6000 \text{ lb}$$

$$M_{(x=8)} = 4000 \times 8 = 32{,}000 \text{ ft-lb}$$

$$M_{(x=16)} = (4000 \times 16) - (5000 \times 8) = 24{,}000 \text{ ft-lb}$$

Thus the maximum bending moment is 32,000 ft-lb, a greater magnitude than found for the loads in the position shown in Fig. 8–15(*a*).

The example previously discussed dealt with loads of equal magnitude; now let us consider a case in which the loads are unequal in magnitude.

Example. Two loads of 8000 and 4000 lb, 6 ft 0 in. apart, roll over a beam whose length is 20 ft 0 in. Compute the maximum bending moment that will result from these moving loads.

SOLUTION. The loads are 8000 and 4000 lb, and their resultant (12,000 lb) has its line of action at some point between them. If we write an equation of moments about the 4000-lb load as a center of moments and let x be the distance of the resultant from the 4000-lb load,

$$8000 \times 6 = 12{,}000 \times x \quad \text{and} \quad x = 4 \text{ ft 0 in.}$$

Thus the position of the resultant is established, and we find that it is 2 ft 0 in. from the 8000-lb load; see Fig. 8–16(a).

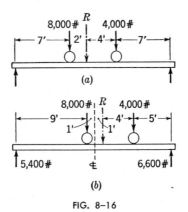

FIG. 8–16

The two loads are now moved to the position shown in Fig. 8–16(b). In accordance with the rule, the 8000-lb load is 1 ft 0 in. to the left of the center of the 20-ft span and the resultant of the two loads is 1 ft 0 in. to the right. When the loads are in this position,

$$20R_1 = (8000 \times 11) + (4000 \times 5) \quad \text{and} \quad R_1 = 5400 \text{ lb}$$

$$20R_2 = (8000 \times 9) + (4000 \times 15) \quad \text{and} \quad R_2 = 6600 \text{ lb}$$

$$M_{(x=9)} = 5400 \times 9 = 48{,}600 \text{ ft-lb}$$

$$M_{(x=15)} = (5400 \times 15) - (8000 \times 6) = 33{,}000 \text{ ft-lb}$$

Thus we find that the maximum bending moment is 48,600 ft-lb. When the loads are in the position shown in Fig. 8–16(a), the maximum bending moment is 46,200 ft-lb.

Problem 8–12–A. A simple beam having a span of 16 ft 0 in. is to support two moving loads of 6000 lb each. If the two loads are at a fixed distance of 4 ft 0 in. apart, compute the maximum bending moment that will occur in the beam.

Problem 8–12–B. Two loads of 12,000 and 8000 lb, at a fixed distance of 10 ft 0 in. apart, roll over a simple beam whose length is 24 ft 0 in. Compute the maximum bending moment that will occur in the beam.

8–13. Bending Moment Determined by Shear Diagram. The
method of determining the value of the bending moment as explained previously in this chapter is probably as simple and direct as any. However, the bending moment may be computed by the use of the shear diagram. Since this method is sometimes used, the following explanation is presented.

In shear diagrams the vertical distances represent forces (pounds) and the horizontal distances represent lengths (feet). *The magnitude of the bending moment at any section of a beam is equal to the area of the shear diagram to the left of the section.* Be sure to note the positive and negative values of the shear; in computing the bending moment, it may be necessary to subtract one area from the other.

Example. Compute the maximum bending moment for the beam shown in Fig. 8–1(*a*).

SOLUTION. The shear diagram, Fig. 8–1(*b*), shows that the shear passes through zero at 4 ft 0 in. from the left support. The vertical dimension of the shear diagram to the left of this section is 15,000 lb, and the horizontal length is 4 ft 0 in. Hence the area of the shear diagram is 15,000 × 4, or 60,000 ft-lb. This is the maximum bending moment.

Example. Compute the maximum bending moment for the beam shown in Fig. 8–2(*a*).

SOLUTION. It was found (Art. 8–2) that the shear passed through zero at 11.6 ft from R_1. The shear diagram, Fig. 8–2(*b*), to the left of this section is made up of a rectangle and triangle; hence the area of this portion of the shear diagram is

$$(3600 \times 8) + \left(\frac{3600 \times 3.6}{2} \right)$$

$$= 35{,}280 \text{ ft-lb, the maximum bending moment}$$

Example. Compute the maximum bending moment for the beam shown in Fig. 8–3(a).

SOLUTION. The shear diagram, Fig. 8–3(b), shows that the shear passes through zero at 6 ft 0 in. from the left support. The area of the shear diagram to the left of this section is composed of two rectangles. Hence

$$(9750 \times 2) + (3750 \times 4)$$

$$= 34{,}500 \text{ ft-lb, the maximum bending moment}$$

Example. Compute the maximum positive and negative bending moments for the beam shown in Fig. 8–14(a).

SOLUTION. From the discussion in Art. 8–11 it was found that the shear passed through zero at two points, 4 ft 0 in. and 9.8 ft from the left end of the beam. Note that the point 9.8 ft from the left end of the beam is 5.8 ft to the right of R_1.

At the left support the shear diagram to the left is a triangle; hence $\dfrac{-3200 \times 4}{2} = -6400$ ft-lb, the maximum negative bending moment.

At 5.8 ft to the right of R_1 the area of the shear diagram consists of two triangles, one positive and one negative. Thus

$$\left(\frac{-3200 \times 4}{2}\right) + \left(\frac{4640 \times 5.8}{2}\right) = -6400 + 13{,}456$$

$$= 7056 \text{ ft-lb, the maximum positive bending moment}$$

Problem 8–13–A–B–C–D–E–F–G–H–I. Compute the magnitude of the maximum bending moment for the beams shown in Figs. 7–6(a), (b), (c), (d), (e), (f), (g), (h), and (i) by the shear-area method.

CHAPTER 9

CONTINUOUS AND
RESTRAINED BEAMS

9–1. Continuous Beams, Theorem of Three Moments. A *continuous beam* is a beam that rests on more than two supports; see Fig. 7–1(e). For most continuous beams the maximum bending moment is smaller than that found in a series of simple beams having the same spans and loads, hence it may be more economical to use. Continuous beams occur very frequently in reinforced concrete construction.

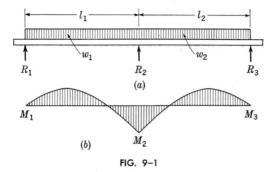

FIG. 9–1

The reactions for a continuous beam cannot be found by the methods previously described in this text. By the use of a formula based on the *theorem of three moments*, the relation among the bending moments at any three consecutive supports may be found. When the bending moments at all the supports are established, the magnitudes of the reactions may be computed, and, by the methods previously described, the shear and moment diagrams may be drawn.

Although a thorough discussion of continuous beams is inappropriate here, simple examples are presented to show how the theorem of three moments is applied. Figure 9–1(a) represents a continuous beam of two spans with uniformly distributed loads. If there is no restraint at the end supports, the bending moments at these two supports must be zero and the bending moment diagram will have the general shape shown in Fig. 9–1(b). There will be a negative bending moment at the middle support.

The formula for a continuous beam of two spans with uniformly distributed loads and constant moment of inertia is based on *the theorem of three moments;* it is

$$M_1 l_1 + 2M_2(l_1 + l_2) + M_3 l_2 = -\frac{w_1 l_1{}^3}{4} - \frac{w_2 l_2{}^3}{4}$$

the various terms being as shown in Fig. 9–1.

9–2. Continuous Beam with Equal Spans. To illustrate the application of the theorem of three moments, consider the following example. This continuous beam has two spans of equal length with the same uniformly distributed load extending the full length of each span.

Example. A continuous beam has two spans of 10 ft 0 in. each with a uniformly distributed load of 100 lb per lin ft extending over its entire length. There is no restraint at the end supports. Let it be required to compute the magnitude of the reactions, shear, and bending moments at critical sections and to construct the shear and moment diagrams.

SOLUTION. The beam and loading are shown in Fig. 9–2(a). Bearing in mind that the moments M_1 and M_3 are each zero, substitute the known values in the formula given above. Then

$$(0 \times 10) + [2M_2(10 + 10)] + (0 \times 10)$$

$$= -\frac{100 \times 1000}{4} - \frac{100 \times 1000}{4}$$

$$40M_2 = -50,000$$

$$M_2 = -1250 \text{ ft-lb}$$

the negative bending moment at the center support.

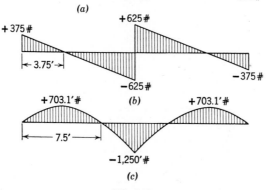

FIG. 9–2

Next we shall write an expression for the bending moment at 10 ft 0 in. from the left support and equate it to the value we have just found, -1250 ft-lb.   Then

$$M_{(x=10)} = (R_1 \times 10) - (100 \times 10 \times 5) = -1250$$

$$10R_1 = 3750$$

$$R_1 = 375 \text{ lb}$$

Since R_1 and R_3 are equal, R_3 also equals 375 lb.   The total load on the entire length of the beam is $2 \times 100 \times 10 = 2000$ lb.   Hence

$$R_1 + R_3 + R_2 = 2000$$

$$375 + 375 + R_2 = 2000$$

$$R_2 = 1250 \text{ lb}$$

Now that the magnitudes of the reactions have been established, we can construct the shear diagram as shown in Fig. 9–2(b).

Let x be the distance in feet from R_1 to the point between R_1 and R_2 at which the shear diagram passes through zero.   Then, writing an expression for the shear at this point and equating it to zero,

$$375 - (100 \times x) = 0 \quad \text{and} \quad x = 3.75 \text{ ft}$$

the section at which we find the maximum positive bending moment.

$$M_{(x=3.75)} = (375 \times 3.75) - \left(3.75 \times 100 \times \frac{3.75}{2}\right) = 703.1 \text{ ft-lb}$$

Since this beam is symmetrical, the positive bending moment between R_2 and R_3 will likewise have a magnitude of 703.1 ft-lb. Now that both the maximum positive and negative moments have been computed, we may construct the bending moment diagram, Fig. 9–2(c).

9–3. Continuous Beam with Unequal Spans. The example in the preceding article dealt with a continuous beam with two equal spans. The following example shows how the formula for the theorem of three moments given in Art. 9–1 may be used for beams of unequal spans.

Example. A continuous beam, having no restraint at the end supports, has two spans of 14 ft 0 in. and 10 ft 0 in. with a uniformly distributed load of 1000 lb per lin ft extending over its entire length, as shown in Fig. 9–3(a). Construct the shear and moment diagrams.

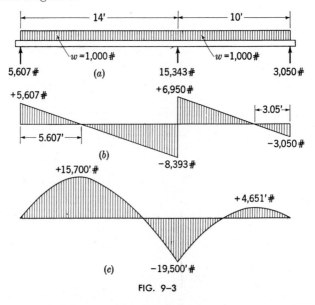

FIG. 9–3

SOLUTION. By data we know that $l_1 = 14$ ft 0 in., $l_2 = 10$ ft 0 in., w_1 and w_2 each equal 1000 lb, and $M_1 = M_3 = 0$.

The first step is to determine M_2, and this requires that we substitute the known values in the formula

$$M_1 l_1 + 2M_2(l_1 + l_2) + M_3 l_2 = -\frac{w_1 l_1{}^3}{4} - \frac{w_2 l_2{}^3}{4}$$

Thus

$$0 + 2M_2(14 + 10) + 0 = -\frac{1000 \times 14^3}{4} - \frac{1000 \times 10^3}{4}$$

$$48M_2 = -936,000$$

$$M_2 = -19,500 \text{ ft-lb}$$

Now let us write an expression for the bending moment at $x = 14$ (at R_2), considering the forces to the left. This expression can be equated to $-19,500$ ft-lb, since we have just established its magnitude. Thus

$$14R_1 - (14 \times 1000 \times 7) = -19,500 \quad \text{and} \quad R_1 = 5607 \text{ lb}$$

Similarly, writing an equation for the bending moment at R_2, considering the forces to the *right*,

$$10R_3 - (10 \times 1000 \times 5) = -19,500 \quad \text{and} \quad R_3 = 3050 \text{ lb}$$

$$R_1 + R_2 + R_3 = (14 \times 1000) + (10 \times 1000)$$

$$5607 + 3050 + R_2 = 24,000 \text{ lb}$$

$$R_2 = 15,343 \text{ lb}$$

Now that the values of R_1, R_2, and R_3 have been determined, we can draw the shear diagram, Fig. 9–3(b).

Let $x =$ the distance from R_1 to the point at which the shear is zero. Then

$$5607 - (1000 \times x) = 0 \quad \text{and} \quad x = 5.607 \text{ ft}$$

the section at which the positive bending moment has its maximum value between R_1 and R_2.

$$M_{(x=5.607)} = (5607 \times 5.607) - \left(5.607 \times 1000 \times \frac{5.607}{2}\right)$$

$$= 15,700 \text{ ft-lb}$$

Similarly, we find that the positive moment has its maximum value at 3.05 ft from R_3, and its value, considering only the forces to the right, is

$$(3050 \times 3.05) - \left(3.05 \times 1000 \times \frac{3.05}{2}\right) = 4651.25 \text{ ft-lb}$$

The bending moment diagram is shown in Fig. 9–3(c).

9–4. Continuous Beam with Concentrated Loads. In the previous examples the loads on the continuous beams were uniformly distributed. Figure 9–4(a) shows a continuous beam of two spans

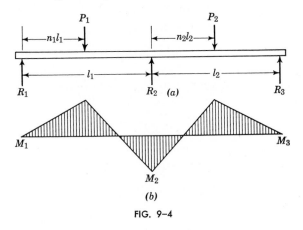

FIG. 9–4

with a concentrated load on each span. The general shape of the bending moment diagram for this beam is shown in Fig. 9–4(b). Using the letters shown in the figure, the formula for the theorem of three moments for this continuous beam is

$$M_1 l_1 + 2M_2(l_1 + l_2) + M_3 l_2$$
$$= -P_1 l_1{}^2[n_1(1 - n_1)(1 + n_1)] - P_2 l_2{}^2[n_2(1 - n_2)(2 - n_2)]$$

Example. A two-span continuous beam has equal spans of 20 ft 0 in. each. At the center of each span is a concentrated load of 4000 lb as shown in Fig. 9–5(a). There is no restraint at R_1 and R_3, the two end supports. Compute the magnitudes of the reactions and bending moments and draw both the shear and bending moment diagrams.

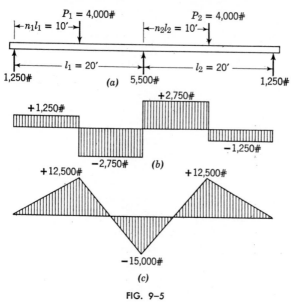

FIG. 9–5

SOLUTION. In this problem note that l_1 and l_2 = 20 ft 0 in., that P_1 and P_2 = 4000 lb each, and that both n_1 and n_2 = 0.5. Then, substituting in the above formula,

$$(M_1 \times 20) + 2M_2(20 + 20) + (M_3 \times 20)$$
$$= -4000 \times 20^2(0.5 \times 0.5 \times 1.5)$$
$$- 4000 \times 20^2(0.5 \times 0.5 \times 1.5)$$

Because there is no restraint at R_1 and R_3, the values of M_1 and M_3 each equal zero. Thus

$$0 + 80M_2 + 0 = -(4000 \times 400 \times 0.375)$$
$$- (4000 \times 400 \times 0.375)$$

or

$$80M_2 = -1,200,000$$

and

$$M_2 = -15,000 \text{ ft-lb}$$

the value of the bending moment at R_2, the center support.

Next, write an expression for the bending moment at R_2 and equate it to $-15,000$ ft-lb, the value we have just found. Thus

$$M_{(x=20)} = (R_1 \times 20) - (4000 \times 10) = -15,000$$

$$20R_1 = 25,000 \quad \text{and} \quad R_1 = 1250 \text{ lb}$$

R_1 and R_3 will have equal magnitudes, hence $R_1 = R_3 = 1250$ lb and $R_2 = (4000 + 4000) - (1250 + 1250) = 5500$ lb. Now that all the vertical forces are known, the shear diagram can be constructed. It is shown in Fig. 9–5(b).

Since the magnitude of R_1 has been established, we can now compute the value of the bending moment under the first concentrated load. Thus $M_{(x=10)} = 1250 \times 10 = 12,500$ ft-lb. This is also the magnitude of the bending moment under the second concentrated load. We know that the bending moment has a magnitude of $-15,000$ ft-lb at R_2. Therefore, we have sufficient data to construct the bending moment diagram for this continuous beam; it is shown in Fig. 9–5(c).

9–5. Continuous Beam with Three Spans. In the two preceding examples it is seen that the problem involved in the design and investigation of continuous beams consists of first determining the negative moments at the supports. After this magnitude is established we can compute the reactions and the positive bending moments. The procedure, when the beam has more than two spans, is to investigate them in pairs, two adjacent spans.

Figure 9–6(a) shows the shear and moment diagrams for a continuous beam having three equal spans and a uniformly distributed load of w pounds per linear foot. The values shown for reactions and shear are coefficients of wl; for the moments the values are coefficients of wl^2. The coefficients for shear and moments for continuous beams of various spans and types of loading may be found in engineering reference books. Such tabulations enable one to determine quickly the bending moments at critical sections.

Example. A continuous beam has three spans of 20 ft 0 in. each and a uniformly distributed load of 800 lb per lin ft extending over the entire length of beam. The ends of the beam are not restrained. Compute the maximum bending moment and the maximum shear.

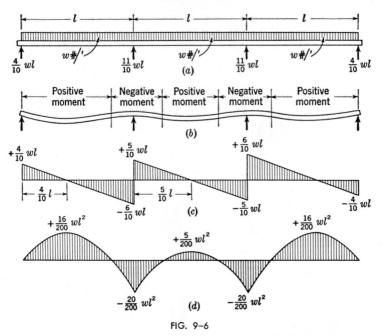

FIG. 9–6

SOLUTION. The values for shear and moments given in Fig. 9–6 may be used for this example. We note that the maximum bending moment is negative, $-\dfrac{1}{10}\,wl^2$; the maximum positive moment is $\dfrac{16}{200}\,wl^2$, a smaller magnitude. Hence

$$M = -\left(\frac{1}{10}\,wl^2\right) = -\left(\frac{1}{10} \times 800 \times 20 \times 20\right)$$

$$= -32{,}000 \text{ ft-lb, the maximum bending moment}$$

The maximum shear is

$$\frac{6}{10}\,wl = \frac{6}{10} \times 800 \times 20 = 9600 \text{ lb}$$

9–6. Restrained Beams. A simple beam may be defined as a beam resting on supports at its ends, *there being no restraint against* *bending at the supports.* The shape a simple beam tends to assume is shown in Fig. 9–7(*a*); we say that the ends are *simply supported.* Figure 9–7(*b*) shows a beam built into a wall at the left end and simply supported at the right end. The left end is *restrained* or *fixed;* the tangent to the elastic curve is horizontal at the face of the wall, at which point there is a negative bending moment. For such a beam, symmetrically loaded, the reactions are not equal in magnitude as they are in simple beams. Figure 9–7(*c*) illustrates

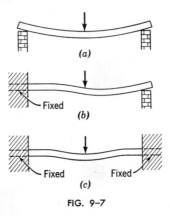

FIG. 9–7

a beam "fixed" at both ends. In this beam negative bending moments occur at the supports and a positive bending moment occurs in a portion of the beam at mid-span. A negative moment always occurs at a fixed support.

For the steel beams found in structures there is usually a certain degree of restraint at the supports that results from riveted connections at columns or girders. Since this restraint is relatively slight, it is customary to consider such beams as simply supported, no restraint.

The reactions for beams with fixed ends cannot be computed by the principle of moments, as in simple beams, and the necessary mathematics involved is beyond the scope of this book. Figures 9–8, 9–9, 9–10, and 9–11 show beams "fixed at both ends" and "fixed at one end and simply supported at the other." For each of these two conditions there are two types of loading, uniformly distributed loads and a concentrated load at the center of the span. For each kind of beam the magnitude of the maximum shear and maximum moment is given in the shear and moment diagrams.

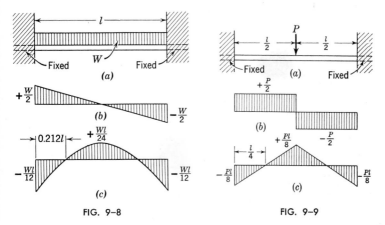

FIG. 9–8   FIG. 9–9

Particular attention is called to Fig. 9–8, which shows a uniformly distributed load on a beam fixed at both ends. This beam is similar to an interior span of a continuous beam with a number

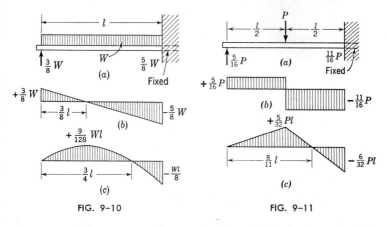

FIG. 9–10   FIG. 9–11

of spans which occurs so frequently in reinforced concrete slabs and beams. Note particularly that the maximum bending moment is negative, $-\dfrac{Wl}{12}$, and that it occurs at the supports. The positive bending moment is only one half this magnitude, $\dfrac{Wl}{24}$; it occurs at the center of the span. The inflection points for this beam are located at $0.212l$ (about $l/5$) from the faces of the supports. In uniformly loaded, fully continuous beams in reinforced concrete construction it is customary to turn up the longitudinal tensile reinforcement at $l/5$ from the faces of the supports.

A beam with fixed ends is both stronger and stiffer than a simple beam similarly loaded.

Example. A beam having a span of 20 ft 0 in. has both ends fixed with a uniformly distributed load of 8000 lb extending over its entire length; see Fig. 9–12(a). Draw the shear and moment diagrams.

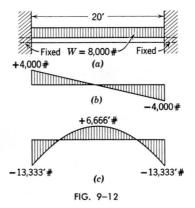

FIG. 9–12

SOLUTION. Referring to Fig. 9–8, we find that each reaction is $\dfrac{W}{2}$, or $\dfrac{8000}{2} = 4000$ lb. Since the load is uniformly distributed, the shear diagram takes the shape shown in Fig. 9–12(b).

The bending moment at the supports, shown in Fig. 9–8(c), is $-\dfrac{Wl}{12}$, or $-\dfrac{8000 \times 20}{12} = -13,333$ ft-lb. The moment at the center of the span is $\dfrac{Wl}{24}$, or $\dfrac{8000 \times 20}{24} = 6666$ ft-lb. The bending moment diagram is shown in Fig. 9–12(c).

Example. A beam having a span of 16 ft 0 in. is fixed at one end and simply supported at the other. A load of 9600 lb is placed at the center of the span; see Fig. 9–13. Draw the shear and moment diagrams.

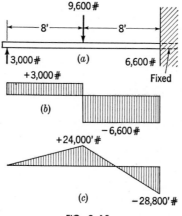

FIG. 9–13

SOLUTION. The critical values for this beam are found in Fig. 9–11. The shear at $R_1 = \frac{5}{16} \times P = \frac{5}{16} \times 9600 = 3000$ lb. The shear at R_2 is $-\left(\frac{11}{16} \times P\right) = -\left(\frac{11}{16} \times 9600\right) = -6600$ lb. These two values enable us to draw the shear diagram, Fig. 9–13(b).

The maximum positive bending moment is $\frac{5}{32} \times Pl$, or $\frac{5}{32} \times 9600 \times 16 = 24,000$ ft-lb. The maximum negative bending moment is $-\left(\frac{6}{32} \times Pl\right)$, or $-\left(\frac{6}{32} \times 9600 \times 16\right) = -28,800$ ft-lb. The moment diagram is shown in Fig. 9–13(c).

Problem 9–6–A. A beam having a span of 22 ft 0 in. is fixed at both ends and has a concentrated load of 16,000 lb at the center of the span. Compute the maximum shear and bending moment and draw the shear and moment diagrams.

Problem 9–6–B. A beam fixed at one end and simply supported at the other has a span of 20 ft 0 in. with a uniformly distributed load of 8000 lb extending over its entire length. Compute the maximum shear and bending moment and draw the shear and moment diagrams.

CHAPTER 10

DEFLECTION OF BEAMS

10–1. Deflection of Beams. When a beam bends, the deformation or change in shape is called the deflection. The vertical distance moved by a point on the neutral surface is the *deflection* of the beam at that point. The trace of the neutral surface on a vertical longitudinal plane is called the *elastic curve* of the beam.

In the design of most beams it is important that the deflection be given consideration. A floor beam may be strong enough to support the load it is required to hold, but it may not be *stiff* enough; that is, the deflection may be so great that a plaster ceiling below might develop cracks or the floor might vibrate unduly. For average conditions the allowable deflection of beams in building construction is limited to $\frac{1}{360}$ of the span. Thus it becomes necessary for the designer, having determined the size of the beam to withstand bending stresses, to compute the actual deflection to see that it does not exceed the allowable deflection.

10–2. Deflection Formulas. The formulas used to determine the deflection of beams may be derived by the use of the calculus. Another method, not involving the calculus, is known as the *moment-area method*. Although the various formulas and their application are presented, it is inappropriate in this volume to derive all the deflection formulas. Three examples are given to show the method employed.

The curved line in Fig. 10–1 represents the elastic curve of a beam that was originally horizontal and straight. *M* and *N* are two points on the curve. *The vertical displacement, D, of point M from the tangent to the elastic curve at point N is equal to the statical moment, with respect to M, of the area of the bending moment diagram between the points M and N divided by EI.* E is the modulus of elasticity of the material of which the beam is composed, and *I* is the moment of inertia of the cross section of the beam.

Consider first the cantilever beam of length l with a concentrated load P at the free end as shown in Fig. 10–2(a). The elastic curve for this beam is shown in Fig. 10–2(b), and Fig. 10–2(c) is the bending moment diagram. Note that the tangent to the elastic curve is horizontal at the support and that the maximum deflection is D. Since the maximum bending moment occurs at the face of the wall and has a magnitude of Pl, the *area* of the moment dia-

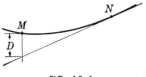

FIG. 10–1

gram between the force P and the face of the wall is $\dfrac{Pl \times l}{2}$, or $\dfrac{Pl^2}{2}$. As the moment diagram has the shape of a triangle, its centroid is $\dfrac{2l}{3}$ distance from the free end of the beam; hence its

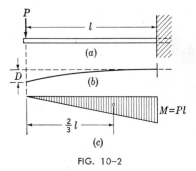

FIG. 10–2

statical moment is $\dfrac{Pl^2}{2} \times \dfrac{2l}{3}$. Therefore, applying the theorem noted above,

$$D = \frac{Pl^2}{2} \times \frac{2l}{3} \times \frac{1}{EI} = \frac{Pl^3}{3EI}$$

the magnitude of the maximum deflection of a cantilever beam with a concentrated load at its free end.

Figure 10–3(*a*) shows a simple beam with a concentrated load at the center of the span. Figures 10–3(*b*) and 10–3(*c*) show the elastic curve and bending moment diagram, respectively. Note that the maximum deflection occurs at the center of the span.

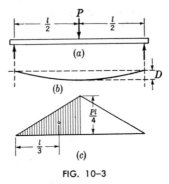

FIG. 10–3

The area of the moment diagram between the center of the span and the left reaction, the hatched area, is $\dfrac{Pl}{4} \times \dfrac{l}{2} \times \dfrac{1}{2}$, or $\dfrac{Pl^2}{16}$. The centroid of the hatched area from the left reaction is $\dfrac{2}{3} \times \dfrac{l}{2}$, or $\dfrac{l}{3}$. Hence the statical moment of this area is $\dfrac{Pl^2}{16} \times \dfrac{l}{3}$, and this quantity divided by EI is $\dfrac{Pl^2}{16} \times \dfrac{l}{3} \times \dfrac{1}{EI}$, or $\dfrac{Pl^3}{48EI}$, the maximum deflection of a simple beam with a concentrated load at the center of the span.

One of the most common beam conditions is a simple beam with a uniformly distributed load extending over its entire length. This beam is shown in Fig. 10–4(*a*). The elastic curve and bending moment diagram are shown in Figs. 10–4(*b*) and (*c*), respectively. The curve of the bending moment diagram is a parabola. The maximum deflection, D, is at the center of the span, and the area of the bending moment diagram from the center of the span to the left reaction, the hatched area, is $\dfrac{2}{3}\left(\dfrac{wl^2}{8} \times \dfrac{l}{2}\right)$. Since the centroid of this area is at a distance of $\dfrac{5}{16}l$ from the left support, the

statical moment of the area is $\dfrac{2}{3}\left(\dfrac{wl^2}{8} \times \dfrac{l}{2}\right) \times \dfrac{5}{16}l$, or $\dfrac{5}{384}wl^4$,

which is $\dfrac{5}{384}Wl^3$. This quantity divided by EI is $\dfrac{5}{384}\dfrac{Wl^3}{EI}$, the
maximum deflection of a simple beam with a uniformly distributed
load.

Simple and cantilever beams with cases of typical loadings are
shown in Fig. 8–4. For each of the six cases the value of the maxi-

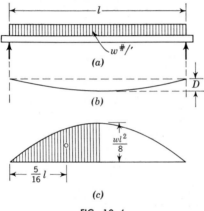

FIG. 10–4

mum deflection is given in the right-hand column in units of
inches. It is important to remember, in using these values, that
l, the length of the span, is in inches.

In designing beams the designer establishes a beam whose size
is ample to resist bending stresses; that is, he selects a beam
that is *strong* enough to support the applied loads. Having done
this, he computes the actual deflection of the beam to see whether
or not it exceeds the allowable, the allowable deflection usually
being $\frac{1}{360}$ of the span.

Example. A 12 I 31.8 is to be used for a simple beam having
a span of 18 ft 0 in. with a uniformly distributed load of 26,000 lb.
Is the deflection excessive?

SOLUTION. On referring to Fig. 8–4, Case 1, we find that the value of the maximum deflection for a simple beam with a uniformly distributed load is $\dfrac{5}{384} \times \dfrac{Wl^3}{EI}$. In this example $W =$ 26,000 lb, $l = 18 \times 12$, or 216 in., $E = 29{,}000{,}000$ psi (Table 5–1), and $I = 215.8$ in.^{4} (Table 6–1). Therefore

$$D = \frac{5}{384} \times \frac{26{,}000 \times 216^3}{29{,}000{,}000 \times 215.8} = 0.545 \text{ in., the actual deflection}$$

The allowable deflection is $\frac{1}{360}$ of the span length; hence $\dfrac{18 \times 12}{360}$ $= 0.6$ in. Since the actual deflection is less than the allowable, the 12 I 31.8 is acceptable with respect to deflection.

Example. An 8 x 10 in. southern pine beam is to be used to support a concentrated load of 4000 lb at the center of a 16 ft 0 in. span. Investigate this beam for deflection.

SOLUTION. The allowable deflection for a 16 ft 0 in. span is $\dfrac{16 \times 12}{360}$, or 0.53 in. Case 2 of Fig. 8–4 shows that the actual deflection for this beam is $\dfrac{1}{48} \times \dfrac{Pl^3}{EI}$. $P = 4000$ lb, $l = 16 \times 12$, or 192 in., $E = 1{,}760{,}000$ psi (Table 5–4), and $I = 535.86$ in.^{4} (Table 6–7). Then

$$D = \frac{1}{48} \times \frac{4000 \times 192^3}{1{,}760{,}000 \times 535.86} = 0.62 \text{ in., the actual deflection}$$

The 8 x 10 in. is *not* acceptable, since the actual deflection exceeds the allowable.

Example. A 16 WF 36 is used for a simple beam having a span of 21 ft 0 in. There are two concentrated loads of 4000 lb each, placed at the third points of span, and also a uniformly distributed load of 800 lb per lin ft extending over the entire length of the beam. Investigate the deflection.

SOLUTION. This beam is symmetrically loaded, and, since the maximum deflection for both the concentrated and uniformly distributed loads occurs at the center of the span, the deflection that each type of loading produces may be computed separately. Their sum is the deflection of the combined loads.

From Table 6–2 we find that I for a 16 $\mathbf{W^F}$ 36 is 446.3 in.[4] The span length is 21 ft 0 in., or 252 in. E for steel beams is 29,000,000 psi, Table 5–1.

For the concentrated loads at the third points of span the maximum deflection is $\dfrac{23}{648} \times \dfrac{Pl^3}{EI}$, Case 3, Fig. 8–4; hence

$$D = \frac{23}{648} \times \frac{4000 \times 252^3}{29,000,000 \times 446.3} = 0.176 \text{ in.}$$

For the uniformly distributed load, Case 1, Fig. 8–4, $D = \dfrac{5}{384} \times \dfrac{Wl^3}{EI}$; thus

$$D = \frac{5}{384} \times \frac{21 \times 800 \times 252^3}{29,000,000 \times 446.3} = 0.271 \text{ in.}$$

the deflection for the distributed load.

The maximum actual deflection that results from the combined loading is $0.176 + 0.271 = 0.447$ in.

The allowable deflection is $\dfrac{21 \times 12}{360} = 0.7$ in., and, since the actual deflection does not exceed this amount, the beam will not deflect excessively.

Problem 10–2–A. A 6 x 12 in. southern pine timber is used for a simple beam having a span of 18 ft 0 in. If the uniformly distributed load it supports is 5300 lb, is the deflection excessive?

Problem 10–2–B. A cantilever beam 8 ft 0 in. in length has a concentrated load of 6000 lb at its unsupported end. If the beam is a 10 $\mathbf{W^F}$ 33, compute the maximum deflection.

Problem 10–2–C. A 12 I 31.8 is used as a contilever beam whose length is 8 ft 0 in. This beam supports a concentrated load of 6000 lb at its unsupported end and also a uniformly distributed load of 3200 lb that extends over its full length. Compute the actual maximum deflection.

Problem 10–2–D. A 6 x 12 in. eastern hemlock timber is used for a simple beam having a span of 12 ft 0 in. If the total uniformly distributed load on the beam is 8500 lb, compute the actual maximum deflection. Is it excessive?

CHAPTER 11

BENDING STRESSES, DESIGN OF BEAMS

11-1. Bending Stresses. A beam is a structural member on which the applied loads tend to produce bending rather than shortening or lengthening. In the discussions in this book we have seen that a beam must resist shearing forces and that these forces are held in equilibrium by resisting shearing stresses in the fibers of the beam. Now we shall investigate the tendency of the external forces to bend a beam (the bending moment) and the corresponding resisting stresses set up in the fibers of the beam (the resisting moment) that hold the beam in equilibrium.

Figure 11-1(a) represents the side elevation of a simple beam before it is affected by any loads; the upper and lower surfaces are plane parallel surfaces. The horizontal dot-and-dash line is the neutral surface, and AB and CD are two parallel lines drawn on the side of the beam. Figure 11-1(b) represents the same side elevation of the beam when it is deformed (bent) by applied loads. Points A and C have moved closer together, and points B and D are farther apart. The fibers of the beam above the neutral surface are in compression and those below are in tension. The maximum compressive stress is in a fiber at the upper surface of the beam. The stresses below the upper surface decrease in magnitude and are zero at the neutral surface. Similarly, the stresses below the neutral surface are tensile, the maximum stress being at the bottom surface of the beam. If the stress in the outermost fibers of the bent beam does not exceed the elastic limit of the material, the lines AB and CD remain straight lines. The deformation (lengthening and shortening) of the fibers, and also the magnitude of the stresses in the fibers, is directly proportional to their distances from the neutral surface.

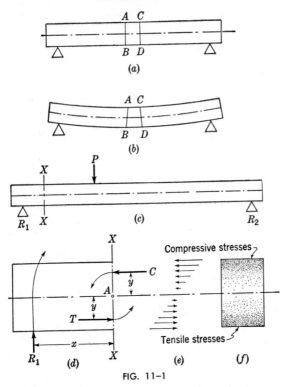

FIG. 11–1

11–2. Resisting Moment. Figure 11–1(c) represents a simple beam subjected to a load. This load is held in equilibrium by the reactions R_1 and R_2. Now consider the portion of the beam to the left of the line X–X; this portion of the beam is drawn on a larger scale in Fig. 11–1(d). The intersection of the neutral surface and the vertical line X–X is the axis A. The bending moment at the section X–X is ($R_1 \times x$); R_1 tends to produce clockwise rotation about the axis A.

In this same figure C and T represent, respectively, the resultants of the horizontal compressive and tensile stresses in the fibers of the beam that are exerted by the right-hand side of the beam. Both C and T tend to produce counterclockwise rotation about the axis A; the sum of the moments of these stresses is called the *resisting moment* because it holds in equilibrium the bending moment; that is, bending moment = resisting moment

$$R_1 \times x \quad = (T \times y) + (C \times y)$$

The lengths of the arrows in Fig. 11–1(e) show how the stresses in the fibers of the beam vary in magnitude. If the beam cross section is symmetrical, as shown in Fig. 11–1(f), the greatest compressive and tensile stresses are at the upper and lower surfaces of the beam, respectively; they decrease in magnitude toward the middle of the beam and at the neutral surface are zero. Figure 11–1(f) indicates the magnitude of the stress distribution, the intensity of the stipple representing the magnitude of the stress.

11–3. Flexure Formula. In Art. 11–2 we have seen that, to maintain equilibrium, the bending moment and the resisting moment are equal in magnitude. We are familiar with the method of

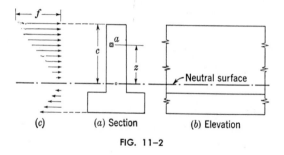

(c)   (a) Section   (b) Elevation

FIG. 11–2

computing the bending moment, and now we shall derive an expression for the resisting moment.

Figure 11–2(a) represents a cross section of a beam subjected to forces that produce bending stresses. Figure 11–2(b) shows a portion of the side elevation of the beam, and Fig. 11–2(c) shows the bending stress distribution.

Let c be the distance of the fiber in the cross section that is farthest from the neutral surface and let f be the unit stress on this fiber at c distance. If f does not exceed the elastic limit of the material, the stresses are directly proportional to their distances from the neutral surface. Hence the unit stress on a fiber at one unit of distance from the neutral surface is $\dfrac{f}{c}$. For example, suppose that $c = 6$ in. and that the unit stress on the fiber 6 in. from the neutral surface is 18,000 psi; that is, $f = 18,000$ psi. At 1 in. the stress is $\dfrac{f}{c}$, or $\dfrac{18,000}{6} = 3000$ psi, at 2 in. it is 2×3000, or 6000 psi, at 3 in. it is 3×3000, or 9000 psi, etc.

Let a be a minutely small area at z distance from the neutral surface, Fig. 11–2(a). Then, from the above, the unit stress on a fiber at z distance is $\dfrac{f}{c} \times z$, and the stress on the tiny area a is $\dfrac{f}{c} \times z \times a$. The *moment* of the stress on the fiber a with respect to the neutral surface is $\dfrac{f}{c} \times z \times a \times z$, z being the lever arm. This quantity may be written $\dfrac{f}{c} \times a \times z^2$. In mathematics the Greek letter Σ, sigma, is often used to indicate the sum of a great number of infinitely small parts. Thus $\dfrac{f}{c} \times \Sigma a \times z^2$ is the sum of the moments of the stresses in all the elementary fibers of the cross section with respect to the neutral axis, and this quantity is the resisting moment. Since the bending moment and resisting moment are equal in magnitude, $M = \dfrac{f}{c} \times \Sigma a \times z^2$. But we know that $\Sigma a \times z^2$ is I, the moment of inertia of the cross section, Art. 6–2. Hence we may write

$$M = \frac{f}{c} \times I \quad \text{or} \quad \frac{M}{f} = \frac{I}{c}$$

For convenience $\dfrac{I}{c}$, called the *section modulus*, Art. 6–5, is represented by the letter S. Thus

$$\frac{M}{f} = S$$

This is known as the *flexure formula;* it is the fundamental formula for the analysis of the bending stresses in homogeneous beams. In designing beams, the architect or engineer first uses the flexure formula to determine the size of the beam for *strength in bending*. To use the formula we simply compute the maximum bending moment and then divide it by the allowable extreme fiber stress of the material. The quotient is the required section modulus of the beam, and the proper size is selected from the table of properties of the various sections. The section thus established is then investigated for shear and deflection.

11–4. Moment of Inertia of a Rectangle. In Art. 6–3 it was stated that I, the moment of inertia, of a rectangular cross section

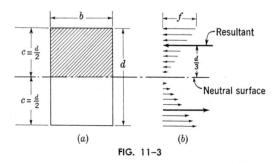

(a)   (b)

FIG. 11–3

with respect to an axis through its centroid and parallel to its base is $\dfrac{bd^3}{12}$. Also, as shown in Art. 6–5, the value of the section modulus of a rectangular cross section S is $\dfrac{bd^2}{6}$. By use of the flexure formula, $\dfrac{M}{f} = S$, we can verify these values.

Figure 11–3(a) shows a rectangle of width b and depth d. The neutral surface lies at a distance of $\dfrac{d}{2}$ from both the upper and lower surfaces; thus $c = \dfrac{d}{2}$. The area in compression (hatched) lies above the neutral surface and is $b \times \dfrac{d}{2}$. Since the unit stress on the most remote fiber is f and is zero at the neutral surface, the *average* unit stress is $\dfrac{f}{2}$; hence the total compressive stress is

$\left(b \times \dfrac{d}{2}\right) \times \dfrac{f}{2}$. The resultant of the compressive forces is $\dfrac{2}{3} \times \dfrac{d}{2}$,

or $\dfrac{d}{3}$, above the neutral surface [see Fig. 11–3(b)]; therefore, the moment of all the compressive stresses with respect to the neutral

surface is $\left(b \times \dfrac{d}{2} \times \dfrac{f}{2}\right) \times \dfrac{d}{3}$, or $f \times \dfrac{bd^2}{12}$. Since there are equal

tensile stresses below the neutral surface, $\left(f \times \dfrac{bd^2}{12}\right) \times 2$, or $f \times$

$\dfrac{bd^2}{6}$, is the sum of the moments of all the stresses in the cross section with respect to the neutral surface, and we know that this is the resisting moment. Since the resisting moment equals the

bending moment, $M = f \times \dfrac{bd^2}{6}$, or $\dfrac{M}{f} = \dfrac{bd^2}{6}$. The flexure for-

mula is $\dfrac{M}{f} = S$; therefore, $S = \dfrac{bd^2}{6}$, the *section modulus*. But $S =$

$\dfrac{I}{c}$; hence $\dfrac{I}{c} = \dfrac{bd^2}{6}$, and, as we know that $c = \dfrac{d}{2}$, $I = \dfrac{bd^2}{6} \times \dfrac{d}{2} =$

$\dfrac{bd^3}{12}$, the value of the *moment of inertia* of the rectangle.

11–5. Design of Beams. The flexure formula is used primarily to determine the size of a beam with respect to *strength in bending*. Experience has shown that beams that fail usually fail by a crushing or tearing of the fibers at the section at which the bending moment is maximum rather than by shear at the supports. The common procedure in designing a beam is to begin by determining its size in accordance with strength in bending, the application of the flexure formula. The beam selected is then investigated for shear and deflection. Short beams with relatively large loads should always be tested with respect to shear. We know how to compute the maximum bending moment, and now that we have the flexure formula, $\dfrac{M}{f} = S$, the design of beams with respect to strength in bending is a very simple matter.

It should be noted that the flexure formula is to be used for *homogeneous beams* only, beams composed of only one material, steel, wood, etc., but not reinforced concrete.

Example. A simple beam having a span length of 22 ft 0 in. is to support a uniformly distributed load of 36,000 lb, which includes the weight of the beam. Design a steel beam for strength in bending.

SOLUTION. The key to the solution of this problem is the flexure formula, $\dfrac{M}{f} = S$. This requires that we first compute the maximum bending moment. *Be certain, when using the flexure formula, that M is in units of inch-pounds.* The beam in this example is a typical condition, and we know that $M = \dfrac{Wl}{8}$, Case 1, Fig. 8–4. Thus

$$M = \frac{36,000 \times 22}{8} = 99,000 \text{ ft-lb}$$

and

$$99,000 \times 12 = 1,188,000 \text{ in-lb}$$

From Table 5–5 we find that f, the allowable extreme fiber stress of structural steel, is 20,000 psi. Then

$$\frac{M}{f} = S$$

$$S = \frac{1,188,000}{20,000} = 59.4 \text{ in.}^3, \text{ the required section modulus}$$

Referring to Table 6–2 we find that a 16 **WF** 40 has a section modulus of 64.4 in.^{3} and therefore is accepted. Other sections having a section modulus of 59.4 in.^{3} or greater are also acceptable. If building conditions permit, the lightest-weight section is usually the most economical.

Example. A simple beam having a span of 14 ft 0 in. has a concentrated load of 7700 lb at 4 ft 0 in. from the left support. With respect to strength in bending, design both a steel and a timber beam to support the 7700-lb load. For the timber beam the allowable extreme fiber stress, f, is 1200 psi.

SOLUTION. Computing the reactions,

$$R_1 \times 14 = 7700 \times 10 \quad \text{and} \quad R_1 = 5500 \text{ lb}$$

$$R_2 \times 14 = 7700 \times 4 \quad \text{and} \quad R_2 = 2200 \text{ lb}$$

The shear diagram is drawn; it shows that the maximum bending moment occurs under the 7700-lb load.

$$M_{(x=4)} = 5500 \times 4 = 22,000 \text{ ft-lb}$$

and

22,000 $\times$ 12 = 264,000 in-lb, the maximum bending moment

For the steel beam, f = 20,000 psi, Table 5–5; therefore

$$\frac{M}{f} = S$$

$$S = \frac{264,000}{20,000} = 13.2 \text{ in.}^3, \text{ the required section modulus}$$

Referring to Table 6–2, we find that an 8 W 17 has a section modulus of 14.1 in.^{3} and therefore is accepted. Note that an 8 I 18.4 (Table 6–1) is also acceptable.

For the timber beam, f = 1200 psi; therefore,

$$\frac{M}{f} = S$$

$$S = \frac{264,000}{1200} = 220 \text{ in.}^3, \text{ the required section modulus}$$

From Table 6–7 select an 8 x 14 in. whose section modulus is 227.81 in.^{3}

In the following problems ignore the weight of the beam and determine the proper sections with respect to strength in bending only.

Problem 11-5-A. A simple beam has a span of 17 ft 0 in. and a uniformly distributed load of 23,000 lb. Determine the size of a wide-flange steel beam to support this load.

Problem 11-5-B. Two loads of 11,000 lb each occur at the third points of span on a simple beam whose length is 18 ft 0 in. What is the lightest-weight standard I-beam that is acceptable?

Problem 11-5-C. Determine the lightest-weight wide-flange section for a simple beam whose length is 20 ft 0 in., having a concentrated load of 20,000 lb at the center of the span and, in addition, a uniformly distributed load of 200 lb per lin ft over its entire length.

Problem 11-5-D. A timber beam of dense structural grade of redwood (see Table 5-4) is to be used for a span of 15 ft 0 in. If there is a concentrated load of 6300 lb at 5 ft 0 in. from one end, what section is acceptable?

Problem 11-5-E. A timber beam, for which $f = 1200$ psi, is to be used for the beam shown in Fig. 7-5 (a). What should be its cross-section dimensions?

Problem 11-5-F. Is an 8 W⁻ 20 sufficiently large to support the cantilever beam shown in Fig. 7-5(c)?

11-6. Computation of Safe Loads. The flexure formula can also be used to determine the safe load or loads a beam of given cross section and span will properly support. The flexure formula is $M = fS$, and, in finding the allowable load, M, the maximum bending moment, is expressed in terms of W or P.

Example. A 10 W⁻ 21 is used for a simple beam whose span is 14 ft 0 in. What is the maximum uniformly distributed load this beam will support?

SOLUTION. From Table 6-2 we find that the section modulus of a 10 W⁻ 21 is 21.5 in.^{3} $M = \dfrac{Wl}{8}$, Case 1, Fig. 8-4. Thus

$$M = \frac{W \times 14 \times 12}{8} = 21W \text{ in-lb}$$

and, since $M = fS$ and $f = 20,000$ psi (Table 5-5),

$21W = 20,000 \times 21.5$

$W = 20,476$ lb, the maximum uniformly distributed load

Example. A simple beam having a span of 20 ft 0 in. has a concentrated load 12 ft 0 in. from the left reaction. If the beam used is a 14 WF 30, what is the greatest load the beam will properly support?

SOLUTION. On referring to Table 6–2, we find that the section modulus of a 14 WF 30 is 41.8 in.^{3}; $f = 20,000$ psi, Table 5–5. Since the span length is 20 ft 0 in. and the concentrated load occurs at 12 ft 0 in. from R_1, $R_1 = \dfrac{2}{5}P$ and $R_2 = \dfrac{3}{5}P$. On constructing the shear diagram, we find that the maximum bending moment will occur under the concentrated load; its magnitude is $\dfrac{2}{5}P \times 12 \times 12 = 57.6P$ in-lb.

$M = fS$; hence $57.6P = 20,000 \times 41.8$ and $P = 14,510$ lb, the maximum concentrated load.

In solving the following problems neglect the weight of the beam and determine the allowable loads only with respect to strength in bending.

Problem 11–6–A. Compute the maximum allowable uniformly distributed load for a simple beam having a span of 17 ft. 0 in. if the section used is a 12 I 31.8.

Problem 11–6–B. An 8 x 12 in. timber beam, for which the allowable extreme fiber stress is 1400 psi, has a span of 15 ft 0 in. with equal concentrated loads at the third points of span. Compute the maximum allowable magnitudes of the loads.

Problem 11–6–C. A 12 WF 27 having a span of 14 ft 0 in. supports s uniformly distributed load of 7000 lb and also a concentrated load at the center of the span. Compute the magnitude of the maximum allowable concentrated load.

Problem 11–6–D. What is the maximum concentrated load that may be placed at the unsupported end of a cantilever beam 9 ft 0 in. in length if the section used is an 8 WF 17?

Problem 11–6–E. A simple beam has a span of 20 ft 0 in. with a concentrated load at 4 ft 0 in. from one of the supports. If the section used is a 16 WF 36, compute the magnitude of the concentrated load.

11–7. Investigation of Beams. Another use of the flexure formula is for the investigation of beams. To investigate a beam, we determine whether it is strong enough to support a certain loading. For such problems we are given as data a span length, magnitude and type of loading, and the size of the beam. Although such problems may be solved by different methods, a simple and direct way is to compute the *actual* extreme fiber stress in the member and to compare it with the stress we know to be the allowable. This means that we compute the value of f in the flexure formula.

Another method of investigation is to compute the required section modulus for the given load and span so that it may be compared with that of the given section.

Example. An 8 I 18.4 is used for a simple beam whose span length is 12 ft 0 in. A concentrated load of 7000 lb is placed at the center of the span. Is the beam safe with respect to strength in bending?

SOLUTION. From Table 6–1 we find that the section modulus of an 8 I 18.4 is 14.2 in.³ The maximum bending moment for this loading is $\dfrac{Pl}{4}$, Case 2, Fig. 8–4; thus $M = \dfrac{7000 \times 12 \times 12}{4}$, or 252,000 in-lb. Since $\dfrac{M}{f} = S$, $f = \dfrac{M}{S} = \dfrac{252,000}{14.2} = 17,730$ psi, the *actual* extreme fiber stress. Since the actual extreme fiber stress is less than 20,000 psi, the allowable (Table 5–5), the beam is safe with respect to strength in bending.

Using the other method of investigation, the required section modulus for this span and load is $S = \dfrac{M}{f} = \dfrac{252,000}{20,000}$, or $S = 12.6$ in.³ Since the section modulus of the 8 I 18.4 is 14.2 in.³, the beam is sufficiently large.

Example. A 6 x 8 in. timber beam is used for a cantilever having a length of 8 ft 0 in.; it supports a uniformly distributed load of 1800 lb. If the allowable extreme fiber stress of the timber is 1400 psi, is the beam safe with respect to strength in bending?

SOLUTION. For a 6 x 8 in. beam, $S = 51.56$ in.³ (Table 6–7). $M = \dfrac{Wl}{2}$, Case 5, Fig. 8–4. Then $M = \dfrac{1800 \times 8 \times 12}{2} = 86,400$ in-lb.

$f = \dfrac{M}{S}$, or $f = \dfrac{86,400}{51.56} = 1670$ psi, the *actual* extreme fiber stress. Since this exceeds 1400 psi, the allowable, the beam is unsafe.

In the following problems neglect the weight of the beam and investigate the beams with respect to strength in bending.

Problem 11-7-A. A 10 I 25.4 is used for a simple beam whose span is 14 ft 0 in. If the uniformly distributed load is 26,000 lb, is the beam safe?

Problem 11-7-B. A cantilever beam has a length of 9 ft 0 in. with a concentrated load of 2000 lb at its unsupported end. If the section used is an 8 WF 17, is the beam safe?

Problem 11-7-C. A simple beam having a span of 19 ft 0 in. has two concentrated loads of 7000 lb each at the third points of span and, in addition, a uniformly distributed load of 25,000 lb. If the beam section is a 16 WF 40, is the beam safe?

Problem 11-7-D. A lintel in a masonry wall has a span of 14 ft 0 in. and supports a triangular load of 58,000 lb. The lintel is composed of two 14 WF 30 beams. Is this lintel safe? See Art. 8–10.

Problem 11-7-E. A simple beam has a span of 20 ft 0 in. with a uniformly distributed load of 12,000 lb extending over a length of 12 ft 0 in. from one of the supports. If the beam section is a 10 I 25.4, is the beam safe?

Problem 11-7-F. The example in Art. 7–5 referred to the beam shown in Fig. 7–8(a). Is the 8 x 12 in. section safe with respect to strength in bending?

BUILT-UP BEAMS OF
TWO MATERIALS

12–1. Beams of Two Materials. Before rolled-steel beams were so readily obtainable, it was common practice to increase the strength of timber beams by the addition of a steel plate or plates. One type of built-up beam frequently used consisted of a steel plate with a timber beam on each side, as shown in Fig. 12–1(a);

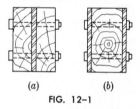

(a)   (b)

FIG. 12–1

it is known as a *flitched beam*. The three components were securely held together with through-bolts and acted as a single unit. Although such sections are not employed today, the computations for determining their strength are interesting and illustrate the phenomenon of two different materials in a beam acting as a unit. It will be seen that using wood and steel in this manner results in an uneconomical use of the two materials.

The computations for designing a beam of this type are based on the fact that *the two materials deform equally*. Let

Δ_s and Δ_w = the deformations per unit of length of the outermost fibers of the steel and wood, respectively, in inches

f_s and f_w = the unit stresses in the most remote fibers of the steel and wood, respectively, in pounds per square inch

E_s and E_w = the moduli of elasticity of the steel and wood, respectively, in pounds per square inch

Since, by definition, the modulus of elasticity of a material is equal to the unit stress divided by the unit deformation,

$$E_s = \frac{f_s}{\Delta_s} \quad \text{and} \quad E_w = \frac{f_w}{\Delta_w}$$

$$\Delta_s = \frac{f_s}{E_s} \quad \text{and} \quad \Delta_w = \frac{f_w}{E_w}$$

Since the deformations of the steel and wood must be equal,

$$\frac{f_s}{E_s} = \frac{f_w}{E_w} \quad \text{and} \quad f_w = f_s \times \frac{E_w}{E_s}$$

Assuming that f_s = 20,000 psi, E_s = 29,000,000 psi, and E_w = 1,760,000 psi,

$$f_w = 20,000 \times \frac{1,760,000}{29,000,000} \quad \text{and} \quad f_w = 1213 \text{ psi}$$

Attention is called to the fact that southern pine and Douglas fir, each having a modulus of elasticity of 1,760,000 psi, are two of our strongest structural woods and are in constant use. However, regardless of their grade and allowable extreme fiber stress, when used with steel in flitched beams their maximum extreme fiber stress is only 1213 psi when the steel is stressed to 20,000 psi.

Example. A flitched beam composed of two 4 x 12 in. southern pine timbers with a $\frac{1}{2}$ x $11\frac{1}{2}$ in. steel plate between, as shown in Fig. 12–1(a), is used as a simple beam having a span of 14 ft 0 in. Compute the allowable uniformly distributed load this built-up beam will support.

SOLUTION. In accordance with the foregoing computations, we shall use f = 20,000 psi for the steel and f = 1213 psi for the timber. Table 6–7 gives 79.9 in.³ as the section modulus for a 4 x 12 in.; hence S for two 4 x 12 in. timbers is 2×79.9, or 159.8 in.³ For a rectangular section $S = \dfrac{bd^2}{6}$, Fig. 6–9. Thus for the steel plate $S = \dfrac{0.5 \times 11.5 \times 11.5}{6} = 11.02$ in.³ in.

Computing the load carried by the wood,

$$M = \frac{Wl}{8} = \frac{W \times 14 \times 12}{8}$$

$= 21W$ in-lb, the maximum bending moment

$M = f \times S$ or $21W = 1213 \times 159.8$

$W = 9200$ lb, the distributed load carried by the two timber beams

To compute the load carried by the steel plate,

     $M = 21W$ in-lb, the maximum bending moment, as for the timber beams

     $M = f \times S$ or $21W = 20{,}000 \times 11.02$

and

     $W = 10{,}490$ lb, the distributed load carried by the steel plate

Thus the distributed load carried by the built-up beam is 9200 + 10,490, or 19,690 lb.

The steel plate has a cross-sectional area of 5.75 sq in. and carries a distributed load of only 10,490 lb. An 8 **WF** 17 has a smaller cross-sectional area, 5 sq in., and for the same span will support a uniformly distributed load of 13,430 lb. When the two 4 x 12 in. timbers are used without the steel plate, they can safely support a total uniformly distributed load of 12,930 lb if $f = 1700$ psi.

Problem 12–1–A. A flitched beam built up of a 10 x 14 in. Douglas fir timber and two $\frac{1}{2}$ x $13\frac{1}{2}$ in. steel plates, as shown in Fig. 12–1(*b*), is used for a simple beam having a span length of 16 ft 0 in. Compute the magnitude of the concentrated load, at the center of the span, that this flitched beam will support.

COLUMNS

13-1. Columns and Posts. The term *column* is applied to a more or less slender structural member that is subject to compression in a direction parallel to its longitudinal axis. A column is generally used in a vertical position. The term *strut* is given to smaller compression members not necessarily in a vertical position. A compression member whose length is so short that its failure is caused by crushing of its fibers is called a *short column* or *post*.

13-2. Slenderness Ratio. A piece of timber whose cross section is 3 x 4 in. (actual dimensions $2\frac{5}{8}$ x $3\frac{5}{8}$ in.) has an area of 9.52 sq in. If the allowable compressive unit stress parallel to the grain is 1200 psi, and the length of the piece is 10 in., it will safely support a compressive load of 9.52 × 1200, or 11,424 lb. If, however, a piece of timber has the same cross-sectional area but a length of 8 ft 0 in., a compressive load of the same magnitude will cause the member to bend and failure will result. It is obvious, therefore, that the relation of length to width of cross section is an important consideration in the determination of the allowable load a compression member will support. This relation is known as the *slenderness ratio*. For timber columns it is l/d, in which l is the unbraced length of the member and d is the dimension of the least side of the cross section. It is impossible to designate the exact ratio of length to least side at which a member should be considered as a column rather than a post. This ratio for timber columns is given in some older building codes and varies from 10 to 14. Current specifications require that simple solid wood columns have l/d values not in excess of 50. For structural steel columns the slenderness ratio is l/r, l being the unsupported length of the member and r the least radius of gyration of the cross section. In Fig. 13–1(d) the column has a total length of L_1 but the unbraced or unstayed length is L_2.

13–3. End Conditions of Columns. Another factor to be considered in determining the allowable load for a column is the condition of the ends. One can readily understand that a column with *rounded* ends will bend more readily and therefore support a smaller load than a column of the same dimensions whose ends are *flat*. Likewise, a member with flat ends will support a smaller load than one having its ends rigidly fixed (see Fig. 13–1). In still another end condition the ends of the columns are *hinged* or *pin-connected;* such end conditions are often found in machines.

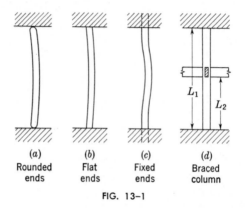

| (a) | (b) | (c) | (d) |
| Rounded ends | Flat ends | Fixed ends | Braced column |

FIG. 13–1

In practice, columns used in building construction generally have both ends flat or fixed and are computed as being equally strong. In succeeding articles certain formulas for simple solid columns are used in the design of wood columns. These formulas are based on pin-end conditions but apply also to square-end conditions as well. For timber columns it is important that the ends be at right angles to the axis of the column and that there be a uniform pressure on the surface on which the column bears.

13–4. Solid Wood Columns. The design of a wood column must conform to the requirements in the governing building code. The designer must employ the column formulas specified in the code; these formulas are changed from time to time. The following formula is recommended by the National Lumber Manufacturers Association. It is used to determine the allowable unit stress in simple solid square or rectangular columns

$$\frac{P}{A} = \frac{0.30E}{(l/d)^2}$$

in which P = the axial load in pounds

$\quad\quad A$ = the area of the column cross section in square inches

$\quad\quad E$ = the modulus of elasticity of the wood species in pounds per square inch (see Table 5–4)

$\quad\quad l$ = the laterally unsupported length of the column in inches

$\quad\quad d$ = the dimension of the least side of the cross section in inches

In using this formula, care must be taken to see that P/A, the allowable unit stress, does not exceed the value of c, the allowable compressive unit stress parallel to the grain. The values of c for various species and grades of woods are found in Table 5–4.

The allowable axial load for a wood column having a circular cross section shall not exceed that of a square column having the same cross-sectional area.

For simple solid columns l/d shall not exceed 50.

Example. Compute the allowable axial load for an 8 x 8 in. column whose unsupported length is 12 ft 0 in. The column is of the select structural grade of Douglas fir.

SOLUTION. On referring to Table 5–4, we find, for this timber, $E = 1,760,000$ psi and $c = 1500$ psi. In Table 6–7 we see that the actual dimensions of this cross section are 7.5 x 7.5 in., the area being 56.25 sq in.

Since the length is 12 ft 0 in., $l/d = (12 \times 12)/7.5 = 19.2$, the slenderness ratio. Then

$$\frac{P}{A} = \frac{0.30E}{(l/d)^2} = \frac{0.30 \times 1,760,000}{19.2 \times 19.2} = 1432 \text{ psi}$$

the allowable unit stress. Note that this does not exceed the value of c, 1500 psi, and consequently may be used to determine the column load. Thus $1432 \times 56.25 = 80,550$ lb, the allowable axial load on the column.

Example. A 10 x 10 in. wood column of the heart structural grade of redwood has a length of 12 ft 0 in. Compute its allowable axial load.

SOLUTION. In Table 5–4 we find that $E = 1,320,000$ psi and $c = 1100$ psi. The actual dimensions of the cross section are 9.5 x 9.5 in., and the cross-sectional area is 90.25 sq in. (Table 6–7). The slenderness ratio is l/d, or $(12 \times 12)/9.5 = 15.2$. Then

$$\frac{P}{A} = \frac{0.30E}{(l/d)^2} = \frac{0.30 \times 1,320,000}{15.2 \times 15.2} = 1714 \text{ psi}$$

In this problem we see that 1714 psi exceeds the value of c, 1100 psi, and therefore the allowable unit stress is only 1100 psi. Hence $1100 \times 90.25 = 99,275$ lb, the allowable axial load.

In accordance with the following data, compute the allowable axial loads that these columns will support.

Problem 13–4–A. Column length, 13 ft 0 in.; nominal cross section, 8 x 8 in.; No. 1 SR grade of southern pine.

Problem 13–4–B. Column length, 10 ft 0 in.; nominal cross section, 6 x 8 in.; heart structural grade of redwood.

Problem 13–4–C. Column length, 11 ft 0 in.; nominal cross section, 10 x 10 in.; 1450 c grade of cypress.

Problem 13–4–D. Column length, 12 ft 0 in.; nominal cross section, 6 x 6 in.; construction grade of Douglas fir.

13–5. Spaced Columns. A spaced column is formed by two or more individual members having their longitudinal axes parallel and separated at the ends and middle points of their length by blocking. They are joined at the ends by timber connectors and bolts capable of developing the required shear resistance for the imposed loads. See Fig. 13–2. They constitute an economical use of material and are used for direct support of axial loads and for compression members in wood trusses. For the individual members of a spaced column l/d shall not exceed 80 nor shall l_2/d exceed 40.

For condition a, relating to the position of the connectors in the end blocks shown in Fig. 13–2, the allowable unit stress for the individual members of a spaced column is found by the column formula

$$\frac{P}{A} = \frac{0.75E}{(l/d)^2}$$

Similarly, for condition b, also shown in Fig. 13–2,

$$\frac{P}{A} = \frac{0.90E}{(l/d)^2}$$

In both formulas P/A, the unit stress, must not exceed the value of c for the particular species and grade of wood as given in Table 5–4.

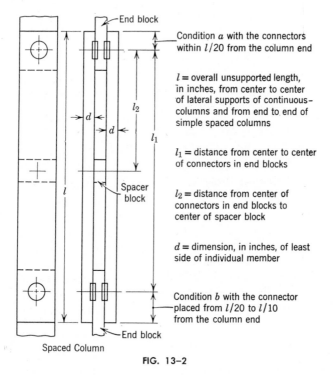

End block

Condition a with the connectors within $l/20$ from the column end

l = overall unsupported length, in inches, from center to center of lateral supports of continuous-columns and from end to end of simple spaced columns

l_1 = distance from center to center of connectors in end blocks

Spacer block

l_2 = distance from center of connectors in end blocks to center of spacer block

d = dimension, in inches, of least side of individual member

Condition b with the connector placed from $l/20$ to $l/10$ from the column end

End block

Spaced Column

FIG. 13–2

Example. A spaced column has a length of 6 ft 0 in. and consists of two 2 x 6 in. members separated at the ends and mid-length by 2-in. blocks. The connectors in the end blocks comply with condition a. If the timber is No. 2 dense SR grade of southern pine, compute the allowable axial load for this spaced column.

SOLUTION. Reference to Table 6–7 shows that the dressed size of a 2 x 6 in. member is $1\frac{5}{8}$ x $5\frac{5}{8}$ in. The cross-sectional area is 9.14 sq in. Table 5–4 shows, for this species and grade of wood, that $E = 1,760,000$ psi and $c = 1050$ psi.

The slenderness ratio, $l/d = \dfrac{6 \times 12}{1.625} = 44.3$. Then $\dfrac{P}{A} = \dfrac{0.75 \times 1,760,000}{44.3 \times 44.3} = 672$ psi. Note that 672 does not exceed c, 1050 psi.

Since $A = 9.14$ sq in., $9.14 \times 672 = 6140$ lb, the allowable load on each individual 2 x 6 in. member. However, there are two 2 x 6 in. pieces; hence $2 \times 6140 = 12,280$ lb, the allowable load on the spaced column.

Problem 13–5–A. A spaced column 8 ft 0 in. in length is made up of two 3 x 8 in. members. The wood used is the select structural grade of hemlock and the end conditions conform with condition a. Compute the allowable axial load.

Problem 13–5–B. Compute the allowable axial load on a spaced column 9 ft 0 in. in length composed of two 3 x 6 in. members made of the construction grade of Douglas fir. The connectors at the ends conform with condition b.

13–6. Slenderness Ratio of Steel Columns.

Consider a timber member 2 x 6 in. in cross section and 3 ft 0 in. long used as a compression member. It is obvious that the member will bend readily and that the bending will be in a plane parallel to the 2-in. side. It is for this reason that the slenderness ratio of rectangular wood columns is the length divided by the dimension of *the least side*, l/d. The slenderness ratio of structural steel columns, however, is l/r, the length divided by the *least radius of gyration*. Suppose that we have a 10 I 25.4 used as a column. We know from Art. 6–6 that $r = \sqrt{\dfrac{I}{A}}$. Table 6–1 gives the moment of inertia with respect to both the X–X and Y–Y axes of standard I-beams. The axis that gives the smaller moment of inertia also gives the smaller radius of gyration. For this particular section the least radius of gyration is 0.97 in. Such a section tends to bend with respect to an axis for which the radius of gyration is the least. Consequently, in determining the slenderness ratio of steel columns, the *least radius of gyration* is considered.

13–7. Formulas for Steel Columns. As for wood columns, many different formulas have been used for the design of structural steel columns. The formulas recommended by the American Institute of Steel Construction have been widely adopted; they are used in the following illustrative examples.

When the A.I.S.C. column formulas for axially loaded columns are used, l/r for main compression members must not exceed 120. For columns with values of l/r not greater than 120, main or secondary members,

$$f = 17{,}000 - 0.485\,\frac{l^2}{r^2} \quad \text{or} \quad f = 17{,}000 - 0.485\left(\frac{l}{r}\right)^2$$

in which $f =$ the allowable compressive unit stress on the cross-sectional area of the column in pounds per square inch

$\quad l =$ the unsupported length of the column in inches

$\quad r =$ the least radius of gyration of the column cross section in inches

For bracing or secondary compression members having values of l/r greater than 120, but not exceeding 200,

$$f = \frac{18{,}000}{1 + \dfrac{l^2}{18{,}000r^2}}$$

in which the terms are similar to those given above.

The designer makes use of safe load tables in determining the proper sizes. If such tables are not available, trial sections are taken and the allowable loads computed.

Example. Design a main structural steel column having an unbraced length of 20 ft 0 in. to support an axial load of 200,000 lb.

SOLUTION. From the formula it is seen that the allowable unit stress cannot exceed 17,000 psi. If l/r is 120, the formula $f = 17{,}000 - 0.485\,\dfrac{l^2}{r^2}$ gives 10,020 lb for the allowable unit stress. For this example assume that the unit stress is 14,000 psi. Then, since the design load is 200,000 lb, $200{,}000 \div 14{,}000 = 14.3$ sq in. This procedure enables us to select a trial section, in this case a 10 **WF** 49 having an area of 14.4 sq in. (Table 6–2). From this same table we note that the least radius of gyration of the trial section is 2.54 in. Then

$$\frac{l}{r} = \frac{20 \times 12}{2.54} = 94.4$$

The slenderness ratio does not exceed 120.

$$f = 17,000 - 0.485 \frac{l^2}{r^2}$$

$$f = 17,000 - 0.485 \frac{240^2}{2.54^2}$$

$$= 12,680 \text{ psi, the allowable unit stress}$$

There are 14.4 sq in. in the cross section; hence $14.4 \times 12,680 = 182,500$ lb, the allowable load on the trial section. But the design load is 200,000 lb, and therefore the trial section is too small. Again take a 10 **WF** 54, a heavier trial section. This section is tested in a similar manner, and the allowable load is found to be 202,000 lb. Therefore, the accepted section is a 10 **WF** 54.

Example. Compute the allowable load on an 8 **WF** 31 column having a length of 22 ft 0 in. This section is to be used as a secondary member.

SOLUTION. From Table 6–2 the cross-sectional area of this section is 9.12 sq in. and the least radius of gyration is 2.01 in.

$$\frac{l}{r} = \frac{22 \times 12}{2.01} = 131.34,$$ the slenderness ratio. This value exceeds 120, and, since it is a secondary, not a main, member, we use the formula

$$f = \frac{18,000}{1 + \dfrac{l^2}{18,000r^2}}$$

$$f = \frac{18,000}{1 + \dfrac{(22 \times 12)^2}{18,000 \times 2.01^2}} = 9190 \text{ psi, the allowable unit stress}$$

The area contains 9.12 sq in., hence $9.12 \times 9190 = 83,700$ lb, the allowable axial load.

Example. A steel pipe column with an external diameter of 4 in. and an internal diameter of 3.548 in. is 10 ft 0 in. in length. Compute its allowable axial load.

SOLUTION. For this hollow circular cross section we must compute the area and radius of gyration. From Fig. 6–9,

$$A = \frac{\pi(d^2 - d_1{}^2)}{4} = \frac{3.1416(4^2 - 3.548^2)}{4}$$

$$= 2.68 \text{ sq in., the cross-sectional area}$$

$$r = \frac{\sqrt{d^2 + d_1{}^2}}{4} = \frac{\sqrt{4^2 + 3.548^2}}{4}$$

$$= 1.34 \text{ in., the radius of gyration}$$

$$\frac{l}{r} = \frac{10 \times 12}{1.34} = 89.6, \text{ the slenderness ratio}$$

$$f = 17,000 - 0.485 \left(\frac{l^2}{r^2}\right) = 17,000 - 0.485 \frac{120^2}{1.34^2}$$

$$= 13,110 \text{ psi, the allowable compressive unit stress}$$

Since the cross-sectional area of the pipe column is 2.68 sq in., $2.68 \times 13,110 = 35,200$ lb, the allowable axial load.

For the following column sections compute the allowable axial loads.

Problem 13–7–A. 12 W℉ 65; unbraced length, 24 ft 0 in.

Problem 13–7–B. 10 W℉ 33; unbraced length, 16 ft 0 in.

Problem 13–7–C. 12 W℉ 40; unbraced length, 14 ft 0 in.

Problem 13–7–D. 8 W℉ 24; unbraced length, 18 ft 0 in. (a secondary member).

Problem 13–7–E. Steel pipe column, outside diameter, 4.5 in.; inside diameter, 4.026 in.; unbraced length, 12 ft 0 in.

13–8. Eccentrically Loaded Columns. The columns previously discussed have been loaded axially. Figure 13–3(a) shows a short column in plan and elevation. The load, P, is axial, located at the intersection of the two major axes, X–X and Y–Y. For this condition, if there is no bending, the stresses are uniformly distributed over the area of the cross section. Figure 13–3(c) shows the stress distribution on the fibers at the face of the column marked mn in plan. Stresses f_1 and f_2 are the stresses on the right and left sides of the column, respectively. When the load is axial, as in Fig. 13–3(a), f_1 and f_2 are equal in magnitude. If A is the area of

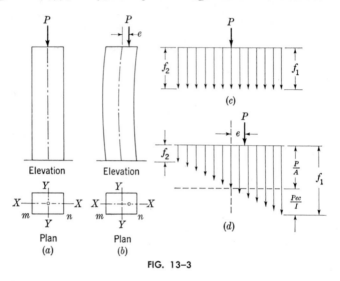

FIG. 13–3

the cross section, the stresses are distributed uniformly and each unit of area has a stress of $\dfrac{P}{A}$. Thus the unit stresses at the face mn of the column, f_1 and $f_2 = \dfrac{P}{A}$.

Now let us consider that the load P is moved the distance e on the axis X–X, as shown in Fig. 13–3(b). The distance e is called the *eccentricity*. There is now a tendency for the column to bend; the stresses are not distributed uniformly over the cross section, the stress f_1 increases in magnitude, and f_2 decreases. If the elastic limit of the column material is not exceeded, the stresses on the unit areas on the mn face of the column increase from f_2 to f_1 at a uniform rate, as shown in Fig. 13–3(d). It is seen from this figure that f_1 is composed of the average stress $\left(\dfrac{P}{A}\right)$ plus the additional stress that results from the tendency to bend. The stress f_2 has decreased by a similar magnitude. This stress that results from bending is the f in the flexure formula, $\dfrac{M}{f} = \dfrac{I}{c}$, or $f = \dfrac{Mc}{I}$. But M, the bending moment, is the load P times its eccentricity; that is, $M = Pe$. Substituting Pe for the value of M, $f = \dfrac{Pec}{I}$. Hence

$$f_1 = \frac{P}{A} + \frac{Pec}{I} \quad \text{and} \quad f_2 = \frac{P}{A} - \frac{Pec}{I}$$

If the column is unduly long, the stress at f_2 may become tensile instead of compressive. A masonry column cannot resist tensile stresses and therefore should always be designed to have such proportions that the entire cross-sectional area is in compression.

In practice, it is common to find columns loaded with both axial and eccentric loads. For such a condition we are concerned with the stress that occurs on the side of the column nearest the eccentric load; this is f_1, the maximum unit stress.

$$f_1 = \frac{P + P'}{A} + \frac{P'ec}{I}$$

in which P = the axial load in pounds
$\qquad P'$ = the eccentric load in pounds

and the remaining terms are similar to those given above. When using this formula, note carefully the axis of the column about which the eccentric load tends to cause bending. As shown in Fig. 13–3(b), this axis is Y–Y.

Example. A 12 **WF** 40 is used as a column whose unbraced length is 12 ft 0 in. This section supports an axial load of 80,000 lb and also an eccentric load of 30,000 lb, the eccentricity of which is 8 in. (see Fig. 13–4). Compute the maximum compressive unit stress on the cross section of the column.

SOLUTION. From Fig. 13–4 it is seen that the eccentric load tends to bend the column about the X–X axis. Hence, referring to Table 6–2, we find that the depth of a 12 **W** 40 is 11.94 in.; therefore $c = \dfrac{11.94}{2} = 5.97$ in.; $I_{X-X} = 310.1$ in.^{4}, and A, the cross-sectional area, is 11.77 sq in.

$$f_1 = \frac{P + P'}{A} + \frac{P'ec}{I}$$

$$= \frac{80,000 + 30,000}{11.77} + \frac{30,000 \times 8 \times 5.97}{310.1}$$

$$= 13,970 \text{ psi, the maximum compressive unit stress}$$

A specification found in certain building codes, relating to combined axial and eccentric loads on columns, states that the max-

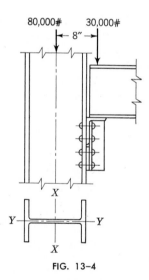

FIG. 13–4

imum unit stress, as found above, must not exceed the stress that would be permitted if only axial stress existed, the stress found by the column formula. For this column, r, the least radius of gyration, is 1.94 in. (Table 6–2). Thus $\dfrac{l}{r} = \dfrac{12 \times 12}{1.94} = 74.2$, the slenderness ratio. Then, in accordance with Art. 13–7,

$$f_r = 17,000 - 0.485 \left(\frac{l}{r}\right)^2 = 17,000 - (0.485 \times 74.2^2)$$

$$= 14,330 \text{ psi}$$

Since the stress 13,970 psi does not exceed this allowable stress, the column section is not overstressed. In computing the allowable stress, 14,330 psi, the *least* radius of gyration was taken irrespective of the position of the eccentric load. This is the usual procedure. The method is conservative and is in common use.

The foregoing discussion explains the theory of investigating the stresses in columns that result from combined axial and eccentric loads. However, the design of an eccentrically loaded column must conform with the requirements found in the governing building code. Frequently the code gives a specific method of design procedure.*

Problem 13–8–A. A 10 WF 33 column having an unbraced length of 16 ft 0 in. supports an axial load of 60,000 lb and an eccentric load of 20,000 lb. The eccentric load is on the $Y–Y$ axis of the column 7 in. from the $X–X$ axis. Is the column overstressed?

13–9. Principle of the Middle Third. Since masonry offers little or no resistance to tension, it is desirable that the stresses resulting from eccentric loads on short piers be entirely compressive. The loads should be of such magnitude and in such positions that the maximum stress does not exceed the allowable compressive stress of the material or the allowable bearing capacity of the foundation bed.

Figures 13–5(a) and (b) represent a short masonry pier in elevation and plan. In plan the pier is d units of length parallel to the $Y–Y$ axis and b units of width parallel to the $X–X$ axis. If P, the load on the pier, is axial, the stresses are distributed uniformly over the cross section and equal $\dfrac{P}{bd}$ or $\dfrac{P}{A}$, A being the cross-sectional area of the pier.

Now assume that P is moved a slight distance on the $Y–Y$ axis, call it e distance. This is an eccentric loading, and the stresses in the pier or on the foundation bed are not uniformly distributed.

---

* See the author's *Simplified Design of Structural Steel*, Second Edition, John Wiley and Sons, New York, 1955.

On the right and left sides of the pier the stresses are f_1 and f_2, respectively, as indicated in Fig. 13–5(c). From Art. 13–8, we know

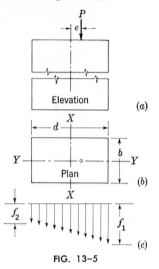

FIG. 13–5

that $f_1 = \dfrac{P}{A} + \dfrac{Pec}{I}$ and $f_2 = \dfrac{P}{A} - \dfrac{Pec}{I}$. Since the pier is a rectangular section in plan, $c = \dfrac{d}{2}$ and $I = \dfrac{bd^3}{12}$. Substituting these values in the formula for f_1 gives

$$f_1 = \frac{P}{A} + \frac{\dfrac{Ped}{2}}{\dfrac{bd^3}{12}} \quad \text{and} \quad f_1 = \frac{P}{A}\left(1 + \frac{6e}{d}\right)$$

Similarly,

$$f_2 = \frac{P}{A}\left(1 - \frac{6e}{d}\right)$$

Figure 13–6(a) represents, in elevation, a similar rectangular pier. Note that the pier width is divided into three thirds, the center and the two outer thirds. P is an *axial* load ($e = 0$), and the stress distribution at the base of the pier is shown in Fig. 13–6(e). For this condition, $f_1 = \dfrac{P}{A}$ and $f_2 = \dfrac{P}{A}$.

Suppose that P is moved to the right on the $Y-Y$ axis of the pier so that e, the eccentricity, is less than $\dfrac{d}{6}$, as shown in Fig. 13–6(b).

P is within the middle third of the base, and $f_1 = \dfrac{P}{A}\left(1 + \dfrac{6e}{d}\right)$

and $f_2 = \dfrac{P}{A}\left(1 - \dfrac{6e}{d}\right)$; see Fig. 13–6($f$). This condition is similar to the pier and load shown in Fig. 13.5.

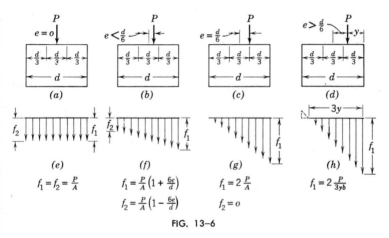

FIG. 13–6

Figure 13–6(c) shows P moved to the outer edge of the middle third; that is, $e = \dfrac{d}{6}$. Substituting this value of e in the formula gives

$$f_1 = \frac{P}{A}\left(1 + \frac{6e}{d}\right) \quad f_1 = \frac{P}{A}\left(1 + \frac{6 \times d}{d \times 6}\right) \quad \text{or} \quad f_1 = 2\frac{P}{A}$$

Similarly,

$$f_2 = 0$$

Thus it is seen that, *if P is at the outer edge of the middle third, the greatest compressive stress is twice the average stress* $\left(f_1 = 2\dfrac{P}{A}\right)$ *and the stress on the opposite side is zero* ($f_2 = 0$). The entire cross-sectional area is under compression as indicated in Fig. 13–6(g).

Another condition is shown in Fig. 13–6(d); P is moved still farther to the right so that e is greater than $\dfrac{d}{6}$. *P is now outside the middle third.* Although the width of the pier is d, only a portion of the width is under compression, Fig. 13–6(h). If P is now y distance from the right side of the pier, the width of pier subjected to compressive stress is $3y$ and the stress at f_1 is twice the average stress over the area of which $3y$ is the width; that is, $f_1 = 2 \times \dfrac{P}{3yb}$. In this equation b is the dimension of the cross section of the pier perpendicular to d; hence $3yb$ is the area subjected to compressive stresses.

In designing masonry piers it is important that the maximum compressive unit stress on the foundation bed not exceed the allowable bearing capacity of the soil. Attention is called to the fact that the foregoing discussion neglects the weight of the pier. As this weight is distributed uniformly over the foundation bed, it may be simply added to determine the unit stress for f_1 or f_2.

Example. A short masonry pier has a cross-sectional area of 30 x 18 in., as shown in Fig. 13–7. The load on the pier is 64,800 lb and is moved to various positions on the $Y–Y$ axis. Neglecting

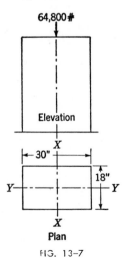

FIG. 13–7

the weight of the pier, compute the maximum stress in pounds per square inch on the foundation bed when $e = 0$, $e = 3$ in., $e = 5$ in., and $e = 7$ in.

SOLUTION.   When $e = 0$, we have a condition of axial loading. Both f_1 and $f_2 = \dfrac{P}{A}$; hence f_1 and $f_2 = \dfrac{64,800}{30 \times 18} = 120$ psi.

If $e = 3$ in.,

$$f_1 = \frac{P}{A}\left(1 + \frac{6e}{d}\right) = \frac{64,800}{30 \times 18}\left(1 + \frac{6 \times 3}{30}\right) = 192 \text{ psi}$$

$$f_2 = \frac{P}{A}\left(1 - \frac{6e}{d}\right) = \frac{64,800}{30 \times 18}\left(1 - \frac{6 \times 3}{30}\right) = 48 \text{ psi}$$

When $e = 5$ in., the load P is at the outer edge of the middle third and the stress at $f_1 = 2\dfrac{P}{A}$, or $f_1 = 2 \times \dfrac{64,800}{30 \times 18} = 240$ psi. The stress at $f_2 = 0$.

When $e = 7$ in., the load P is outside the middle third and only a portion of the base of the pier is in compression.   One half the width of the pier is $\dfrac{30}{2}$, or 15 in.; hence $y = 15 - 7$, or 8 in.   The area under compression is $3yb$, or $3 \times 8 \times 18 = 432$ sq in.

$$f_1 = 2 \times \frac{P}{3yb} = 2 \times \frac{64,800}{432} = 300 \text{ psi}$$

Problem 13–9–A.   In the foregoing illustrative example assume that the load of 64,800 lb is moved to various positions on the axis of the cross section that is parallel to the 18-in. side.   Neglecting the weight of the pier, compute the maximum compressive stress on the foundation bed when $e = 0$, $e = 2$ in., $e = 3$ in., and $e = 4$ in.

Problem 13–9–B.   A short masonry pier is 2 ft square in cross section and supports a load of 57,600 lb.   This load is moved to various positions on one of the major axes of the cross section.   Neglecting the weight of the pier, compute the maximum compressive stress on the foundation bed when $e = 0$, $e = 2$ in., $e = 4$ in., $e = 5$ in., and $e = 6$ in.

CHAPTER 14

RIVETS AND WELDS

14–1. Connections. Rivets, bolts, and welds are used to join individual structural steel members. At the present time riveting is employed most frequently, but welding affords certain advantages and its use is constantly increasing. Bolts are used as temporary connections for riveting and welding and for permanent connections in certain lower-stressed members. High strength bolts are discussed in Art. 14–14.

14–2. Rivets. A rivet is a cylindrical shank of metal with a head on one end. When heated, the rivet is inserted in a hole either punched or bored in the members to be connected and another head is formed on the projecting end of the shank. Rivet holes are $\frac{1}{16}$ in. larger than the diameter of the rivet. Riveting is accomplished by a power-driven hammer, and the heated rivets completely fill the holes. On cooling, the shrinkage in the length of the rivet draws the connected pieces tightly together. The size of a rivet is designated by the diameter of the shaft, the most commonly employed sizes for structural steel being $\frac{3}{4}$, $\frac{7}{8}$, and 1 in.

14–3. Failure of a Riveted Joint. A riveted joint may fail in several different ways, the most common being shear, bearing, and tension. Figure 14–1(a) represents two plates held together by a single rivet. If tensile (or compressive) forces are applied to the plates, there is a tendency for the rivet to fail by shear at the plane of contact of the two plates. Since there is only one section of the rivet to fail, we say that the rivet is in *single shear*. The portion of the rivet resisting single shear is the cross-sectional area of the shank of the rivet.

Another type of failure is the tendency of the rivet to crush or tear through one or more of the connected plates. This is called a *bearing* failure and is illustrated in Fig. 14–1(b). If the two plates are of unequal thickness, failure will occur first in the thinner plate. When only two pieces of metal are connected, the rivets are in *single shear* and in *single bearing*.

Figure 14–1(c) shows a *tension* failure. The cross-sectional area of the plate is reduced by the rivet hole, and a possible failure is a tearing of the plate at a section taken through the rivet hole.

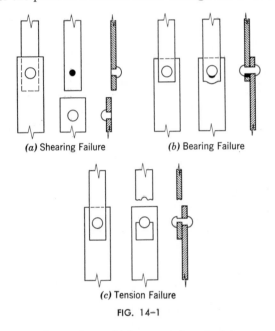

(a) Shearing Failure (b) Bearing Failure

(c) Tension Failure

FIG. 14–1

Figure 14–2 shows three thicknesses of material connected by a rivet. This condition occurs frequently in practice, an example being a gusset plate between the legs of two angles in a roof truss as shown in Fig. 14–6(b). When we have a plate enclosed between two others, as shown in Fig. 14–2, there is a tendency for the rivet to shear at two different sections; we say the rivet is in *double shear*. For such a condition the rivet also is in *double bearing* on the enclosed member.

14–4. Shearing Stresses in a Rivet. Figure 14–3 shows two $2\frac{1}{2}$ x $\frac{5}{16}$ in. plates connected by a $\frac{7}{8}$-in. rivet. Let us investigate this joint to determine the maximum load, P, that this connection will safely carry.

For this particular problem the rivet is in *single shear* and the allowable load on the rivet is the cross-sectional area of the rivet

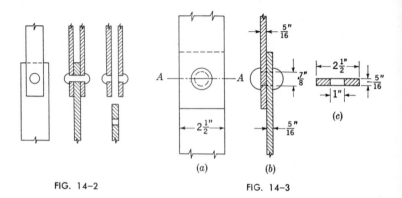

FIG. 14–2

FIG. 14–3

multiplied by the allowable shearing unit stress, 15,000 psi, as given in Table 5–5. The cross-sectional area of a $\frac{7}{8}$-in. rivet is $\dfrac{\pi D^2}{4}$, or $\dfrac{3.1416 \times 0.875^2}{4} = 0.6013$ sq in. Thus $P = f \times A$, or $P = 15,000 \times 0.6013 = 9020$ lb, the allowable working value of one $\frac{7}{8}$-in. rivet in single shear. Note that the cross-sectional area and working value are both given in Table 14–1.

14–5. Bearing Stress in a Rivet. Again referring to Fig. 14–3, consider the bearing of the $\frac{7}{8}$-in. rivet on the $\frac{5}{16}$-in. plate. Since the surfaces in contact are curved, the stress transferred from the rivet to the plate is not distributed uniformly. Nevertheless, we assume that the stress is uniformly distributed over a rectangular area, the sides of which are the diameter of the rivet and the thickness of the plate, in this instance $\frac{7}{8} \times \frac{5}{16}$ in. From Table 5–5 we find that the allowable bearing unit stress of a rivet in single bearing is 32,000 psi. Therefore,

$$P = f \times A \quad \text{or} \quad P = 32,000 \times (0.875 \times 0.3125) = 8750 \text{ lb}$$

the allowable working value of a $\frac{7}{8}$-in. rivet in single bearing on a $\frac{5}{16}$-in. plate. Refer to Table 14–1 and note that this working value is given.

14–6. Tensile Stress in a Plate. If the $2\frac{1}{2}$ x $\frac{5}{16}$ in. plate fails by tension, it will fail at section A–A [Fig. 14–3(a)], where its area has been reduced by the rivet hole. Punched rivet holes are $\frac{1}{16}$ in. larger than the diameter of the cold rivet. Because the material around the rivet hole is injured by punching, it is customary to assume that the diameter of the hole is $\frac{1}{8}$ in. greater in diameter than the diameter of the rivet. Therefore, since in this instance the diameter of the rivet is $\frac{7}{8}$ in., we assume that the diameter of the hole is $\frac{7}{8} + \frac{1}{8}$, or 1 in. The net area of the plate that resists tension is shown in Fig. 14–3(c), $(2\frac{1}{2} - 1) \times \frac{5}{16}$, or 0.46875 sq in. The allowable tensile unit stress of steel (Table 5–5) is 20,000 psi. Thus

$$P = f \times A = 20,000 \times 0.46875$$

$$= 9375 \text{ lb, the allowable tensile load on the punched plate}$$

We have now found for this problem that the allowable loads on the connection are single shear, 9020 lb, single bearing, 8750 lb, tension in plate, 9375 lb. Of the three, 8750 lb is the smallest, and this is the maximum load that the connection will safely support.

14–7. Double Bearing. Figure 14–4 shows a 3 x $\frac{7}{16}$ in. plate enclosed by two 3 x $\frac{1}{4}$ in. plates, the three plates being connected by

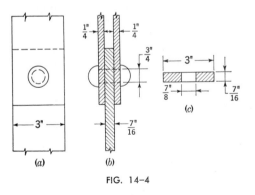

FIG. 14–4

a $\frac{3}{4}$-in. rivet. If the rivet fails by shear, there are two sections that must fail, and therefore the allowable working value is twice the value of the rivet in single shear. We say the rivet is in *double shear*. In a riveted connection, where a rivet bears on a plate that is enclosed between two adjacent plates, the enclosed plate and rivet are said to be in *double bearing*. The pressure exerted by the rivet on the enclosed plate is more uniformly distributed than that exerted by a rivet in single bearing, and the crushing of the enclosed plate is restrained by the outer plates. Consequently, a greater allowable bearing stress is permitted for a rivet in double bearing. Table 5–5 gives 40,000 psi for the allowable stress for double bearing. Attention is called to the fact that when a rivet is in double shear it is also in double bearing. The allowable working value for the rivet in this connection with respect to double bearing is

$$P = f \times A \quad \text{or} \quad P = 40,000 \times (0.75 \times 0.4375) = 13,100 \text{ lb}$$

This value is found in Table 14–1.

Example. For the connection shown in Fig. 14–4, determine the maximum allowable load.

SOLUTION. The rivet is in double shear, and from Table 14–1 we find the area of a $\frac{3}{4}$-in. rivet to be 0.4418 sq in. For shear the allowable stress is 15,000 psi (Table 5–5).

$$P = f \times A \quad \text{or} \quad P = 15,000 \times 0.4418 \times 2 = 13,250 \text{ lb}$$

the allowable working value of the rivet in double shear. This value is given in Table 14–1. In the above equation we multiply by 2 because there are two sections at which the rivet must fail in shear.

For double bearing the allowable working value was found to be 13,100 lb.

For single bearing we have a $\frac{3}{4}$-in. rivet bearing on *two* $\frac{1}{4}$-in. plates, and therefore the allowable working value is twice the value of the rivet bearing on one plate. For single bearing the allowable unit stress given in Table 5–5 is 32,000 psi. Therefore,

$$P = f \times A \quad \text{or} \quad P = [32,000 \times (0.75 \times 0.25)] \times 2 = 12,000 \text{ lb}$$

If this connection fails by tension in the plates, the $\frac{7}{16}$-in. enclosed plate will fail before the two $\frac{1}{4}$-in. plates because the $\frac{7}{16}$-in. plate contains less material in its cross section. The net or reduced area is at a section taken through the rivet, shown in Fig. 14–4(c). As the rivet is $\frac{3}{4}$ in. and the diameter of the hole is taken to be $\frac{1}{8}$ in.

greater, the width of the hole is $\frac{7}{8}$ in. Thus the net area of the plate is $(3 - 0.875) \times 0.4375$, or 0.931 sq in.

$$P = f \times A = 20,000 \times 0.931$$

$$= 18,620 \text{ lb, the allowable tensile load on the plate}$$

The allowable loads just computed are

$$
\begin{array}{ll}
\text{double shear} & = 13,250 \text{ lb} \\
\text{double bearing} & = 13,100 \text{ lb} \\
\text{single bearing} & = 12,000 \text{ lb} \\
\text{tension in plate} & = 18,620 \text{ lb}
\end{array}
$$

Of these values, 12,000 lb is the smallest, and this is the allowable load that the connection will safely support.

14–8. Allowable Working Values for Rivets. In the preceding articles the allowable working values for various rivet sizes and plates have been computed. However, it is unnecessary to do this, for Table 14–1 gives these working values, and in practice they may be taken directly from the table. Attention is called to the unit stresses given at the head of the table. These are the same stresses that are listed in Table 5–5 and that are found in many building codes. Certain blank spaces occur in this table. When no stress is given, the bearing value exceeds the value for shear and the bearing value would have no purpose. To illustrate the use of this table, consider the following example.

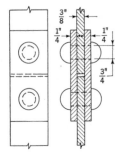

FIG. 14–5

Example. Two $\frac{3}{8}$-in. plates are connected by means of $\frac{3}{4}$-in. rivets and $\frac{1}{4}$-in. outer plates, as indicated in Fig. 14–5. Neglecting the tensile stresses in the plates, determine the allowable load that this joint will safely support.

SOLUTION. The following allowable working values are found in Table 14–1:

$\frac{3}{4}$-in. rivets in double shear = 13,250 lb
$\frac{3}{4}$-in. rivets in double bearing on $\frac{3}{8}$-in. plate = 11,300 lb
$\frac{3}{4}$-in. rivets in single bearing on two $\frac{1}{4}$-in. plates
= 2 × 6000 = 12,000 lb

Of these values, 11,300 lb is the smallest and therefore is the maximum allowable load that this connection will safely support.

TABLE 14–1. ALLOWABLE WORKING VALUES FOR POWER-DRIVEN RIVETS

Unit Shearing Stress = 15,000#/in²

Unit Bearing Stress $\begin{cases} \text{Single Bearing} = 32,000 \text{\#/in}^2 \\ \text{Double Bearing} = 40,000 \text{\#/in}^2 \end{cases}$

Diameter of Rivet		$\frac{5}{8}''$		$\frac{3}{4}''$		$\frac{7}{8}''$		$1''$		$1\frac{1}{8}''$	
Area of Rivet		0.3068		0.4418		0.6013		0.7854		0.9940	
Single Shear, Pounds		4,600		6,630		9,020		11,780		14,910	
Double Shear, Pounds		9,200		13,250		18,040		23,560		29,820	
Bearing		Single, Lb	Double, Lb	Single, Lb	Double, Lb	Single, Lb	Double, Lb	Single, Lb	Double, Lb	Single, Lb	Double, Lb
Thickness of plate in inches	$\frac{1}{4}$	....	6,250	6,000	7,500	7,000	8,750	8,000	10,000	9,000	11,250
	$\frac{5}{16}$	....	7,810	....	9,380	8,750	10,900	10,000	12,500	11,300	14,100
	$\frac{3}{8}$	....	9,380	....	11,300	....	13,100	12,000	15,000	13,500	16,900
	$\frac{7}{16}$	....	.....	....	13,100	....	15,300	.....	17,500	....	19,700
	$\frac{1}{2}$	....	.....	....	.....	....	17,500	.....	20,000	....	22,500
	$\frac{9}{16}$	....	....	....	.....	....	.....	.....	22,500	....	25,300
	$\frac{5}{8}$	....	.....	....	.....	....	.....	.....	.....	....	28,100

Compiled from data in "Manual of Steel Construction." by permission of the American Institute of Steel Construction.

14–9. Design of Riveted Joints. For many riveted joints that occur in practice, determining the required number of rivets is a relatively simple matter. Data for such problems include the thicknesses of the material to be connected, the size of the rivets, and the load to be transferred by the rivets. The controlling allowable working value of one rivet is found by the use of Table 14–1, and the required number of rivets is determined by dividing the load on the joint by this value. In truss joints the number of rivets should never be less than 2 for the end of each member.

Example. The upper and lower chord members of a truss at the supports have loads of 60,000 lb in compression and 54,000 lb in tension, respectively, as indicated in Fig. 14–6(a). Each of these

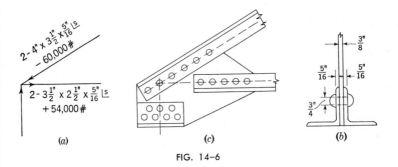

(a)　　　　　　　(c)　　　　　　　(b)

FIG. 14–6

two members is composed of two angle sections separated by the thickness of the gusset plate ($\frac{3}{8}$ in.). The thickness of the angles for both members is $\frac{5}{16}$ in. Assuming that the rivets are $\frac{3}{4}$ in., determine the required number of rivets to be used in the end of each member.

SOLUTION. The thickness of the gusset is $\frac{3}{8}$ in., the angle legs are $\frac{5}{16}$ in. thick, and the rivets are $\frac{3}{4}$ in. in diameter, the gusset being the enclosed plate. With these data we make the diagram shown in Fig. 14–6(b). Next, by the use of Table 14–1, we note the allowable working values for *one* rivet. Thus

double shear $= 13,250$ lb
double bearing $= 11,300$ lb
single bearing $= [(0.3125 \times 0.75) \times 32,000] \times 2 = 15,000$ lb

Table 14–1 does not give the value of a $\frac{3}{4}$-in. rivet in single bearing on a $\frac{5}{16}$-in. plate; it is shown in the above formula to be 7500 lb. Note that this value exceeds the value for single shear and therefore is not a factor. Since there are two $\frac{5}{16}$-in. plates, $2 \times 7500 = 15,000$ lb, the working value for single bearing.

Of the three working values, double bearing, 11,300 lb, is the smallest and consequently is the controlling rivet value for both the upper and lower chords. Then, for the upper chord,

$$60,000 \div 11,300 = 5+ \qquad \text{Use 6 rivets.}$$

For the lower chord,

$$54,000 \div 11,300 = 4+ \qquad \text{Use 5 rivets.}$$

The truss joint is shown in Fig. 14–6(c).

Example. Two $\frac{1}{2}$-in. plates are connected by means of a butt joint, as shown in Fig. 14–7. The outer plates are $\frac{1}{4}$ in. thick, and

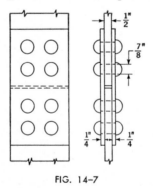

FIG. 14–7

the rivets are $\frac{7}{8}$-in. Determine the required number of rivets if the tensile load on the $\frac{1}{2}$-in. plates is 50,000 lb.

SOLUTION. The following allowable working values are found by means of Table 14–1:

$$
\begin{aligned}
\text{double shear} &= 18,040 \text{ lb} \\
\text{double bearing} &= 17,500 \text{ lb} \\
\text{single bearing, } 2 \times 7000 &= 14,000 \text{ lb}
\end{aligned}
$$

Single bearing, 14,000 lb, is the controlling value; therefore, $50,000 \div 14,000 = 3+$. Use 4 rivets on each side of the joint.

Problem 14–9–A. Compute the allowable working values of a $\frac{3}{4}$-in. rivet in (a) single shear, (b) single bearing, and (c) double bearing on a $\frac{1}{4}$-in. plate. Check the values with those given in Table 14–1.

Problem 14–9–B. Compute the allowable working values of a $\frac{7}{8}$-in. rivet in (a) single shear, (b) single bearing, and (c) double bearing on a $\frac{5}{16}$-in. plate. Check the values with those given in Table 14–1.

Problem 14–9–C. Two $2\frac{1}{2}$ x $\frac{1}{4}$ in. plates are connected with a $\frac{3}{4}$-in. rivet as arranged in Fig. 14–3. Compute the maximum allowable load that this joint will safely support.

Problem 14–9–D. A $2\frac{1}{4}$ x $\frac{1}{2}$ in. plate is connected to two $2\frac{1}{4}$ x $1\frac{5}{16}$ in. plates by a $\frac{7}{8}$-in. rivet as arranged in Fig. 14–4. Compute the maximum allowable load that this joint will safely support.

Problem 14–9–E. A connection arranged as indicated in Fig. 14–5 is composed of a 3 x $\frac{1}{2}$ in. enclosed plate with two 3 x $\frac{1}{4}$ in. outer plates. If 1-in. rivets are used, compute the maximum safe load the joint will support.

Problem 14–9–F. A tension member of a truss is composed of two 3 x $2\frac{1}{2}$ x $\frac{3}{8}$ in. angle sections. The thickness of the enclosed gusset plate is $\frac{3}{8}$ in., the rivets are $\frac{3}{4}$ in., and the load on the member is 62,000 lb. Compute the required number of rivets at an end connection of the member.

14–10. Welding. In addition to riveting, connections between steel elements are also made by welding. Among the materials that can be successfully welded are structural and cast steel, cast iron, aluminum, copper, and bronze. Gas welding employs the oxyacetylene flame and the weld material. The electric-arc fusion welding process is generally used for welding in building construction. By holding the electrode at the proper distance, an electric arc is formed between the base metal and the electrode; the heat melts the electrode, and this molten metal builds up a bead and is fused with the material to be joined. Many advantages are claimed for welding both in assembling in the fabrication shop and in the field. For joining structural elements there are three types of welds, the fillet weld, the butt weld, and the plug or slot weld. For butt joints the edges of the plates to be joined are usually beveled to provide access and to afford a more perfect fusion of the base metal. Since the parts to be connected meet in different manners, the welds have various shapes.

14–11. Fillet Welds. The *fillet* weld is used more frequently in welding structural steel than any other type of weld. It is used to connect elements having two surfaces at right angles to each other, and its cross section is theoretically triangular in shape, as shown in Fig. 14–8(*a*). In this figure point *B* is the *root* of the weld. The *throat* of a fillet weld is the distance from the root to the hypotenuse of the largest isosceles right triangle that can be inscribed within the weld cross section; for this figure the throat is distance *B–D*. The *size* of a fillet weld is the length of the leg of largest inscribed isosceles right triangle; in Fig. 14–8(*a*) it is *AB* or *BC*. An actual fillet weld has an exposed surface more nearly like that indicated in Fig. 14–8(*b*); the throat may be somewhat greater than that shown in Fig. 14–8(*a*). This additional weld material

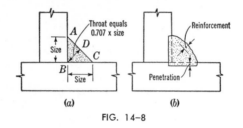

FIG. 14–8

is called *reinforcement;* it is not considered in determining the strength of the weld.

Assume that the dimension (size) of *AB*, in the equal-leg, 45° triangle shown in Fig. 14–8(*a*), is 1 unit of length. Then $(AD)^2 + (BD)^2 = 1^2$. Since *AD* and *BD* are equal, $2 \times (BD)^2 = 1^2$ and $BD = 0.707$. Hence *the throat of a fillet weld is equal to the size of the weld multiplied by 0.707.*

The stress in a fillet weld is considered to be shear on the throat regardless of the direction of the applied load. The allowable shearing unit stress on a section taken through the throat of a fillet weld is frequently given in building codes as 13,600 psi.

Example. A $\frac{3}{8}$-in. fillet weld 6 in. in length is used to connect two pieces of steel. What allowable load will this weld support?

SOLUTION. The size of the weld is $\frac{3}{8}$ in.; hence the throat dimension is $\frac{3}{8} \times 0.707$, or 0.265 in. One linear inch of weld, therefore, contains 0.265 sq in. of weld material in the throat. If the allowable stress is 13,600 psi, $0.265 \times 13,600 = 3600$ lb, the allowable unit stress *per linear inch of weld;* see Table 14–2. As the weld is 6 in. in length, $6 \times 3600 = 21,600$ lb, the allowable load on the weld.

TABLE 14–2. ALLOWABLE WORKING STRESSES OF FILLET WELDS

Size of Fillet Weld, in Inches	Allowable Unit Stress, in Pounds per Linear Inch
$\frac{1}{4}$	2,400
$\frac{5}{16}$	3,000
$\frac{3}{8}$	3,600
$\frac{1}{2}$	4,800
$\frac{5}{8}$	6,000
$\frac{3}{4}$	7,200

The allowable working stresses for various fillet weld sizes are given in Table 14–2. This table is based on an allowable shearing unit stress of 13,600 psi on the throat of the weld.

The size of fillet weld to use depends on the thickness of plate, or edge of rolled section, and the load to be transmitted. Minimum weld sizes are given in Table 14–3. The $\frac{5}{16}$-in. weld may be formed

TABLE 14–3. MINIMUM SIZES OF FILLET WELDS

Size of Fillet Weld, in Inches	Maximum Thickness of Part, in Inches
$\frac{3}{16}$	$\frac{1}{2}$
$\frac{1}{4}$	$\frac{3}{4}$
$\frac{5}{16}$	$1\frac{1}{4}$
$\frac{3}{8}$	2
$\frac{1}{2}$	6
$\frac{5}{8}$	Over 6

by a single pass of the electrode and is commonly used. The maximum sizes are shown in Figs. 14–9(a) and (b). For the square edge of plate or shape the maximum size is $\frac{1}{16}$ in. less than the thickness of the edge. For the rounded edge of an angle section or rounded edge of flange the weld size should not exceed three

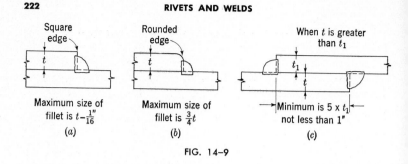

FIG. 14-9

fourths the thickness of the angle or nominal thickness of the flange. The minimum *length* of a fillet weld should not be less than four times the weld size. For a lap joint, as indicated in Fig. 14-9(c), the length of lap should not be less than five times the thickness of the thinner plate and never less than 1 in.

Example. A $2\frac{1}{2}$ x $\frac{3}{8}$ in. bar is to be welded to the back of a channel section. What should be the length of the welds to develop the full tensile strength of the bar? See Fig. 14-10.

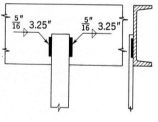

FIG. 14-10

SOLUTION. Since the bar is $2\frac{1}{2}$ x $\frac{3}{8}$ in., its cross-sectional area is 0.375×2.5, or 0.9375 sq in. The allowable tensile stress of the steel is 20,000 psi; therefore $0.9375 \times 20,000 = 18,750$ lb, the allowable tensile load the bar will develop.

The size of the fillet weld should not exceed $\frac{1}{16}$ in. less than the thickness of the bar, $0.375 - 0.0625 = 0.3125$ in.; therefore a $\frac{5}{16}$-in. weld is used. Table 14-2 gives for the allowable stress of a $\frac{5}{16}$-in. fillet weld 3000 lb *per lin in.* Thus $18,750 \div 3000 = 6.275$ in., the minimum required length of $\frac{5}{16}$-in. fillet weld. There are several different arrangements of welds for this connection. Figure

14–10 shows a method commonly used: two $3\frac{1}{4}$-in. lengths of $\frac{5}{16}$-in. fillet welds.

Example. An ∟ $5 \times 3\frac{1}{2} \times \frac{3}{8}$ resists a tensile load of 60,000 lb. It is to be welded to a plate by the use of fillet welds. Compute the dimensions of the welds. See Fig. 14–11.

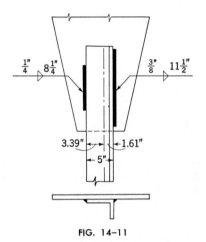

FIG. 14–11

SOLUTION. When the member to be welded is unsymmetrical in cross section, the welds should be so proportioned that eccentricity is avoided and that the stresses in the welds are proportioned in accordance with the distributed area.

Referring to Table 6–6, we find that the back of the short leg is 1.61 in. from the centroidal axis of the angle; hence $5 - 1.61 = 3.39$ in., the distance of the axis from the toe of the long leg. These dimensions are shown in Fig. 14–11. Assuming that the 60,000-lb load has its line of action at the centroidal axis and taking the center of moments at the back of the short leg,

$$60,000 \times 1.61 = \text{stress in left weld} \times 5$$

$$\text{stress in left weld} = 19,320 \text{ lb}$$

Therefore

$$60,000 - 19,320 = 40,680 \text{ lb, the stress in the right weld}$$

The edge of the leg of the angle section is curved; hence, in accordance with Fig. 14–9, $\frac{3}{4} \times \frac{3}{8} = 0.281$ in., the maximum size of the left fillet weld. We shall use a $\frac{1}{4}$-in. weld, for which Table 14–2 gives a stress of 2400 lb per lin in. Since the stress is 19,320 lb, $19,320 \div 2400 = 8.05$ in., the minimum length of the left weld.

At the right side there is no curved edge, and we can use a $\frac{3}{8}$-in. fillet weld. The stress for this weld is 3600 lb per lin in. (Table 14–2). As the stress is 40,680 lb, $40,680 \div 3600 = 11.3$ in., the minimum length of the right weld.

Problem 14–11–A. A $5 \llcorner 6.7$ resists a tensile load of 36,000 lb. If it is welded to a gusset plate with $\frac{5}{16}$-in. welds, what should be the total combined length of welds?

Problem 14–11–B. An $\llcorner 3\frac{1}{2} \times 3 \times \frac{3}{8}$ is used to resist a tensile load of 40,000 lb. If the long leg of the angle is welded to a gusset plate, determine the dimensions of the welds.

14–12. Butt Welds. For butt welds the material to be connected (base metal) is generally grooved or beveled in preparation for the welding process. The various types of butt welds are designated by the groove or bevel. Butt welds are formed by welding from either or both sides. Figures 14–12(*a*), (*b*), and (*c*) indicate butt welds formed by welding from both sides, and Figs. 14–12(*d*), (*e*), and (*f*) are welded from one side. Butt welds welded from one side, as shown in Fig. 14–12(*d*), are used only in relatively thin material. In general, the effective throat of a butt weld is considered to be the thickness of the thinner part joined. For the welds shown in Figs. 14–12(*e*) and (*f*) the effective throat thickness is three fourths the thickness of the base metal.

The allowable stresses for butt welds in structural steel are 20,000 psi for both tension and compression; for shear the allowable stress is 13,000 psi. Butt welds are commonly employed in the construction of tanks and boilers, and for this type of work the allowable stress is often given as a percentage of the allowable stress of the base metal, 90 per cent for double-V welds and 70 per cent for single-V welds.

Example. Two steel plates, $\frac{5}{16}$ and $\frac{3}{8}$ in. thick, are to be connected by means of a double-V butt weld to resist a tensile load. Compute the allowable load the weld will support.

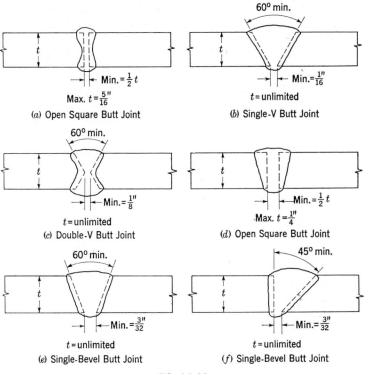

60° min.

Min. = $\frac{1}{2}t$

Max. $t = \frac{5}{16}''$

(a) Open Square Butt Joint

Min. = $\frac{1''}{16}$

t = unlimited

(b) Single-V Butt Joint

60° min.

Min. = $\frac{1''}{8}$

t = unlimited

(c) Double-V Butt Joint

Min. = $\frac{1}{2}t$

Max. $t = \frac{1''}{4}$

(d) Open Square Butt Joint

60° min.

Min. = $\frac{3''}{32}$

t = unlimited

(e) Single-Bevel Butt Joint

45° min.

Min. = $\frac{3''}{32}$

t = unlimited

(f) Single-Bevel Butt Joint

FIG. 14–12

SOLUTION. Since the two plates are of unequal thickness, the throat of this butt weld is the dimension of the thinner of the two plates, in this instance $\frac{5}{16}$ in. The allowable tensile stress of the weld being 20,000 psi, $0.3125 \times 20,000 = 6250$ lb per lin in. of weld, the allowable load.

14–13. Plug and Slot Welds. Two pieces of metal are sometimes welded together by welds in holes made in one of the two connected parts, as indicated in Figs. 14–13(a), (b), and (c). Holes for plug welds should be circular, the diameter being not less than the thickness of the part containing the hole plus $\frac{5}{16}$ in., rounded to the next greater odd sixteenth. The diameter of the hole should not be greater than three times the thickness of the weld metal. The width of the slot, as shown in Fig. 14–13(c), should not be less than the diameter of plug welds, and the maximum length should not exceed ten times the thickness of the part containing the slot.

If the material containing the hole is not over $\frac{5}{8}$ in. thick, the hole should be filled with weld material; if the hole is over $\frac{5}{8}$ in. in thickness, the hole should be filled with weld metal to a depth of

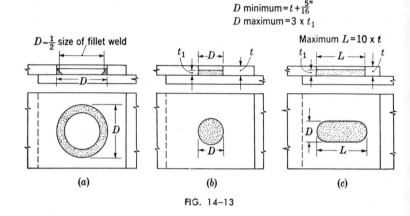

(a)   (b)   (c)

FIG. 14–13

at least $\frac{5}{8}$ in. When the hole is filled with weld metal [Figs. 14–13(b) and (c)], the effective shearing area of the weld is the nominal cross-sectional area of the hole or slot in the plane of the faying surface.

Example. A $\frac{5}{8}$-in. plate has a hole $1\frac{1}{8}$ in. in diameter, which is filled with weld metal. What shearing load will this plug weld support?

SOLUTION. The effective cross-sectional area is circular, the area of a circle whose diameter is $1\frac{1}{8}$ in., or $D^2 \times 0.7854 = 1.125^2 \times 0.7854 = 0.994$ sq in. As the allowable shearing stress of weld metal is 13,600 psi, $0.944 \times 13,600 = 12,840$ lb, the shearing load this plug weld will support.

Sometimes a continuous fillet weld is made at the outer edge of a hole, as indicated in Fig. 14–13(a). The allowable load on this type of plug weld is equal to the allowable working stress of the fillet weld multiplied by its length, the length being the circumference *at the center line of the throat* of the weld.

Example. A hole whose diameter is $2\frac{1}{2}$ in. is made in a plate that is to be welded to another plate by means of a plug weld. The weld is to consist of a continuous $\frac{5}{16}$-in. fillet weld at the outer edge of the hole as shown in Fig. 14–13(a). Compute the allowable load this weld will support.

SOLUTION. The diameter of a circle at the center line of the throat of the fillet weld is the diameter of the hole minus one half the size of the weld. The weld is $\frac{5}{16}$-in.; therefore, $2.5 - \dfrac{0.3125}{2} =$ 2.344 in., the diameter. Hence the length of the fillet is the circumference of a circle of which 2.344 in. is the diameter, or $2.344 \times 3.1416 = 7.38$ in. The allowable working stress of a $\frac{5}{16}$-in. fillet weld is 3000 lb per lin in. (Table 14–2); therefore, $7.38 \times 3000 = 22{,}140$ lb, the allowable load on the weld.

Problem 14–13–A. A plug weld is made by filling a hole 1 in. in diameter with weld metal. Compute the allowable load the weld will support.

Problem 14–13–B. The hole for a slot weld is 5 in. in length overall and 1 in. in width, the ends of the slot being semicircular. Compute the allowable load this slot weld will support.

Problem 14–13–C. A $\frac{5}{16}$-in. plate has a hole 2 in. in diameter in which a continuous $\frac{1}{4}$-in. fillet weld is to be made at the outer edge of the hole. What load will this plug weld support?

14–14. High Strength Bolts. In addition to rivets and welds, another method of connecting structural steel members employs bolts and nuts. Turned and unfinished bolts are commonly used, but their use is often restricted by building codes to buildings of limited height or to field connections in work of minor importance. These connections are designed in the manner described for rivets, and their allowable stresses are given in Table 5–5.

The design of a riveted connection takes into consideration both bearing and shearing stresses in the rivets. On cooling, a heated rivet contracts and thus draws together the parts that are to be connected. The frictional stress that is developed, however, is ignored in computations.

In recent years considerable investigation has been made in structural steel joints using ASTM A325 bolts. These are high-strength steel bolts tightened to a high tension in holes slightly larger than the nominal bolt size. This type of connection is particularly advantageous where there is a reversal of stress, impact, or vibration or where slippage would tend to loosen a rivet. This is known as a friction-type connection. The basic principle involved is to clamp the members together tightly so that the stresses are transferred from one member to another by friction between the connected parts.

The principal means of transferring loads between connected parts in high-strength bolted connections is the friction developed between the connected parts; thus slipping and movement within the joint does not take place, and a joint which is much superior under fatigue type loading results. The control of the tensile stresses required of the fasteners to produce the requisite clamping forces is insured by the use of pneumatic impact wrenches or torque wrenches. The bolts and nuts are manufactured to conform to ASTM Specification A325, which requires a tensile strength of approximately 115,000 psi and a yield point of approximately 81,000 psi. When properly installed, the fasteners are tightened to not less than 78,000 psi.

These high-stress bolts are more expensive than undriven rivets, but this is offset by lower installation costs. Because of their many advantages, it is predicted that high-strength bolts will supplant rivets as connectors for structural steel.

CHAPTER 15

TORSIONAL STRESS, SHAFTS, AND HORSEPOWER

15–1. Torsion. When a bar is firmly secured at one end and a force is applied to the other end so that the bar tends to twist, the stresses developed in the bar are *torsional stresses*. Figures 15–1(*a*) and (*b*) represent a bar subjected to two equal forces, *P*,

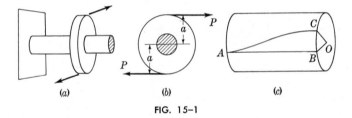

(*a*)	(*b*)	(*c*)

FIG. 15–1

that cause torsional stresses. Each force is *a* distance from the center of the bar, and the *twisting moment* or *torque* has a magnitude of $2Pa$. It is important to realize that the forces do not *bend* the bar; they tend to twist it.

At any section of the bar, between the left (fixed) end and the section at which the loads are applied, the bar tends to shear off from the section adjacent to it. Figure 15–1(*c*) represents a portion of a bar or shaft that is subjected to torsional stresses, the left end being fixed. Before torsional stresses are applied, *AB* is a straight line on the surface of the cylinder parallel to a longitudinal axis through its center of gravity. When the shaft is subjected to torque, both stresses and deformation occur. The line *AB* takes the position of *AC*. If the maximum stress, the stress on the outermost fiber of the shaft, remains within the elastic limit of the material, the radial line *OC* remains straight. The unit shearing

229

stress at any point in the shaft is directly proportional to its distance from the axis O.

15–2. Torsion Formula. Torque or twisting moment is the product of the resultant force and its distance from the axis about which it tends to turn. In Figs. 15–1(a) and (b) there are two forces of P pounds each and the moment arm of each force is a. If a is in units of inches, T, the torque, is $2Pa$ in-lb. For equilibrium T the torque or twisting moment must equal T_r, the resisting moment. The torsion formula for round shafts is

$$T = \frac{f_s J}{c}$$

in which T = the torque or twisting moment in inch-pounds

f_s = the shearing unit stress on the fibers at the surface of the shaft in pounds per square inch

J = the polar moment of inertia of the cross section of the shaft in inches to the fourth power

c = the distance of the outermost fiber of the shaft (the radius) from the axis in inches.

J, the *polar moment of inertia* of a surface about an axis through its centroid perpendicular to the surface, is equal to the sum of the products of all the elementary areas of the surface multiplied by the squares of their distances from the axis. For a circular area of which D is the diameter, $J = \dfrac{\pi D^4}{32}$.

For a hollow circular area the cross-sectional area of a pipe or hollow shaft, in which D is the outside diameter and D_1 is the inside diameter,

$$J = \frac{\pi(D^4 - D_1{}^4)}{32}$$

The torsion formula is $T = \dfrac{f_s J}{c}$. Thus for a solid round shaft $c = \dfrac{D}{2}$ and $\pi = 3.1416$ and

$$T = \frac{f_s \times \dfrac{3.1416 \times D^4}{32}}{\dfrac{D}{2}} \quad \text{or} \quad T = 0.196 f_s D^3$$

Similarly, for a hollow shaft,

$$T = \frac{0.196 f_s (D^4 - D_1{}^4)}{D}$$

In using these torsion formulas, the unit stress must not exceed the elastic limit of the material; T must be in units of inch-pounds and D in inches.

Example. A pulley wheel on a solid shaft has a diameter of 2 ft 0 in., and the resultant load on the wheel is 1200 lb. If the shaft is 3 in. in diameter, compute the maximum shearing unit stress in the shaft.

SOLUTION. The diameter of the wheel is 2 ft 0 in.; therefore, the moment arm of the 1200-lb force is 1 ft 0 in., or 12 in. Thus $T = 1200 \times 12$, or 14,400 in-lb.

$$T = 0.196 f_s D^3$$

$$f_s = \frac{T}{0.196 \times D^3} = \frac{14,400}{0.196 \times 3^3}$$

$f_s = 2720$ psi, the maximum shearing unit stress

Example. The resultant load on a pulley wheel 20 in. in diameter on a solid shaft is 10,000 lb. If the maximum shearing unit stress in the shaft is 8000 psi, what is the diameter of the shaft?

SOLUTION. The pulley wheel being 20 in. in diameter, the moment arm of the 10,000-lb load is 10 in.; therefore, T, the torque, is $10,000 \times 10$, or 100,000 in-lb.

$$T = 0.196 \times f_s \times D^3$$

$$D^3 = \frac{T}{0.196 \times f_s}$$

$$D^3 = \frac{100,000}{0.196 \times 8,000}$$

$D = 4$ in., the diameter of the shaft

Example. A hollow shaft has outside and inside diameters of 4 and 2 in., respectively. A load of 9000 lb on a pulley wheel on the shaft has a moment arm of 10 in. Compute the maximum shearing unit stress in the shaft.

SOLUTION. The torque $T = 9000 \times 10$, or 90,000 in-lb.

$$T = \frac{0.196 \times f_s(D^4 - D_1^4)}{D}$$

Therefore $90,000 = \dfrac{0.196 \times f_s(4^4 - 2^4)}{4}$ and $f_s = 7640$ psi, the maximum shearing unit stress in the shaft.

Problem 15-2-A. A load of 19,600 lb is applied to a pulley wheel 20 in. in diameter attached to a solid shaft. Compute the diameter of the shaft if the maximum shearing unit stress in the shaft is 8000 psi.

Problem 15-2-B. The load on a pulley wheel 2 ft 0 in. in diameter on a 4-in. solid shaft is 4000 lb. Compute the maximum shearing unit stress in the shaft.

Problem 15-2-C. A hollow shaft has an outside diameter of 3 in. and an inside diameter of 1 in. Attached to the shaft is a pulley wheel 22 in. in diameter to which a 3800-lb load is applied. Compute the maximum shearing unit stress in the shaft.

15–3. Keys in Pulleys. One of the most commonly used methods of securing a pulley wheel to a shaft is by means of a key fitted into slots in the pulley and shaft as indicated in Fig. 15–2. The

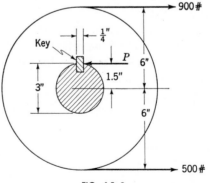

FIG. 15–2

keyway in the shaft reduces its cross-sectional area and thus results in increased stresses in the shaft at a cross section taken through the keyway. Some specifications require that the torque on a shaft with a keyway be 25 per cent less than on a shaft in which there is no keyway. The stress on the key is shear, the area resisting shear being the length of the key multiplied by its width.

Example. Figure 15–2 represents a 3-in. shaft to which is keyed a pulley wheel 12 in. in diameter. There are two forces acting in opposite directions on the wheel as shown. The key is $1\frac{1}{4}$ in. in length and $\frac{1}{4}$ in. wide. Compute the shearing unit stress in the key.

SOLUTION. Since the loads on the wheel tend to cause rotation in opposite directions, the resultant of the loads is $900 - 500$, or 400 lb, and it causes a clockwise rotation. The wheel is 12 in. in diameter; hence the moment arm is 6 in., and the torque is 400×6, or 2400 in-lb. This same torque must be transferred to the shaft.

Therefore, if P is the force to be transmitted and its moment arm is 1.5 in., the radius of the shaft, $2400 = P \times 1.5$, and $P = 1600$ lb.

The area of the key resisting this force is 1.25×0.25 in., or 0.3125 sq in. Hence $\dfrac{1600}{0.3125} = 5120$ psi, the shearing unit stress in the key.

Problem 15–3–A. A pully wheel 18 in. in diameter on a 4-in. shaft is secured by a key whose length and width are $1\frac{1}{2}$ and $\frac{1}{4}$ in., respectively. If the resultant belt load on the wheel is 900 lb, what is the shearing unit stress in the key?

15–4. Shaft Couplings. In the design of shafting, it is frequently necessary to join two pieces of shafting end to end. Shafts may be forged with flanges that serve as couplings, or the couplings may be made separately and attached to the shafts. In any event, the coupling must be strong enough to transfer the torque from one piece of shafting to the other. The flanges or faces of couplings are bolted together by a number of bolts arranged in a circle. These bolts tend to shear at the plane of contact of the couplings.

Example. The ends of two shafts are joined by the coupling shown in Fig. 15–3. A torque of 160,000 in-lb is transmitted from one shaft to the other by six bolts $\frac{3}{4}$ in. in diameter arranged in a circle 12 in. in diameter. Compute the shearing unit stress in the bolts.

SOLUTION. Let P be the force transferred by *each* bolt. Then $6P$ is the force transferred by the 6 bolts. Since the circle of bolts has a radius of 6 in., $(6 \times 6 \times P)$ in-lb is the torque exerted by the 6 bolts. This torque must equal 160,000 in-lb. Therefore, $6 \times 6 \times P = 160{,}000$, and $P = 4440$ lb, the shearing stress on each bolt. As a bolt $\frac{3}{4}$ in. in diameter has a cross-sectional area of 0.4418 sq in., $4440 \div 0.4418 = 10{,}000$ psi, the shearing unit stress in the bolts.

Problem 15-4-A. A shaft coupling contains a circle 16 in. in diameter in which are arranged bolts $\frac{7}{8}$ in. in diameter. If the torque transferred from one piece of shafting to the other is 200,000 in-lb and the allowable shearing unit stress in the bolts is 8000 psi, how many bolts are required?

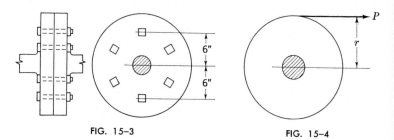

FIG. 15-3   FIG. 15-4

15-5. Work, Horsepower. Figure 15-4 represents a pulley on a shaft; the force acting on the pulley is P, and the radius of the pulley is r. When a force acts on a body, moving it a certain distance, the *work* done is the product of the force by the distance:

$$\text{work} = \text{force} \times \text{distance}$$

Thus, in Fig. 15-4, if r is the radius, the circumference is $2\pi r$, and the work done while the pulley is making one revolution is

$$\text{work} = P \times 2\pi r$$

Let N be the number of revolutions per minute made by the pulley; then the work (power) done per minute is

$$\text{work} = P \times 2\pi r \times N$$

In Fig. 15-4 the torque $T = P \times r$ and $P = T/r$. Thus, substituting in the above equation,

$$\text{work (power)} = 2\pi T N$$

Power is the time rate at which work is done. A horsepower (hp) is the power required to move 33,000 lb per ft per min. Thus

$$\text{horsepower (hp)} = \frac{2\pi TN}{33,000} = \frac{TN}{5240}$$

in which T, *the torque, must be in units of foot-pounds* and N is the number of revolutions per minute.

If T is in units of inch-pounds, $\text{hp} = \dfrac{TN}{63,000}$.

Example. A solid shaft 4 in. in diameter revolves 240 revolutions per minute (rpm). If the maximum shearing stress in the shaft is 8000 psi, how many horsepower are transmitted by the shaft?

SOLUTION. First let us compute the torque. (See Art. 15–2.)

$$T = 0.196 \times f_s \times D^3 \text{ or } T = 0.196 \times 8000 \times 4^3 = 100,300 \text{ in-lb}$$

Since the torque has been found in units of inch-pounds and $N = 240$,

$$\text{hp} = \frac{TN}{63,000} = \frac{100,300 \times 240}{63,000} = 382$$

the number of horsepower transmitted by the shaft.

Example. A pulley wheel 24 in. in diameter has a belt load of 500 lb. If the pulley wheel revolves 200 rpm, what horsepower can be transmitted?

SOLUTION. Since the diameter of the pulley wheel is 24 in., the moment arm is 1 ft 0 in.; thus $T = 500 \times 1 = 500$ ft-lb, the torque. Note that, in this example, the torque is in units of foot-pounds; therefore

$$\text{hp} = \frac{TN}{5240} = \frac{500 \times 200}{5240}$$

$= 19.1$, the number of horsepower that can be transmitted

Problem 15–5–A. A solid shaft 3 in. in diameter revolves at 200 rpm. If the maximum shearing stress in the shaft is 8000 psi, what horsepower is being transmitted by the shaft?

Problem 15–5–B. How many revolutions per minute are necessary to transmit 50 hp if the torque on a shaft is 20,000 in-lb?

CHAPTER 16

STRESSES IN PIPES
AND TANKS

16-1. Stresses in Pipes and Tanks. When pressure from water, gas, or steam is exerted internally in a thin cylindrical container, such as a pipe or tank, tensile stresses are set up. A cylinder or pipe is considered "thin" when the thickness of the wall is small in comparison with the diameter. For such containers it is assumed that the tensile stresses are distributed uniformly over the thickness of the wall. These stresses must, of course, fall within the allowable tensile stress of the material of which the pipe or tank is made. Figures 16-1(a) and (b) show a short section of a pipe in elevation and plan. The length of the pipe is l, the inside diameter is d, and the thickness of the pipe material is t. The radial arrows in Fig. 16-1(b) show the direction of the steam or water pressure; the pressure is normal to the internal surface of the pipe. Internal pressure tends to produce two different types of failure. The pipe may fail in tension by a longitudinal opening parallel to the longitudinal axis of the pipe, possibly along a seam. The other type of failure is a tension failure along a line parallel to the circumference of the pipe. For these two types of failure the stresses are tensile, but, with the same internal pressure, the two stresses are unequal in magnitude.

Imagine that the pipe is cut in half at section A–A, as shown in Fig. 16-1(b). The total internal pressure on the half pipe is p, the pressure per unit of area, multiplied by a rectangular area the dimensions of which are the length, l, and the diameter, d. Thus the total pressure on the half pipe is $p \times ld$; its resultant is shown by the arrow at the center of the pipe [Fig. 16-1(c)], although it is distributed over the curved inner surface. This resultant force, $p \times ld$, must be held in equilibrium by the stresses in the two cut

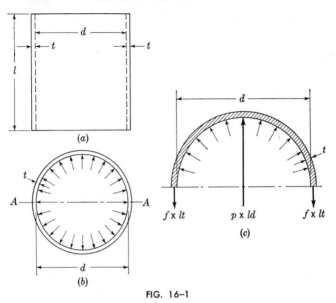

FIG. 16-1

sections of the pipe as shown in the figure. Let f be the tensile unit stress in the pipe metal, and, since $l \times t$ is the area of pipe resisting tension, $f \times lt$ is the stress at each side, as shown in the figure. Then $(f \times lt) + (f \times lt) = p \times ld$, or

$$2flt = pld \quad \text{and} \quad f = \frac{pd}{2t}$$

Steam and water pressures are generally given in pounds per square inch; therefore, in the above formula, d and t are in inches and f is in units of pounds per square inch.

Example. A steel pipe 12 in. in inside diameter has a shell thickness of $\frac{3}{8}$ in. If this pipe is used as a water main in which the water pressure is 100 psi, what is the tensile unit stress in the pipe parallel to its longitudinal axis?

SOLUTION. In this problem $p = 100$ psi, $d = 12$ in., and $t = 0.375$ in. Then

$$f = \frac{pd}{2t} = \frac{100 \times 12}{2 \times 0.375}$$

$$= 1600 \text{ psi, the tensile unit stress}$$

Assume that the container shown in Figs. 16–1(a) and (b) is a closed tank in which there is steam or water pressure of p pounds per square inch. This pressure also tends to force off the head of the tank. This internal pressure results in tensile stresses across a transverse section, along a section that has the shape of the circumference of a cylinder. The pressure that tends to produce this failure is the pressure on the head. The area of the head is $\dfrac{\pi d^2}{4}$, and, if the internal pressure is p pounds per square inch, the pressure on the head is $p \times \dfrac{\pi d^2}{4}$. The area of metal resisting this force is approximately the circumference of the container multiplied by the thickness of the metal, $\pi d \times t$. Now, if the tensile stress in the metal is f pounds per square inch, $f \times \pi dt$ is the tensile stress in the cross section of the pipe or tank and therefore

$$f\pi dt = \frac{p\pi d^2}{4} \quad \text{and} \quad f = \frac{pd}{4t}$$

Example. A capped steel pipe having an inside diameter of 12 in. has a wall thickness of $\frac{3}{8}$ in. If the pressure in the pipe is 100 psi, what is the unit stress in the metal on a section corresponding to a seam or joint on the circumference?

SOLUTION.

$$f = \frac{pd}{4t} \quad \text{or} \quad f = \frac{100 \times 12}{4 \times 0.375} \quad \text{and} \quad f = 800 \text{ psi}$$

Note that this stress is one half the unit stress in the pipe on a section parallel to the longitudinal axis, although the pipe size and internal pressure are the same.

Problem 16–1–A. A steel pipe has an inside diameter of 14 in., a wall thickness of 0.33 in., and the water pressure is 80 psi. (a) Compute the tensile unit stress in the pipe on a section parallel to the longitudinal axis of the pipe. (b) Compute the tensile unit stress on a transverse cross section of the pipe.

CHAPTER 17

REINFORCED CONCRETE

17–1. Theoretical Assumptions. A reinforced concrete beam is a structural member composed of concrete in which steel bars are embedded. Whereas concrete in its hardened state is well able to resist compressive stresses, it is relatively weak in tension, and the steel reinforcement, in general, is placed in beams to resist the tensile stresses. In a simple beam the tensile stresses occur in the lower part of the beam, where the bending moment is positive; hence the longitudinal tensile reinforcing bars are placed near the bottom of the beam. For continuous beams tensile stresses are developed at the upper part of the beam over the supports (the negative bending moment), and here the reinforcing bars are placed near the upper side of the beam. Basically, the concrete and steel resist compressive and tensile stresses, respectively.

For homogeneous symmetrical beams the neutral surface lies at the mid-depth of the beam. Its position in a reinforced concrete beam must be computed. A reinforced concrete beam is a unit composed of two materials having different moduli of elasticity, E_s and E_c, the modulus of elasticity of steel and concrete, respectively. Their ratio, E_s/E_c, is represented by the letter n, or $n = E_s/E_c$. For most of the reinforced concrete used in building construction, $n = 8$, 10, or 12, depending on the strength of the concrete.

In developing bending formulas, certain assumptions are made. Among them are the following:

1. The tensile stresses in the concrete are ignored; it is assumed that steel reinforcement resists all the tensile stresses.

2. The deformations and unit stresses of the steel and concrete are directly proportional to their distances from the neutral sur-

face. Thus a plane cross section of a beam before bending remains a plane section after bending.

3. Perfect adhesion exists between the concrete and the steel reinforcement. Deformations of the materials do not break the bond between them.

17–2. Notation Used in Reinforced Concrete. The following notation is used in developing flexure formulas for reinforced con-

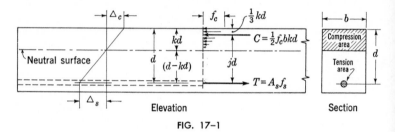

FIG. 17–1

crete beams. The terms relating to dimensions are shown in Fig. 17–1.

Δ_c and Δ_s = deformations, per unit of length, of the concrete and steel, respectively

E_s = modulus of elasticity of steel in pounds per square inch (in reinforced concrete E_s is taken to be 30,000,000 psi)

E_c = modulus of elasticity of concrete in compression in pounds per square inch, depending on the quality of the concrete (3,000,000 psi, etc.)

n = ratio of modulus of elasticity of steel to modulus of elasticity of concrete, $n = \dfrac{E_s}{E_c}$, 10, 12, etc.

f_c = compressive unit stress on the concrete at the surface most remote from the neutral surface in pounds per square inch

f_s = tensile unit stress in the longitudinal steel reinforcement in pounds per square inch

b = width of a rectangular beam in inches

d = the depth of a rectangular beam from the face of

the beam in compression to the center of the longitudinal steel reinforcement in inches. (This is the *effective depth*. The total depth includes the protective concrete below the reinforcement.)

k = the ratio of the distance of the neutral axis of the beam from the extreme fibers in compression to the effective depth of the beam

kd = the distance from the extreme fibers in compression to the neutral axis of the beam in inches

j = the ratio of the distance between the resultant of the compressive stresses and the center of the tensile stresses to d, the effective depth of the beam

jd = the distance between the resultant of the compressive stresses and the center of the tensile stresses in inches (it is the moment arm of the resisting couple)

A_s = the total area of the cross section of the longitudinal tensile steel reinforcement in square inches

p = the ratio of the area of the cross section of the longitudinal steel reinforcement to the effective area of the concrete beam, $p = \dfrac{A_s}{bd}$

M_c = the resisting moment of the compressive stresses in the concrete in inch-pounds

M_s = the resisting moment of the tensile stresses in the longitudinal steel reinforcement in inch-pounds

M = the bending moment in the beam resulting from the external forces in inch-pounds

C = the sum of the horizontal compressive stresses in the concrete in pounds

T = the sum of the horizontal tensile stresses in the longitudinal steel reinforcement in pounds

17–3. Flexure Formulas for Rectangular Reinforced Concrete Beams and Slabs.

By assumption, the deformation of any fiber of a beam is directly proportional to its distance from the neutral surface (Fig. 17–1). Likewise, the stresses in the fibers are directly proportional to their deformations as well as to their distances from the neutral surface. By definition,

$$E \text{ (modulus of elasticity)} = \frac{\text{unit stress}}{\text{unit deformation}}$$

Hence

$$E_s = \frac{f_s}{\Delta_s} \quad \text{and} \quad E_c = \frac{f_c}{\Delta_c}$$

Transposing,

$$\Delta_s = \frac{f_s}{E_s} \quad \text{and} \quad \Delta_c = \frac{f_c}{E_c}$$

Since the deformations are directly proportional to their distances from the neutral surface,

$$\frac{f_c/E_c}{f_s/E_s} = \frac{kd}{d - kd}$$

or

$$\frac{f_c E_s}{f_s E_c} = \frac{k}{1 - k} \tag{a}$$

Substituting in (a) the value $n = \dfrac{E_s}{E_c}$,

$$\frac{n f_c}{f_s} = \frac{k}{1 - k} \quad \text{or} \quad \frac{f_c}{f_s} = \frac{k}{n(1 - k)} \tag{b}$$

from which

$$f_c = \frac{f_s k}{n(1 - k)} \tag{1}$$

and

$$f_s = \frac{n f_c (1 - k)}{k} \tag{2}$$

From (2),

$$k = \frac{n f_c (1 - k)}{f_s} \quad \text{or} \quad k = \frac{n - nk}{f_s/f_c}$$

and

$$k = \frac{n}{n + (f_s/f_c)} \tag{3}$$

The compressive stresses in the concrete vary from zero at the neutral surface to f_c at kd distance; hence the average stress is $\frac{1}{2}f_c$. The area of beam in compression is $b \times kd$. Therefore,

$\frac{1}{2}f_cbkd = C$, the sum of all the compressive stresses. The forces C and T (Fig. 17–1) constitute a mechanical couple, the lever arm of which is jd. Hence, for the resisting moment in the concrete,

$$M_c = \tfrac{1}{2}f_cjkbd^2 \qquad (c)$$

Next, consider the resisting moment with respect to the tensile stresses in the steel reinforcement. The area of the steel is A_s, the unit stress is f_s, and therefore T, the sum of all the tensile stresses, is A_sf_s. Again the moment arm of the couple is jd; therefore, for the resisting moment of the steel,

$$M_s = A_sf_sjd$$

But

$$p = \frac{A_s}{bd} \quad \text{or} \quad A_s = pbd$$

Therefore,

$$M_s = A_sf_sjd \quad \text{or} \quad M_s = pf_sjbd^2 \qquad (d)$$

The two resisting moments M_c and M_s are, of course, equal in magnitude; hence, equating (c) and (d),

$$pf_sjbd^2 = \tfrac{1}{2}f_cjkbd^2$$

from which

$$2pf_s = f_ck \quad \text{or} \quad \frac{f_c}{f_s} = \frac{2p}{k} \qquad (e)$$

Placing the values of $\dfrac{f_c}{f_s}$, in (b) and (e), equal to each other,

$$\frac{k}{n(1 - k)} = \frac{2p}{k}$$

$$k^2 = 2pn(1 - k) \quad \text{or} \quad k^2 + 2pnk = 2pn$$

Completing the square and solving for k,

$$k = \sqrt{2pn + (pn)^2} - pn \qquad (4)$$

The resultant of the compressive stresses is $\frac{1}{3}kd$ from the uppermost fiber, and, since the distance between the resultant of the compressive stresses and the resultant of the tensile stresses is jd (Fig. 17–1),

$$jd = d - \frac{kd}{3} \quad \text{or} \quad j = 1 - \frac{k}{3} \tag{5}$$

Since the magnitudes of the bending moment and the resisting moment must be equal, (c) may be written

$$M = \tfrac{1}{2}f_c jkbd^2 \quad \text{or} \quad d^2 = \frac{M}{\tfrac{1}{2}f_c jkb}$$

and

$$d = \sqrt{\frac{M}{\tfrac{1}{2}f_c jkb}}$$

As a matter of convenience, let $K = \tfrac{1}{2}f_c jk$; then

$$d = \sqrt{\frac{M}{Kb}} \tag{6}$$

The bending moment may also be substituted for the resisting moment, M_s, in (d). Then

$$M = A_s f_s jd$$

and

$$A_s = \frac{M}{f_s jd} \tag{7}$$

By definition,

$$p = \frac{A_s}{bd}$$

Therefore,

$$A_s = pbd \tag{8}$$

Equation (e) gives

$$2pf_s = f_c k$$

Transposing,

$$p = \frac{kf_c}{2f_s} \tag{9}$$

17–4. Summary of Flexure Formulas. The formulas developed in the preceding article apply to rectangular reinforced concrete beams with respect to flexure or bending. They may also be used in the design of slabs, for, in reality, a slab is a beam whose width is considerable when compared to its depth. To the beginner these formulas may seem complex. It is surprising, however, to find how readily they are applied in the design of beams. The terms or notation are those commonly used and are listed in Art. 17–2.

For convenience, the most commonly used formulas are summarized as follows. No other flexure formulas are needed for the design of rectangular beams.

$$f_c = \frac{f_s k}{n(1 - k)} \tag{1}$$

$$f_s = \frac{n f_c (1 - k)}{k} \tag{2}$$

$$k = \frac{n}{n + (f_s/f_c)} \tag{3}$$

$$k = \sqrt{2pn + (pn)^2} - pn \tag{4}$$

$$j = 1 - \frac{k}{3} \tag{5}$$

$$d = \sqrt{\frac{M}{\frac{1}{2}f_c j k b}} = \sqrt{\frac{M}{Kb}} \tag{6}$$

$$A_s = \frac{M}{f_s j d} \tag{7}$$

$$A_s = pbd \tag{8}$$

$$p = \frac{k f_c}{2 f_s} \tag{9}$$

17–5. Allowable Stresses in Concrete and Steel. Because the ingredients of concrete may be combined in various proportions, concrete varies in strength and quality. The symbol f_c' represents the ultimate compressive strength of concrete at the age of 28 days. Commonly used grades of concrete are $f_c' = 2500$ psi, $f_c' = 3000$ psi, and $f_c' = 3750$ psi.

The allowable unit stresses, compression, shear, and bond, are given as percentages of f_c'. For example, if we are using 3000 psi concrete, we find in certain building codes that f_c, the allowable compressive unit stress on the concrete at the surface farthest from the neutral surface, is $0.45 f_c'$, or $0.45 \times 3000 = 1350$ psi.

Some older codes stipulate $0.4f_c'$ for this stress which, of course, is 1200 psi.

Table 17–1 gives certain selected allowable unit stresses for three grades of concrete. The allowable tensile unit stress in the longi-

TABLE 17–1. ALLOWABLE UNIT STRESSES IN CONCRETE

Description		For any strength of concrete as fixed by test $n = \dfrac{30,000}{f_c'}$	When strength of concrete is fixed by the water content		
			$f_c' = 2500$ psi $n = 12$	$f_c' = 3000$ psi $n = 10$	$f_c' = 3750$ psi $n = 8$
Flexure: f_c Extreme fiber stress in compression	f_c	$0.45f_c'$	1125	1350	1688
Shear: v Beams with no web reinforcement	v_c	$0.03f_c'$	75	90	90
Beams with stirrups or bent bars	v	$0.08f_c'$	200	240	240
Bond: u Deformed Top bars	u	$0.07f_c'$	175	210	245
All others	u	$0.10f_c'$	250	300	350

Compiled from data in *Building Code Requirements for Reinforced Concrete*, by permission of the American Concrete Institute.

tudinal steel reinforcement is generally given to be 20,000 psi for rail-steel and 18,000 psi for billet-steel bars.

17–6. Modulus of Elasticity of Concrete. The modulus of elasticity of concrete varies according to its strength. For the grades $f_c' = 2500$ psi, $f_c' = 3000$ psi, and $f_c' = 3750$ psi the moduli of elasticity are 2,500,000, 3,000,000, and 3,750,000 psi, respectively. The symbol n is the ratio of the modulus of elasticity of steel to the modulus of elasticity of concrete, $n = E_s/E_c$. For the steel reinforcement in concrete $E_s = 30,000,000$ psi. Thus, when 2500-, 3000-, and 3750-psi concretes are used, $n = 12$, 10, and 8, respectively. See Table 17–1.

17–7. Formula Coefficients for Rectangular Sections. Let us assume that we are to use a concrete for which $f_c' = 3000$ psi, and that $f_s = 20,000$ psi, the allowable tensile unit stress in the steel reinforcement. Then $n = \dfrac{E_s}{E_c} = \dfrac{30,000,000}{3,000,000}$, or $n = 10$. From Table 17–1, $f_c = 1350$ psi. Now let us determine the values of k, j, p, and K, using the formulas given in Art. 17–4.

Formula (3),

$$k = \frac{n}{n + (f_s/f_c)}$$

or

$$k = \frac{10}{10 + (20,000/1350)} = 0.403$$

Formula (5),

$$j = 1 - \frac{k}{3}$$

or

$$j = 1 - \frac{0.403}{3} = 0.866$$

Formula (9),

$$p = \frac{kf_c}{2f_s}$$

or

$$p = \frac{0.403 \times 1350}{2 \times 20,000} = 0.0136$$

Formula (6),

$$K = \tfrac{1}{2}f_c jk$$

or

$$K = \frac{1350 \times 0.866 \times 0.403}{2} = 236$$

TABLE 17–2. FORMULA COEFFICIENTS FOR RECTANGULAR BEAM SECTIONS

$n = 12$ ($f_c' = 2500$ psi)

f_s	f_c	K	k	j	p
18,000	875	141	0.368	0.877	0.0089
	950	161	0.388	0.871	0.0102
	1000	173	0.400	0.867	0.0111
	1125	207	0.429	0.857	0.0134
20,000	875	133	0.344	0.885	0.0075
	950	152	0.363	0.879	0.0086
	1000	164	0.375	0.875	0.0094
	1125	196	0.403	0.866	0.0113

$n = 10$ ($f_c' = 3000$ psi)

f_s	f_c	K	k	j	p
18,000	1050	169	0.368	0.877	0.0107
	1125	189	0.385	0.872	0.0120
	1200	208	0.400	0.867	0.0133
	1350	248	0.429	0.857	0.0161
20,000	1050	160	0.344	0.885	0.0090
	1125	178	0.360	0.880	0.0101
	1200	197	0.375	0.875	0.0113
	1350	236	0.403	0.866	0.0136

$n = 8$ ($f_c' = 3750$ psi)

f_s	f_c	K	k	j	p
18,000	1300	209	0.366	0.878	0.0132
	1400	234	0.384	0.872	0.0149
	1500	260	0.400	0.867	0.0167
	1688	309	0.428	0.857	0.0200
20,000	1300	197	0.342	0.886	0.0111
	1400	221	0.359	0.880	0.0126
	1500	246	0.375	0.875	0.0141
	1688	294	0.403	0.866	0.0170

In the design of reinforced concrete members the coefficients found in the formulas are used constantly. As has been shown, these coefficients are readily computed. However, the coefficients for various unit stresses have been computed and are compiled in Table 17–2. This table will be of great convenience in designing structural members. Refer to this table and verify the values for k, j, p, and K that have just been computed.

Problem 17–7–A. Compute the values of k, j, p, and K for $f_c' = 3000$-psi concrete when $f_c = 1350$ psi and $f_s = 18,000$ psi.

Problem 17–7–B. For 2500-psi concrete compute the values of k, j, p, and K when $f_c = 1125$ psi and $f_s = 20,000$ psi.

Check the values of k, j, p, and K, just found, with those given in Table 17–2.

17–8. Design of a Rectangular Reinforced Concrete Beam for Flexure. The derivations of the formulas used in the design of reinforced concrete beams, as given in Art. 17–3, are, perhaps, tedious. The application of these formulas, however, is a relatively simple matter. They save much time and labor and result in a comparatively simple design procedure. Our first step in the design of a beam is to show how the dimensions and longitudinal steel reinforcement in a rectangular beam are determined.

Example. A simple reinforced concrete beam has a span of 16 ft 0 in. with a uniformly distributed load, including its own weight, of 2800 lb per lin ft. Determine the dimensions of the beam and the required longitudinal tensile reinforcement. Specification data:

$$n = 10$$
$$f_c' = 3000 \text{ psi}$$
$$f_s = 20,000 \text{ psi}$$
$$f_c = 1350 \text{ psi}$$

SOLUTION. Referring to Table 17–2, we find the following formula coefficients: $K = 236$, $k = 0.403$, and $j = 0.866$.

Since this is a simple beam, $M = \dfrac{Wl}{8}$ (Fig. 8–4). Then

$$W = 2800 \times 16 = 44,800 \text{ lb}$$

and

$$M = \frac{44{,}800 \times 16 \times 12}{8} = 1{,}075{,}000 \text{ in-lb}$$

the value of the maximum bending moment.

In designing a rectangular beam, it is customary to assume a width and then to compute the depth accordingly. Sometimes building conditions determine the width, as, for instance, the width of a wall. In general, a rectangular beam should have a width of one half to three fourths its effective depth. In this problem let us assume b, the width, to be 12 in.

Then

$$d = \sqrt{\frac{M}{Kb}} \text{ , formula (6)} \quad \text{and} \quad d = \sqrt{\frac{1{,}075{,}000}{236 \times 12}} = \sqrt{380} = 19.5$$

This is the effective depth. We add 2.5 in. of concrete, below the center of the longitudinal reinforcement, for protection of the steel. Thus the total depth of the beam is $19.5 + 2.5 = 22$ in. See Fig. 17–2.

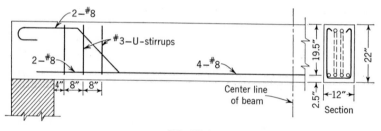

FIG. 17–2

To find the required area of tensile reinforcement we use formula (7),

$$A_s = \frac{M}{f_s jd} \quad \text{or} \quad A_s = \frac{1{,}075{,}000}{20{,}000 \times 0.866 \times 19.5} = 3.16 \text{ sq in.}$$

On referring to Table 17–3, we find that one #8 bar has a cross-sectional area of 0.79 sq in. Thus, 4-#8 deformed bars provide an area of 4 x 0.79, or 3.16 sq in., and are accepted for the longitudinal tensile reinforcement.

Table 17–3 gives the areas and perimeters for the bars that are used in reinforced concrete. All bars are round. The bars are designated as #2, #3, #4, etc., the numbers being based on the

TABLE 17–3.   AREAS AND PERIMETERS OF ROUND BARS

Designation	#2	#3	#4	#5	#6	#7	#8	#9	#10	#11
Diameter, inches	¼	⅜	½	⅝	¾	⅞	1.0	1.128	1.270	1.410
Area, sq in.	0.05	0.11	0.20	0.31	0.44	0.60	0.79	1.00	1.27	1.56
Perimeter, inches	0.786	1.178	1.571	1.963	2.356	2.749	3.142	3.544	3.990	4.430

nearest number of $\frac{1}{8}$ in. included in the nominal diameter of the bar. As an example, #5 and #6 bars have $\frac{5}{8}$ and $\frac{6}{8}$ in. diameters, respectively. The bars may be plain or deformed, but bar #2 comes in plain bars only. Because of their greater ability to resist bond stress, deformed bars are used almost exclusively.

Since this example concerns a simple beam, the maximum bending moment is at the center of the span; it diminishes in magnitude on each side of the center and is zero at the supports. The 3.16-sq in. area of tensile reinforcement was determined in accordance with the maximum moment and, consequently, is required only at the mid-span. Two of the bars will extend the full length of the beam, and the remaining two are turned up at points $\frac{1}{7}$ of the clear span from the faces of the supports. The bent portions of these bars aid in resisting shearing stresses. See Fig. 17–2.

In the example just completed the dimensions of the beam and the required longitudinal reinforcement were determined. The complete design, however, requires that shear and bond stresses be investigated and, if necessary, web reinforcement (stirrups) be designed. This is discussed in subsequent articles.

Example. An interior span of a continuous beam has a clear span of 20 ft 0 in. with a uniformly distributed load, including its own weight, of 1150 lb per lin ft extending over the entire length of the beam. Determine the dimensions of the beam and the required longitudinal tensile reinforcement. Specification data:

$$n = 12$$

$$f_c' = 2500 \text{ psi}$$

$$f_s = 20{,}000 \text{ psi}$$

$$f_c = 1125 \text{ psi}$$

SOLUTION. The formula coefficients for the stresses given as data are found in Table 17–2. They are $K = 196$, $k = 0.403$, and $j = 0.866$.

Since this is an interior span of a continuous beam, we have a condition similar to that shown in Fig. 9–8, a beam with a uniformly distributed load with both ends fixed. For this beam note that the maximum bending moment is at the supports, $M = \dfrac{Wl}{12}$. This is the negative moment. The positive moment, $M = \dfrac{Wl}{24}$, is at the center of the span; its value is only one half the magnitude of the negative moment. For such beams we use the maximum value in determining the dimensions of the beam and provide the same amount of longitudinal tensile reinforcement at the center of the span as at the supports.

The total distributed load is

$$W = 1150 \times 20 = 23{,}000 \text{ lb}$$

Then

$$M = \frac{Wl}{12} = \frac{23{,}000 \times 20 \times 12}{12} = 460{,}000 \text{ in-lb}$$

Assuming b, the width, to be 10 in., and using formula (6),

$$d = \sqrt{\frac{M}{Kb}} = \sqrt{\frac{460{,}000}{196 \times 10}} = \sqrt{234.6} = 15.3 \text{ in.}$$

Adding 2.5 in. of concrete below the center of the steel for protection, $15.3 + 2.5 = 17.8$ in. It is well to use an even number of inches. Therefore, we accept 18 in. for the total depth of the beam: $18 - 2.5 = 15.5$ in., the effective depth of the beam. See Fig. 17–3.

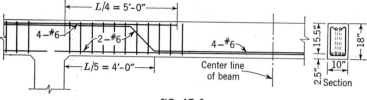

FIG. 17–3

Using formula (7) to find the required area of longitudinal tensile reinforcement,

$$A_s = \frac{M}{f_s jd} \quad \text{or} \quad A_s = \frac{460,000}{20,000 \times 0.866 \times 15.5} = 1.72 \text{ sq in.}$$

Reference to Table 17–3 shows that one #6 bar has a cross-sectional area of 0.44 sq in. Thus $0.44 \times 4 = 1.76$ sq in., and we accept 4-#6 bars for the tensile reinforcement.

Two of the four bars are straight bars placed at the bottom of the beam and extended into the supports a distance of at least 6 in. The remaining two bars are bent. They are turned up at the fifth points of span and continued over the supports to the quarter points of the adjacent spans. This arrangement provides 4-#6 bars for both the positive and negative bending moments. See Fig. 17–3.

Problem 17–8–A. A simple reinforced concrete beam has a span of 20 ft 0 in. with a uniformly distributed load, including its own weight, of 1200 lb per lin ft. Determine the dimensions of the beam and also the required longitudinal tensile reinforcement. Specification data:

$$f_s = 20,000 \text{ psi}$$
$$f_c = 1350 \text{ psi}$$
$$n = 10$$

Problem 17–8–B. Determine the dimensions and required area of the longitudinal tensile reinforcement for an interior span of a continuous beam. The clear span has a length of 18 ft 0 in. and a uniformly distributed load, including its own weight, of 1200 lb per lin ft. Specification data:

$$f_s = 20,000 \text{ psi}$$
$$f_c = 1125 \text{ psi}$$
$$n = 12$$

17–9. Design of a Reinforced Concrete Slab. A reinforced concrete slab with the longitudinal tensile reinforcement extending in one direction only (a one-way slab) is actually a rectangular beam whose width is great in comparison to its depth. In the design of such a floor or roof slab, the load is given as so many pounds per square foot. The design is accomplished by the consideration of a strip of slab 12 in. wide. For this portion of the slab the depth and longitudinal tensile reinforcement are then determined. Some building codes give 4 and $3\frac{1}{2}$ in. as the minimum thicknesses of floor and roof slabs, respectively. The spacing of reinforcement in one-way slabs should never exceed three times the slab thickness. Web reinforcement (stirrups) is never used in slabs.

Example. An interior span of a continuous one-way reinforced concrete slab has a length of 10 ft 0 in. and a uniformly distributed load, including its own weight, of 245 lb per sq ft. Compute the slab thickness and the longitudinal tensile reinforcement. Specification data:

$$f_s = 20,000 \text{ psi}$$

$$f_c = 1350 \text{ psi}$$

$$n = 10$$

SOLUTION. Table 17–2 gives the following formula coefficients: $K = 236$ and $j = 0.866$.

The total load on a *12-in. wide strip of slab*, 10 ft in length, is 245×10, or 2450 lb. Since this slab has a condition similar to a beam with fixed ends, as shown in Fig. 9–8, the maximum bending moment is

$$M = \frac{Wl}{12} \quad \text{or} \quad M = \frac{2450 \times 10 \times 12}{12} = 24,500 \text{ in-lb}$$

Using formula (6),

$$d = \sqrt{\frac{M}{Kb}} \quad \text{or} \quad d = \sqrt{\frac{24,500}{236 \times 12}} = \sqrt{8.66} = 2.95, \text{ say 3 in.,}$$

the effective depth

If we allow 0.25 in. for one half a bar diameter and 0.75 in. for protection for the steel, $3 + 0.25 + 0.75 = 4$ in., the total depth of the slab.

To determine the longitudinal tensile reinforcement we use formula (7),

$$A_s = \frac{M}{f_s jd} \quad \text{or} \quad A_s = \frac{24,500}{20,000 \times 0.866 \times 3} = 0.47 \text{ sq in.}$$

the area of tensile reinforcement required for each 12-in. wide strip of slab. Then $0.47/12 = 0.039$ sq in., the required steel area for each 1-in. wide strip of slab. A #4 bar has a cross-sectional area of 0.2 sq in. (Table 17–3); therefore, $0.2/0.039 = 5$ in., the required spacing of the #4 bars. Consequently, we accept a slab having a total thickness of 4 in., with #4 bars spaced 5 in. on centers with $\frac{3}{4}$ in. of protective concrete below the tensile reinforcement.

As the slab is fully continuous (fixed ends), bend up alternate bars at the fifth points of span and extend them to the quarter points of the adjacent spans. See Fig. 17–4. The remaining bars

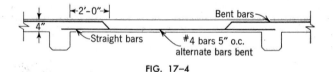

FIG. 17–4

are straight, placed in the bottom of the slab and extending at least 6 in. into the supports or made continuous. In Fig. 17–4 the reinforcement for the adjacent spans is not shown.

Problem 17–9–A. An interior span of a continuous reinforced concrete one-way slab has a length of 11 ft 0 in. The uniformly distributed load on the slab, including its own weight, is 275 lb per sq ft. Compute the thickness of the slab and the required tensile reinforcement. Specification data:

$$f_s = 20,000 \text{ psi}$$
$$f_c = 1350 \text{ psi}$$
$$n = 10$$

17–10. Diagonal Tension, Web Reinforcement. When a beam is subjected to forces that tend to bend it, both compressive and tensile stresses are present, as has been explained. In addition, there are inclined tensile stresses which tend to produce the tension cracks indicated in Fig. 17–5(a). The stresses that cause these cracks are known as *diagonal tension*. To help the concrete to resist diagonal tension we use reinforcing bars called *stirrups*. These bars are usually $\frac{3}{8}$ or $\frac{1}{2}$ in. in diameter, #3 and #4, bent into the shape of the letter U or the letter W. In Fig. 17–5(c) they are shown as the vertical lines, and in Fig. 17–5(d) they are U-shaped with hooked ends and are placed outside the longitudinal tensile reinforcement. Theoretically, these bars might be inclined

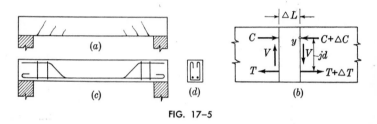

FIG. 17–5

and placed at right angles to the direction taken by the cracks. For practical reasons, however, they are invariably placed in a vertical position.

Figure 17–5(b) represents a side elevation of a portion of a beam. The portion of the beam under consideration is an infinitely short length, marked ΔL. It is in equilibrium under the compression, tension, and shearing stresses shown by the arrows in the figure. Since, by the laws of equilibrium, the algebraic sum of the moments of all the forces about any point is zero, we can write, taking point y as the center of moments,

$$\Delta L \times V = \Delta T \times jd$$

The compressive and tensile stresses are larger on one side of the section than on the other because the bending moment in the beam varies from section to section. Hence ΔT is the horizontal shear; it is resisted by a plane the dimensions of which are ΔL and b, b being the width of the beam. Therefore, letting v be the shearing unit stress,

$$\Delta T = v \, \Delta L b$$

Substituting this value of ΔT in the above equation gives

$$\Delta LV = v \,\Delta Lbjd$$

or

$$V = vjbd \quad \text{or} \quad v = \frac{V}{jbd}$$

In computations for shear (diagonal tension), j is taken to have a value of 0.875, and this equation can be written

$$v = \frac{V}{0.875bd} \quad \text{or} \quad v = \frac{8V}{7bd}$$

This is the formula used to determine the shearing unit stress. shear being a measure of diagonal tension. The symbol v_c represents the allowable shearing unit stress permitted on the concrete. In Table 17–1, we find that v_c is 90 psi for 3000-psi concrete. When v, the shearing unit stress in a beam, exceeds v_c, stirrups, known as web reinforcement, are required; $v - v_c = v'$, the excess shear to be resisted by the stirrups. Frequently 240 psi is the maximum allowable unit stress for v.

17–11. Portion of Beam Requiring Stirrups. For beams in which v does not exceed v_c, web reinforcement (stirrups) is not required. If, however, v does exceed v_c, stirrups are necessary. Let us now derive a formula that can be used to tell us the distance from the supports in which the stirrups are to be placed.

We have seen [Fig. 8–5(b)] that the shear diagram for a simple beam having a *uniformly distributed load* has the shape of two triangles. Figure 17–6 shows one half of the shear diagram for a

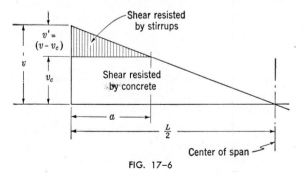

FIG. 17–6

simple beam having a uniformly distributed load. The terms v, v_c, and v' have the significance given in the preceding article and are shown in Fig. 17–6; they are in units of pounds per square inch. In Fig. 17–6, L is the span of the beam in feet, and a, also in feet, is the length of beam from the supports in which stirrups are required.

Referring to Fig. 17–6, by similar triangles the following relation is found:

$$\frac{L}{2} : \left(\frac{L}{2} - a\right) :: v : v_c$$

or

$$\frac{L}{2} \times v_c = \left(\frac{L}{2} \times v\right) - av$$

from which

$$a = \frac{\dfrac{L}{2}(v - v_c)}{v}$$

Substituting v' for $(v - v_c)$, we have

$$a = \frac{L}{2}\left(\frac{v'}{v}\right)$$

This formula enables us to determine the length of beam in which stirrups are required. *Note particularly that this formula applies only to beams having uniformly distributed loads.*

17–12. Spacing of Stirrups. Stirrups are generally made of #3 or #4 bars bent in the shape of the letters U or W. In the formula used to determine the spacing of stirrups we use the symbol A_v to represent the total cross-sectional area of one stirrup. A #3 bar has a cross section of 0.11 sq in.; hence for a U-shaped stirrup, there being two vertical legs, $A_v = 0.22$ sq in. Similarly, for a #4 U-stirrup $A_v = 0.4$ sq in.

The symbol f_v represents the allowable tensile unit stress in the stirrup. It is usually 18,000 or 20,000 psi.

If b is the width of the beam in inches, s is the spacing (in a direction parallel to the length of the beam) of the stirrups in inches, and v' is the shearing unit stress to be taken by the stirrups, the stirrup stress is $v'bs$. Since A_v is the cross-sectional area of a stirrup and f_v is the allowable tensile unit stress, $A_v \times f_v$ is the total stirrup stress.   Therefore,

$$A_v f_v = v'bs$$

and

$$s = \frac{A_v f_v}{v'b}$$

This is the formula to use in determining the stirrup spacing. It is customary to place the first stirrup at $\dfrac{s}{2}$ distance from the support.   Regardless of the magnitude of s determined by the formula, the *maximum* stirrup spacing permitted is $\dfrac{d-m}{2}$, in which d is the effective depth of the beam and m is the distance from the center of the reinforcement to the bottom surface of the beam.   Both of these terms are in inches.

The horizontal component of the diagonal tension is resisted by the longitudinal tensile reinforcement in the beam, but the vertical component is resisted by the vertical stirrups and the concrete. Since the stirrups resist tensile stresses, hooks are formed on the ends of the bars.

Example.   For the simple beam having a span of 16 ft 0 in. with a uniformly distributed load of 2800 lb per lin ft, discussed in the first example given in Art. 17–8, design the web reinforcement (stirrups).   Specification data:

$$v_c = 90 \text{ psi}$$

$$v = \text{limited to } 240 \text{ psi}$$

$$f_v = 20{,}000 \text{ psi}$$

SOLUTION.   For this beam we found that $b = 12$ in., $d = 19.5$ in., and the longitudinal tensile reinforcement consisted of 4-#8 bars.

To determine whether stirrups are required, let us compute the magnitude of v, the shearing unit stress.

The total load is 2800×16, or 44,800 lb, and, since the beam is symmetrically loaded, $R_1 = R_2 = 44{,}800 \times \frac{1}{2} = 22{,}400$ lb. Hence $V = 22{,}400$ lb, the maximum shear.

The formula to use for finding v is given in Art. 17–10, $v = \dfrac{V}{jbd}$.

Thus $v = \dfrac{22,400}{0.875 \times 12 \times 19.5} = 109$ psi, the maximum shearing unit stress.

Since this value exceeds v_c, 90 psi, stirrups are required. Then $v' = v - v_c$ and $v' = 109 - 90 = 19$ psi, the shearing stress to be resisted by the stirrups.

To find the distance from the supports in which stirrups are required, we use the formula $a = \dfrac{L}{2}\left(\dfrac{v'}{v}\right)$ given in Art. 17–11. Then $a = \dfrac{16}{2}\left(\dfrac{19}{109}\right) = 1.4$ ft, say 1 ft 5 in.

Let us assume that #3 U-stirrups will be used. By use of Table 17–3, $A_v = 2 \times 0.11$, or $A_v = 0.22$ sq in. The formula that determines the stirrup spacing is $s = \dfrac{A_v f_v}{v'b}$; hence $s = \dfrac{0.22 \times 20,000}{19 \times 12}$ = 19.4 in. However, we know that the maximum spacing permitted is $\dfrac{d - m}{2}$, or $\dfrac{19.5 - 2.5}{2} = 8.5$ in. Consequently, we accept an 8-in. spacing for the stirrups. The first stirrups are placed at $s/2$, or 4 in. from the face of the support, and then two more at 8-in. spacing. Thus three stirrups are used at each end of the beam as shown in Fig. 17–2.

Problem 17-12-A. A simple reinforced concrete beam has a length of 20 ft 0 in. with a uniformly distributed load, including its own weight, of 3200 lb per lin ft extending over its entire length. Building conditions limit the width of the beam to 12 in. Determine the effective depth and longitudinal tensile steel and investigate the web reinforcement. If it is required, of what should it consist? Specification data:

$$f_c' = 3000 \text{ psi}$$

$$n = 10$$

$$f_v = 20,000 \text{ psi}$$

$$f_s = 20,000 \text{ psi}$$

$$f_c = 1350 \text{ psi}$$

$v_c = 90$ psi

$v = $ limited to 240 psi

$u = $ limited to 210 and 300
psi for top bars and all
others, respectively

Problem 17–12–B. A simple reinforced concrete beam has a span of 14 ft 0 in. and a total uniformly distributed load of 2000 lb per lin ft extending over its entire length. If the width and effective depth are 12 and 20 in., respectively, what web reinforcement should be used? Specification data:

$$v_c = 40 \text{ psi}$$

$$f_v = 18,000 \text{ psi}$$

17–13. Bond Stress.

In the derivation of flexure formulas for reinforced concrete beams, it is assumed that there is a perfect bond between the concrete and the reinforcing bars and that the two materials deform under stress without the bond between them being broken. The bond between the two materials results from the adhesion between them and is further increased by the use of *deformed bars*. Deformed bars are bars rolled with lugs or projections on their surface, their purpose being to provide a mechanical bond. A bar with a hooked end also helps to prevent slipping in the concrete.

For 3000-psi concrete Table 17–1 gives for u, the allowable bond stress, 210 psi for deformed top bars and 300 psi for all others. The design procedure is to determine first the size of the bars required for the longitudinal tensile reinforcement. This having been done, u, the unit bond stress, is computed to see whether the stresses are excessive. Deformed bars are used almost exclusively.

Referring to Fig. 17–5(b) and writing an equation of moments of the various forces about point y,

$$V \times \Delta L = \Delta T \times jd$$

The force ΔT is the force that tends to pull the short length of reinforcement through the concrete. Σ_0 is the perimeter of the bar, and its length is ΔL; hence $\Sigma_0 \times \Delta L$ is the area of the surface of the bar in contact with the concrete. If u is the unit bond stress, $\Sigma_0 \times \Delta L \times u$ is the force resisting the tendency of the reinforcement to pull through the concrete; we know that this force is ΔT. Therefore,

$$\Delta T = \Sigma_0 \times \Delta L \times u$$

Substituting the value of ΔT in the above equation gives

$$V \times \Delta L = \Sigma_0 \times \Delta L \times u \times jd$$

from which

$$V = \Sigma_0 \times u \times jd$$

or

$$u = \frac{V}{\Sigma_0 jd}$$

This is the formula used to compute the unit bond stress. In computations for bond stress the value of j is generally taken to be 0.875. If more than one bar is used for the longitudinal tensile reinforcement, Σ_0 is the sum of the perimeters of all the bars.

In designing a reinforced concrete beam, one of the first steps is to compute the effective depth. Following this, A_s, the required area of longitudinal tensile reinforcement, is computed. This area is expressed as an exact number of bars of a certain size, 4-#7, etc.

One of the succeeding steps is to compute u, the unit bond stress, to see that it does not exceed the allowable stress given as data. If u is excessive, the bond stress can be reduced by employing a greater depth of beam or by using a greater number of smaller bars.

Example. In the first example given in Art. 17–8 the longitudinal tensile reinforcement was found to consist of 4-#8 deformed bars. Investigate the bond stress. For deformed bars the allowable bond stress for 3000-psi concrete is 210 psi for top bars and 300 psi for all others.

SOLUTION. This is a simple beam, and, theoretically, there are no "top bars"; all the tensile reinforcement could be placed in the lower part of the beam.

The total distributed load on the beam is 44,800 lb; therefore, each reaction is $44,800 \times \frac{1}{2}$, or 22,400 lb. This is also the value of V, the maximum vertical shear. Reference to Table 17–3 shows that the perimeter of one #8 bar is 3.142 in.; hence $\Sigma_0 = 4 \times$ 3.142, or 12.57 in. In computations used in determining shear and bond stresses, the value of j is taken to be 0.875. The effective depth, d, in this example was found to be 19.5 in.

Then

$$u = \frac{V}{\Sigma_0 jd} \quad \text{or} \quad u = \frac{22,400}{12.57 \times 0.875 \times 19.5} = 105 \text{ psi}$$

the unit bond stress. Since this stress does not exceed 300 psi, the bond stress is acceptable.

Example. Investigate the bond stress for the tensile reinforcement in the continuous beam given in the second example in Art. 17–8. Specification data: For deformed bars, $u = 210$ psi for top bars and 300 psi for all others.

SOLUTION. The total distributed load on the beam is 1150×20, or 23,000 lb; hence $\frac{1}{2} \times 23,000 = 11,500$ lb, the maximum vertical shear. The tensile reinforcement consists of 4-#6 bars; therefore, since Table 17–3 gives the perimeter of one #6 bar as 2.356 in., $\Sigma_0 = 4 \times 2.356$, or 9.42 in. The effective depth is 15.5 in.

Then

$$u = \frac{V}{\Sigma_0 jd} = \frac{11,500}{9.42 \times 0.875 \times 15.5} = 90 \text{ psi}$$

the unit bond stress. The bars over the supports, in this example (see Fig. 17–3) are top bars. Since 90 psi does not exceed the allowable stress of 210 psi, the bond stress is acceptable.

Example. Compute the unit bond stress for the reinforcement in the one-way slab given in the example in Art. 17–9.

SOLUTION. The effective depth of this slab, d, was found to be 3 in. and the tensile reinforcement consisted of #4 bars at 5-in. spacing.

Since the bars are placed 5 in. apart, each 12-in. width of slab contains an equivalent of $\frac{12}{5}$ or 2.4 bars. Table 17–3 shows the perimeter of a #4 bar to be 1.571 in.; therefore, $\Sigma_0 = 1.571 \times 2.4 = 3.77$ in. The total load on a 12-in. width of slab is 2450 lb; hence $V = \frac{1}{2} \times 2450 = 1225$ lb, the maximum vertical shear.

Then

$$u = \frac{V}{\Sigma_0 jd} = \frac{1225}{3.77 \times 0.875 \times 3} = 124 \text{ psi}$$

the unit bond stress.

Problem 17-13-A. A symmetrically loaded continuous beam has a total distributed load of 31,000 lb on a clear span of 22 ft. The effective depth of the beam is 17.5 in., and the tensile reinforcement consists of 2-#10 bars. Compute the unit bond stress.

Problem 17-13-B. A 12-in. wide strip of a one-way reinforced concrete slab supports a distributed load, including its own weight, of 2500 lb. The effective depth of the slab is 4 in., and the tensile reinforcement consists of #4 bars with $5\frac{1}{2}$-in. spacing. Compute the unit bond stress.

17–14. Reinforced Concrete Columns. Reinforced concrete columns are generally *short columns*, columns for which the length is not greater than ten times the least lateral dimension of the cross section. The length of short columns does not enter in the computations for its design. Current specifications require a minimum diameter of 12 in., or, in the case of rectangular columns, a minimum thickness of 8 in. and a minimum gross area of 120 sq in.

A *tied column* is a column in which the reinforcement consists of longitudinal bars and separate lateral ties as indicated in Fig. 17–7(a). The *ties* are steel bars at least $\frac{1}{4}$-in. (#2) in diameter spaced not farther apart than the least lateral dimension of the column. The reinforcement for a tied column should be protected by a covering of concrete, cast monolithically with the core, having a thickness not less than $1\frac{1}{2}$ in. The ratio of the cross-sectional area of vertical reinforcement to the gross column area should not be less than 0.01 nor more than 0.04. The minimum vertical reinforcement should be 4 bars having a minimum bar size of #5.

A *spiral column* has longitudinal bars and a closely spaced continuous spiral hooping, as indicated in Fig. 17–7(b).

The load a reinforced concrete column will support is made up of the load supported by the concrete and the load supported by the longitudinal (vertical) steel reinforcement. The steel and concrete act as a unit, and the two different materials must have equal deformations when column loads are applied. The stresses, therefore, in the two materials are proportional to their moduli of elasticity.

Let

Δ_s and Δ_c = the unit deformation in the steel and concrete, respectively

f_s and f_c = the compressive unit stresses in the steel and concrete, respectively

E_s and E_c = the moduli of elasticity of steel and concrete, respectively

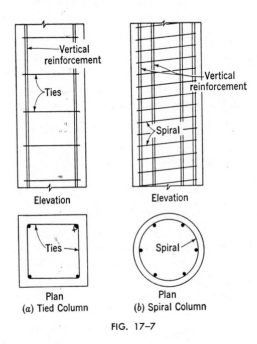

Elevation

Vertical reinforcement

Ties

Plan

Ties →

(a) Tied Column

Elevation

Vertical reinforcement

Spiral

Plan

Spiral

(b) Spiral Column

FIG. 17–7

Since, by definition, the modulus of elasticity of a material is the unit stress divided by the unit deformation,

$$E_s = \frac{f_s}{\Delta_s} \quad \text{and} \quad E_c = \frac{f_c}{\Delta_c}$$

or

$$\Delta_s = \frac{f_s}{E_s} \quad \text{and} \quad \Delta_c = \frac{f_c}{E_c}$$

Since Δ_s and Δ_c must be equal,

$$\frac{f_s}{E_s} = \frac{f_c}{E_c} \quad \text{or} \quad f_s = \frac{f_c E_s}{E_c}$$

but $\dfrac{E_s}{E_c} = n$; hence $f_s = nf_c$.

Now, if P equals the axial load on the column and A_c and A_s are the effective cross-sectional areas of the concrete and steel, respectively,

$$P = A_c f_c + A_s f_s$$

Let A_g equal the gross cross-sectional area of the column and let p_g equal the ratio of A_s to A_g. Then $A_s = p_g A_g$ and $A_c = A_g - p_g A_g$. We have found that $f_s = nf_c$. Therefore, substituting these values in the above equation for P,

$$P = (A_g - p_g A_g)f_c + p_g A_g nf_c$$

or

$$P = f_c A_g (1 - p_g + p_g n)$$

and

$$P = f_c A_g [1 + p_g (n - 1)]$$

The equation in this form is found in older building codes as the formula to be used in the design of tied columns. It has been developed here to show how two materials having different moduli of elasticity act as a unit when used as a reinforced concrete column.

A formula found in recent specifications is

$$P = 0.8 \times A_g (0.225 f_c' + f_s p_g)$$

The symbols in this formula are similar to those given above, f_c' being the ultimate compressive stress of the concrete at the 28-day curing period. This formula, being in common use, is used in the following examples and problems.

Example. Compute the allowable axial load on a 10 x 12 in. tied column 8 ft 0 in. in length and reinforced with 4-#5 bars. Specification data: $f_c' = 3000$ psi and $f_s = 20,000$ psi.

SOLUTION. The least side of this column is 10 in.; $10 \times 10 = 100$ in., or 8 ft 4 in., the maximum permissible length for a column of this cross section when its load is computed as a short column.

Since this column does not exceed the limit (ten times the dimension of the least side), the formula is applicable.

The area of one #5 bar is 0.31 sq in. (Table 17–3). Four bars have an area of 4×0.31, or 1.24 sq in. Then $p_g = \dfrac{A_s}{A_g} = \dfrac{1.24}{10 \times 12}$ $= 0.0103$. This is the minimum percentage of reinforcement that is permitted in a tied column. Then

$$P = 0.8 \times A_g(0.225f_c' + f_s p_g)$$

$$= 0.8 \times 120[(0.225 \times 3000) + (20{,}000 \times 0.0103)]$$

and

$$P = 84{,}570 \text{ lb, the allowable axial load on the column}$$

Example. A 20 x 20 in. tied column, 16 ft 0 in. in length, has vertical reinforcement consisting of 8-#7 bars. Compute the allowable axial load on the column in accordance with these specification data: $f_c' = 3000$ psi and $f_s = 20{,}000$ psi.

SOLUTION. $20 \times 10 = 200$ in., or 16 ft 8 in., the maximum allowable column length. Since the column in this example is 16 ft 0 in. in length, the column formula is applicable. One #7 bar has an area of 0.6 sq in. (Table 17–3); eight bars have an area of 8×0.6, or 4.8 sq in. Thus $p_g = \dfrac{4.8}{20 \times 20}$, or 0.012. This percentage of vertical reinforcement is acceptable, since it falls between 0.01 and 0.04. Then

$$P = 0.8 \times A_g(0.225f_c' + f_s p_g)$$

$$= 0.8 \times 400[(0.225 \times 3000) + (20{,}000 \times 0.012)]$$

$$= 292{,}800 \text{ lb, the allowable axial column load}$$

Problem 17–14–A. Compute the allowable axial load on a 12 x 12 in. reinforced concrete tied column having 4-#9 vertical reinforcing bars and a length of 10 ft 0 in. Specification data: $f_c' = 3000$ psi and $f_s = 20{,}000$ psi.

Problem 17–14–B. A 16 x 16 in. tied reinforced concrete column has vertical reinforcement consisting of 8-#10 bars. The length of the column is 13 ft 0 in. Will this column support safely an axial load of 285,000 lb? Specification data: $f_c' = 2500$ psi and $f_s = 20{,}000$ psi.

CHAPTER 18

RETAINING WALLS AND DAMS

18–1. General Considerations. A *retaining wall* is a wall whose purpose is to resist the lateral pressure (thrust) of earth or other granular material. A *dam* is a retaining wall used to resist the lateral pressure of water or other liquid.

In general, there are three types of retaining walls. The *gravity wall*, illustrated in Figs. 18–1(a) and (b), is made of such propor-

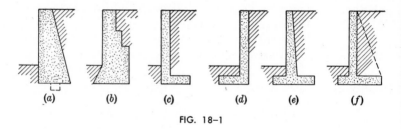

| (a) | (b) | (c) | (d) | (e) | (f) |

FIG. 18–1

tions that its weight alone is sufficient to resist the thrust of the retained material. The *cantilever wall*, shown in Figs. 18–1(c), (d), and (e), is constructed of reinforced concrete. The types shown in Figs. 18–1(c) and (e) make use of the weight of the earth to prevent the wall from overturning at its outer edge. Figure 18–1(f) shows the *counterfort wall*. It is similar to the *cantilever wall* with the exception that vertical triangular-shaped cross walls are tied to the base and vertical slab at regular intervals. The shapes in which retaining walls are made depend on conditions. Sometimes the exposed surface of the wall shown in Fig. 18–1(a) is a sloping surface. The base slab in the cantilever and counterfort walls is sometimes extended beyond the exposed face, as shown in Figs. 18–1(e) and (f); this helps to prevent overturning.

The type of wall to select is the wall that may be constructed most economically under existing conditions. Low walls are invariably of the gravity type. They are constructed of brick, stone masonry, or mass concrete. It is usually economical to use the counterfort wall when the height is 20 ft or more. The cantilever wall is used for walls of intermediate height.

The design of a retaining wall is accomplished by first selecting a cross section known from past experience to be desirable. This section is then tested for the three different ways in which retaining walls are most likely to fail, and the proportions of the component parts are modified as may be necessary.

All retaining walls should have their foundations well below the frost line and care should be exercised to see that drainage holes are provided to permit the escape of water from the back of the wall.

18-2. Earth Pressure. In investigating the stability of a retaining wall, it is necessary to determine the resultant of the forces corresponding to the weight of the wall and the force that results from the retained earth, the thrust. When the dimensions of the wall are known, its weight may be determined accurately. The earth pressure, however, depends on several factors, the types of retained material, sand, broken stone, gravel, clay, etc. When sand or loose earth is deposited on a flat surface, it does not spread out as a liquid but piles up in a mound. This piling up is caused by friction between the individual particles as they slide one on the other. The slope of the side of such a mound of material is called the *slope of repose*, and the angle between the surface of the material and the horizontal is known as the *angle of repose*. The material within the angle of repose exerts no pressure on a retaining wall. The angle of repose varies with different materials, but for average conditions retained soil is assumed to have a slope of 1.5 to 1, which corresponds to an angle of 33° 41′.

When the surface of the retained earth is horizontal, as shown in Fig. 18-2(a), P, the resultant earth pressure, is assumed to be horizontal at a height of $\dfrac{h}{3}$ from the base of the retained earth. Its magnitude is

$$P = 0.286 \frac{wh^2}{2}$$

in which P = the magnitude of the resultant earth pressure in pounds

w = the weight of the retained soil or other material in pounds per cubic foot

h = the height of the retained earth in feet.

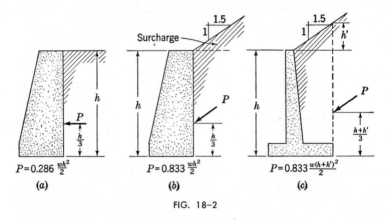

$$P = 0.286 \frac{wh^2}{2}$$
(a)

$$P = 0.833 \frac{wh^2}{2}$$
(b)

$$P = 0.833 \frac{w(h+h')^2}{2}$$
(c)

FIG. 18-2

When the wall is required to retain a *surcharge*, a slope of earth above the top of the wall, as shown in Figs. 18–2(b) and (c), $P = 0.833 \dfrac{wh^2}{2}$. For the three retaining walls in Fig. 18–2, P, the thrust of the earth, is shown in direction, line of action, and magnitude. Note that the direction of the thrust is parallel to the upper surface of the retained earth.

In designing a retaining wall, it is customary to consider a strip of wall 12 in. in length. As an example, if a concrete retaining wall has a cross-sectional area of 3 x 9 ft, the cross section contains 27 sq ft. Hence a strip of wall 12 in. in length contains 27 cu ft, and its weight is 27 × 150, or 4050 lb.

18–3. Resultant of Weight of Wall and Earth Pressure. The resultant of a system of forces is a single force that produces the same effect as the system of individual forces. If the system is composed of two nonparallel forces, the resultant passes through the point of intersection of their lines of action. The magnitude, direction, and line of action of the resultant can be found graphically by constructing the parallelogram of forces as explained in Arts. 2–9 and 2–10.

Figure 18–3(a) represents a cross section of a retaining wall whose weight is W. The weight W is downward and acts through the centroid of the cross-sectional area. P is the pressure of the earth on the wall. The line of action of P is extended until it meets the line of action of W. At this point a parallelogram of

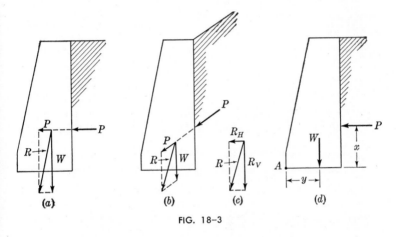

FIG. 18–3

forces of P and W is constructed, and R, the resultant, is determined in magnitude, direction, and line of action. For this particular case note that the vertical component of R is W and that the horizontal component of R is P.

Figure 18–3(b) illustrates a wall retaining soil on which there is a surcharge. Hence P, the thrust of the earth, is not horizontal. By constructing a parallelogram of forces, R, the resultant of P and W is determined. R is again drawn in Fig. 18–3(c). The horizontal and vertical components of R are R_H and R_V, respectively. They are not P and W as in Fig. 18–3(a). When the two components of the resultant are determined, we can proceed to investigate the stability of the wall.

18–4. Stability of Retaining Walls. In general, a retaining wall may fail in one of three ways: (1) by overturning, (2) by undue settlement at the toe, and (3) by sliding horizontally on its base.

The tendency of the wall to overturn is the moment of the force P with respect to the point A [Fig. 18–3(d)]; the overturning moment is $P \times x$. The force W multiplied by its lever arm y is $W \times y$, the moment that resists the overturning moment. The resisting moment divided by the overturning moment determines the factor of safety against overturning. A factor of safety of 2 is considered to be ample.

The point at which the resultant of W and P cuts the base of the retaining wall determines the pressure on the foundation bed at the toe of the wall [point A in Fig. 18–3(d)]. If the resultant cuts the base of the wall at the center of its width, the pressure on the foundation wall is uniformly distributed. If it cuts the base at any other point, there is an unequal distribution of pressure and the maximum pressure may be found, as explained in Art. 13–9. For important work, test borings should be made to determine the allowable pressure on the foundation bed. Table 18–1 is given as

TABLE 18–1. ALLOWABLE BEARING CAPACITIES OF FOUNDATION BEDS, IN TONS PER SQUARE FOOT

Alluvial soil.............................	$\frac{1}{2}$
Soft clay.................................	1
Firm clay................................	2
Wet sand................................	2
Sand and clay mixed..............	2
Fine dry sand.................... .	3
Hard clay..........................	4
Coarse dry sand......	4
Gravel............................	6
Gravel and sand, well cemented....	8
Hardpan or hard shale.	10
Medium rock.................... .	20
Rock under caissons...............	25
Hard rock.	80

a reference; the allowable bearing capacities in this table are taken from various building codes. Regardless of the magnitude of the maximum pressure, it is good practice to have the wall of such proportions that the resultant falls within the middle third of the base.

The force that tends to cause the retaining wall to slide horizontally is the horizontal component of the resultant. The force resisting this tendency to slide is the product of the vertical component of the resultant and the coefficient of friction of the material composing the foundation bed. Average coefficients of friction of masonry on various foundation beds are: on wet clay, 0.3; on dry clay, 0.5; on sand, 0.4; on gravel, 0.6. The factor of safety against sliding is the resisting force divided by the force that tends to cause sliding. A minimum value for the factor of safety is considered to be 1.5. When this value is exceeded, the width of the wall may be increased, thus increasing its weight, or a key may be formed on the base as shown in Fig. 18–1(a). As all retaining walls extend below the frost line, the soil abutting the wall also aids in resisting the tendency to slide.

18–5. Design of a Dam. A dam is a retaining wall whose purpose is to resist the pressure of water or other liquid. Liquid pressure is always perpendicular to the retaining surface. If the face of the dam is vertical, the water pressure is horizontal, and, with the exception of the magnitude, we have a condition similar to that shown in Fig. 18–2(a).

Example. Let it be required to design a masonry dam to retain a stream of water whose depth is 15 ft 0 in. at the face of the dam. The dam has gravel for a foundation bed.

SOLUTION. The first step is to draw a trial cross section of the dam, giving dimensions to the sides. Such a section is shown in Fig. 18–4(a); it is 15 ft in height, 3 ft in width at the top, and 9 ft in width at the base. This particular cross section will be investigated for stability and modified if necessary.

We shall confine our computations to a strip of dam 1 ft long.

The intensity of water pressure varies directly with the depth, and we remember that water weighs 62.5 lb per cu ft. In this problem we have a depth of 15 ft; hence on a vertical surface of the dam 15 ft below the upper surface of the water we have a pressure of (15×62.5) psf. Since the pressure at the top of the dam is zero, the *average* pressure is $\left(\dfrac{15 \times 62.5}{2}\right)$ psf. The column of water is 15 ft high; therefore

$$\frac{15 \times 62.5}{2} \times 15 = 7031 \text{ lb}$$

the total horizontal water pressure on the 1-ft length of dam. This is force P; it acts at one third the distance from the base of the dam to the top, as shown in Fig. 18–4(a).

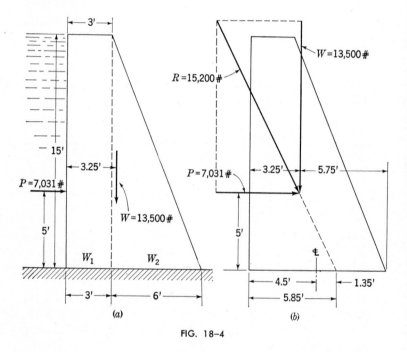

FIG. 18–4

To find the weight of the 1-ft length of dam, we divide the cross section into two parts, W_1 and W_2, the rectangle and triangle as shown. Assuming that the dam is of concrete weighing 150 lb per cu ft, the weight $W_1 = 3 \times 15 \times 1 \times 150$, or 6750 lb. Its moment with respect to the left face of the wall is 6750×1.5, or 10,125 ft-lb. Similarly, for the area W_2, its weight is $\dfrac{6 \times 15}{2} \times 1 \times 150$ or 6750 lb. Its moment about an axis at the left side of the wall is 6750×5, or 33,750 ft-lb. These computations are tabulated thus:

Section	Weight	Moment Arm	Moment
W_1	$3 \times 15 \times 1 \times 150 = 6{,}750\#$	$1.5'$	$6{,}750 \times 1.5 = 10{,}125'\#$
W_2	$\dfrac{6 \times 15}{2} \times 1 \times 150 = 6{,}750\#$	$5'$	$6{,}750 \times 5 = 33{,}750'\#$
	Total weight, $W = 13{,}500\#$		Sum of moments $= 43{,}875'\#$

The total weight of this strip of dam is 13,500 lb. To find the line of action of this force (the position of the centroid of the cross section), we can employ the principle, "the sum of the moments of the parts is equal to the moment of the whole." Let us call x feet the distance of the centroid from the left side of the section. Then

$$13{,}500 \times x = 43{,}875 \quad \text{and} \quad x = 3.25 \text{ ft} \quad \text{See Fig. 18–4}(a).$$

Now that P and W have been established, the line of action of P is extended until it meets the line of action of W, Fig. 18–4(b). At this point we construct the parallelogram of forces. By scaling, R, the resultant, equals 15,200 lb. Its horizontal and vertical components are 7031 and 13,500 lb, respectively. We also find, by scaling, that the line of action of the resultant cuts the base of the dam at 5.85 ft from the left side. Since the base is 9 ft in width, the resultant cuts the base at 1.35 ft from the center line. This is within the middle third.

The overturning moment about the toe, the lower right-hand edge of the dam, is 7031×5, or 35,155 ft-lb. The moment resisting this tendency to overturn is $13{,}500 \times 5.75$, or 77,625 ft-lb. The factor of safety against overturning is $77{,}625 \div 35{,}155$, or 2.2, and is acceptable.

Since the foundation bed is of gravel, we know the allowable bearing capacity to be 6 tons, or 12,000 psf (Table 18–1). Now let us find the maximum pressure on the foundation bed. This pressure will occur at the right-hand side of the base, and the magnitude is found by the formula

$$f_1 = \frac{P}{A}\left(1 + \frac{6e}{d}\right) \qquad \text{See Art. 13-9.}$$

Then

$$f_1 = \frac{13{,}500}{9}\left(1 + \frac{6 \times 1.35}{9}\right) \quad \text{and} \quad f_1 = 2850 \text{ psf}$$

As the allowable pressure is 12,000 psf, there will be no undue settlement.

The force tending to cause sliding horizontally is 7031 lb. The force resisting sliding is 13,500 lb, and the coefficient of friction for gravel is 0.6. Thus $13{,}500 \times 0.6 = 8100$ lb. The factor of safety against sliding is $8100 \div 7031 = 1.15$. This is not high enough. Actually, the base of the dam is below the frost line, and the abutting soil assists in resisting sliding. An additional aid would be a key on the base, as shown in Fig. 18-1(a), or the thickness of the dam may be increased.

18-6. Design of a Retaining Wall with Surcharge. The water pressure on the dam designed in the preceding article was a horizontal force. When a retaining wall is loaded with a surcharge, the thrust is oblique with the horizontal, as shown in Figs. 18-2(b) and (c).

Example. A retaining wall has a total height of 12 ft 0 in. and retains not only the fill in back of the wall but also a surcharge, the slope of which is 1.5 to 1.0. The wall is to be reinforced concrete of the cantilever type, as indicated in Fig. 18-2(c), and the foundation bed is gravel. Design the wall, investigating the three usual types of failure but omitting the required reinforcing bars in the concrete.

SOLUTION. In the design of a reinforced concrete retaining wall, proper proportions of the components are first determined to insure stability. Then the structural elements, base and vertical slab, are further investigated with respect to the unit stresses in the concrete and the reinforcing bars.

A retaining wall having a total height of 12 ft 0 in. with the dimensions shown in Fig. 18-5(a) is taken as a trial section. This section is investigated for stability, the computations being confined to a strip of wall 12 in. in length. The weight of concrete is taken to be 150 lb per cu ft, and that of the retained soil, 100 lb per cu ft.

As shown in Fig. 18–2(c), the resultant earth pressure is parallel to the slope of the surcharge and its magnitude is $0.833 \dfrac{w(h + h')^2}{2}$.

Thus $P = 0.833 \times \dfrac{100(12 + 3)^2}{2}$, or $P = 9370$ lb.   Its line of action passes through a point at $\dfrac{12 + 3}{3}$, or 5 ft above the inside base of the wall.   See Fig 18–5 (a).

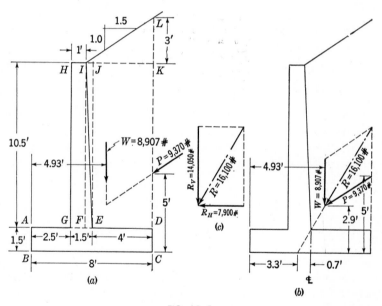

FIG. 18–5

To find the combined weight of the wall and the earth above the base, the section is divided into the six components, rectangles and triangles, shown in Fig. 18–5(a). In order to establish the line of action of this vertical force, we take the moments of the weights of the various parts with respect to an axis passing through the left side of the base, line AB. Thus the weight of the base,

ABCD, is (1.5 × 8 × 1 × 150), or 1800 lb. Its centroid from line *AB* is 8 ÷ 2, or 4 ft, and its moment is 1800 × 4, or 7200 ft-lb.

In a similar manner, the weights and moments of the various parts are computed as shown in the following tabulation. Bear in mind that the centroid of a triangle lies at a point one third the distance from the base to the apex, as explained in Art. 6–1.

Section	Weight		Moment Arm		Moment
ABCD	1.5 × 8 × 1 × 150	= 1800#	8 × ½ =	4'	1800 × 4 = 7,200'#
GFIH	1 × 10.5 × 1 × 150	= 1575#	2.5 + 0.5 =	3'	1575 × 3 = 4,725'#
FEI	0.5 × 10.5 × ½ × 1 × 150	= 394#	3.5 + 0.17 =	3.7'	394 × 3.7 = 1,458'#
EJI	0.5 × 10.5 × ½ × 1 × 100	= 263#	3.5 + 0.3 =	3.8'	263 × 3.8 = 999'#
EDKJ	4 × 10.5 × 1 × 100	= 4200#	4 + 2 =	6'	4200 × 6 = 25,200'#
KLI	4.5 × 3 × ½ × 1 × 100	= 675#	3.5 + 3 =	6.5'	675 × 6.5 = 4,387'#
	Total weight = 8907#				Sum of moments = 43,969'#

Adding the weights of the various parts, we find that the total weight is 8907 lb. The sum of the moments of the parts is equal to the moment of the whole, and, if we let x feet be the distance from the center of gravity of the resultant force of 8907 lb to the left side of the base,

$$8907 \times x = 43{,}969 \quad \text{and} \quad x = 4.93 \text{ ft}$$

Thus we have established the magnitude and lines of action of *W*, the total weight, 8907 lb, and *P*, the thrust of the soil, 9370 lb. as shown in Fig. 18–5(*a*).

To avoid a confusion of lines, the wall is again drawn [Fig. 18–5(*b*)], and the forces *W* and *P* are shown in their proper positions. The resultant of these two forces acts through their point of intersection. Therefore, *P* is extended on its line of action until it meets the line of action of *W*. At this point we construct the parallelogram of forces, thus establishing *R*, the resultant. Its line of action is shown in Fig. 18–5(*b*), and its magnitude is found by scaling to be 16,100 lb.

The resultant, *R*, is again drawn [Fig. 18–5(*c*)], and the vertical and horizontal components are found by scaling to be 14,050 and 7900 lb, respectively.

The force that tends to overturn the wall about point B [Fig. 18–5(a)] is 7900 lb, and its moment arm is 2.9 ft. Hence 7900 × 2.9 = 22,910 ft-lb, the overturning moment. The force resisting the tendency to overturn is 14,050 lb, and its moment arm is 4.93 ft. Thus 14,050 × 4.93 = 69,266 ft-lb. Then the factor of safety against overturning is 69,266 ÷ 22,910, or 3.02. This is acceptable since it exceeds 2.

In Fig. 18–5(b) we see that the resultant of W and P intersects the base of the wall 3.3 ft from the left side. Since the base is 8 ft 0 in. in width, (8 ÷ 2) − 3.3 = 0.7 ft, the distance from the center line of the base. This indicates that the resultant cuts the base within the middle third, and the formula used to determine the maximum pressure on the foundation bed, the pressure at point B, is

$$f_1 = \frac{P}{A}\left(1 + \frac{6e}{d}\right) \qquad \text{Art. 13–9}$$

Then

$$f_1 = \frac{14,050}{8}\left(1 + \frac{6 \times 0.7}{8}\right) = 2680 \text{ psf}$$

The foundation bed is gravel, and from Table 18–1 we find that the allowable bearing capacity of the soil is 6 tons (12,000 psf). Since the maximum pressure is only 2680 psf, it is well within the allowable.

The force that tends to cause the wall to slide is the horizontal component of the resultant of the forces acting on the wall. This horizontal component is 7900 lb [Fig. 18–5(c)]. The force resisting the tendency to slide is the vertical component of the resultant, 14,050 lb, multiplied by the coefficient of friction of gravel, 0.6, or 14,050 × 0.6 = 8430 lb. Then the factor of safety against sliding is 8430 ÷ 7900, or 1.07. This factor of safety is too low, but, since the wall extends below the frost line, the soil abutting the wall helps to resist the tendency to slide. A projection below the base, as shown in Fig. 18–1(a), materially increases the resistance to sliding. Another way to aid in preventing the wall from sliding is to incline upward the left end of the base.

Thus far the discussion relating to this retaining wall has concerned only its stability. A trial cross section was drawn, and a wall of these dimensions was tested for various types of stability failure. But this does not complete the design. The material used in its construction is reinforced concrete, and it is now necessary to compute the required areas of reinforcing steel in the base and vertical slab and to investigate the stresses in the concrete. The result of these computations may reveal the need of certain revisions in the dimensions of the trial section.*

* For the complete design of a similar retaining wall see the author's *Simplified Design of Reinforced Concrete*, second edition, John Wiley and Sons, New York, 1960.

INDEX

Abbreviations, 2
Allowable stresses, 68, 77
  for bolts, 80
  for concrete, 245
  for fillet welds, 221
  for reinforcement, 245
  for structural steel, 80
  for woods, 78
Allowable working values for rivets, 215
Aluminum alloys, 68
Aluminum Company of America, 113
Aluminum sections, 113
American Institute of Steel Construction, 113
American Society for Testing Materials, 67
American Standard channels, 109
American Standard I-beams, 105
Angle of repose, 269
Angles, properties of, 110, 111
Areas of bars, 251

Bars, areas and perimeters of, 251
Beams, bending moment in, 139
  built-up, 128, 190
  cantilever, 114, 146, 147
  concrete, formulas for, 240, 244
  continuous, 159, 160, 162, 164, 165
  deflection of, 172
  design of, 183

Beams, fixed, 167
  investigation of, 187
  length of, requiring stirrups, 257
  maximum deflection of, 139
  of two materials, 190
  overhanging, 150
  reinforced concrete, bond stresses in, 261
    formula coefficients for, 248
  restrained, 167
  shear in, 139
  simple, 114, 140
  types of, 114
Bearing stresses in rivets, 212
Belgian truss, 31
Bending moment, 157
  for triangular loading, 148
  for typical loadings, 139
  in beams, 139
  positive and negative, 133
Bending moment diagrams, 133
Bending stresses, 178
Blocks, concrete, 81
Bluestone, 81
Bolts, high strength, 227
  stresses for, 80
Bond stress in concrete, 261
Bow's notation, 14
Breaking strength, 72
Brick masonry, 68, 81
Built-up beams, shear in, 129
Butt welds, 224

Cantilever beam, 114
　with concentrated load, 147
　with distributed load, 145
Cantilever retaining wall, 268
Capstan, 62
Cast iron, 68
Center of gravity, 85
Center of moments, 47
Centroids, 85
Character of stress, 34
Clockwise direction, 14, 47
Columns, 193
　eccentrically loaded, 201
　end conditions of, 194
　reinforced concrete, 264
　spaced, 196
　spiral, 264
　steel, 198, 199
　tied, 264
　wood, 194
Components, 8
Compression, 5
Concentrated loads, 115
　on cantilever beams, 147
　on simple beams, 142, 143, 144
Concrete, allowable stresses in, 245
　modulus of elasticity of, 247
Concrete blocks, 81
Concrete columns, 264
Concurrent forces, 8
Continuous beams, 114, 159, 164, 165
Coplanar forces, 7
Counterclockwise direction, 15
Counterfort wall, 268
Couple, mechanical, 18
Couplings, shaft, 233
Curvilinear motion, 7
Cypress, 78

Dam, design of, 273
Deflection, 69, 172
Deformation, 69
Deformed bars, 261
Design, 1
Diagonal tension, 255
Direct stress, 65
Distributed loads, 115

Distributed loads, on cantilever
　beams, 145
　on continuous beams, 159
　on simple beams, 140
Double bearing in rivets, 213
Douglas fir, 78
Ductility, 67

Earth pressure, 269
　resultant, 271
Eccentrically loaded columns, 201
Elasticity, 66
Elastic limit, 66, 68, 70, 71
Elements of a force, 6
End conditions of columns, 194
Equal leg angles, 110
Equilibrant, 12
Equilibrium, 7
　laws of, 49, 51
　three forces in, 20
Equilibrium polygon, 18

Factor of safety, 75
Fan truss, 31
Fillet welds, 219
　allowable working stresses for, 221
　minimum sizes of, 221
Fixed beams, 114, 168
Flexure formula, 180
　for reinforced concrete beams, 241,
　244
Flitched beams, 190
Force, 4
　elements of, 6
　moment of, 47
　of gravity, 4
Force polygon, 13, 15
Forces, concurrent, 8
　coplanar, 7
　exerted by spheres, 41
　found by mathematics, 61
　moments of, 49
　required for motion, 43
Formula, flexure, 180
　for bending moments, 139
　for deflection, 139, 172
　for reinforced concrete, 241, 244

Formula, for shear, 139
    for steel columns, 199
    for timber columns, 194, 196
Foundation beds, allowable pressure
    on, 272
Free body, 37
Friction, 40
Funicular polygon, 17, 20

Granite, 81
Gravity retaining wall, 268

Hemlock, 79
High strength bolts, 227
Horizontal shear, 123
Horsepower, 234
Howe truss, 29

Inclined plane, 40
Inertia, moment of, 89, 91
Inflection point, 150
Investigation, 1, 187

Keys in pulleys, 232
Kinetics, 1

Laws of equilibrium, 49, 51
Lever arm, 47
Limestone, 81
Loads, concentrated, 115
    distributed, 115
    moving, 154
    triangular, 148
Lumber, allowable stresses for, 78
    species and grades of, 78

Malleability, 67
Marble, 81
Masonry, allowable stresses for, 81
Mass, 4
Materials, brittleness of, 67
    ductility of, 67
    elasticity of, 66
    malleability of, 67
    physical properties of, 68
    plasticity of, 67

Materials, stiffness of, 66
    strength of, 66
    used in construction, 67
    weights of, 68
Mechanical couple, 18
    moment of, 49
Mechanics, 1
Middle third, principle of, 205
Miscellaneous shapes, 108
Modulus of elasticity, 68, 73
    computation of, 73
    of cast iron, 68
    of concrete, 247
    of lumber, 78, 79
    of structural steel, 68
    of wrought iron, 68
Moment, bending, 133
    of a force, 47, 133
    of a mechanical couple, 49
    resisting, 179
    statical, 124
Moment-area method, 172
Moment arm, 47
Moment diagram, 133
Moment of inertia, 89, 91
    of various areas, 104
    polar, 230
    transfer of, 95
Moments, center of, 47, 133
    denomination of, 47, 63
Motion, 7
Moving loads, 154

National Lumber Manufacturers
    Association, 81
Negative bending moment, 150
Neutral axis, 85
Neutral surface, 85
Nonconcurrent forces, 8

Overhanging beam, 150

Parallelogram of forces, 9
Perimeters of bars, 251
Permanent set, 72
Physical properties of materials, 68
Piers, eccentrically loaded, 208

Pine, southern, 79
Pipes, stresses in, 236
Plane motion, 7
Plasticity, 67
Plates, tensile stresses in, 213
Plug welds, 225
Point of contraflexure, 150
Polar moment of inertia, 230
Positive bending moment, 150
Posts, 193
Pratt truss, 29, 36
Pressure, earth, 269
   water, 273
Principle of the middle third, 205
Properties of American Standard
   channels, 109
  of American Standard I-beams, 105
  of angles, 110, 111
  of sections, 103, 104
  of wide-flange shapes, 106, 107
  of yard lumber and timbers, 112
Proportional limit, 71
Pulleys, keys in, 232

Radius of gyration, 100
Reactions, computations of, 55
  found by moments, 55
  found graphically, 25
  relation of, to loads, 60
  truss, 26, 28
Redwood, 79
Reinforced concrete, beams, design
   of, 249
  bond stress in, 261
  columns, 264
  flexure formulas for, 241, 244
  formula coefficients for, 247
  notation used in, 240
  slab, design of, 254
Reinforcement, allowable stresses in,
  245
  areas and perimeters of, 251
Resisting moment, 179
Restrained beams, 167
Resultants, 8, 11, 20
  of parallel forces, 21
  of wall and earth pressure, 271

Retaining wall, 268
  design of, 276
  stability of, 271
Riveted joints, design of, 217
Rivets, 210
  allowable working values of, 215
  bearing stresses in, 212
  double bearing in, 213
  failure of, 210
  shear in, 211
  stresses for, 80
Roller bearings, 28, 30
Rubble, 81

Safe loads, computations of, 186
Sandstone, 81
Scalar, 6
Section modulus, 99, 183
Sections, properties of, 103
Shaft couplings, 233
Shear, 5
  horizontal, 123
  in beams, 139
  in built-up beams, 128
  in rivets, 211
  in steel beams, 127
  vertical, 117
Shear diagram, 118
Simple beam, 114
  with concentrated loads, 142, 143,
   144
  with distributed loads, 140
  with triangular loading, 148
Slab, reinforced concrete, 254
Slenderness ratio, 193, 198
Slope of repose, 269
Slot welds, 225
Southern pine, 79
Spaced columns, 196
Space diagram, 13
Space motion, 7
Spacing of stirrups, 258
Spheres, forces exerted by, 41
Spiral column, 264
Spruce, 79
Stability of retaining walls, 271
Standard channels, 109

Standard I-beams, 105
Statical moment, 124
Statics, 1
Steel, structural, 68
    allowable stresses in, 80
Steel beams, design of, 183
    shear in, 127
Steel columns, 198, 199
Stiffness, 66
Stirrups, 256
    portion of beam requiring, 257
    spacing of, 258
Stone masonry, 68
Strain, 70
Strength of materials, 1, 66
Stress, 5
    character of, 34
    direct, 65
Stress diagram, 31
Stresses, bending, 178
    in frames, 16
String polygon, 18
Structural tile, 81
Structural steel, 68
    allowable stresses in, 80
Strut, 193
Surcharge, 270

Tanks, stresses in, 236
Tensile stress in plates, 213
Tension, 5
Theorem of three moments, 159
Three forces in equilibrium, 29
Three-force members, 39
Tied columns, 264
Tile, clay, 81
Timber, 68
    allowable stresses for, 78
    properties of standard sizes of, 112

Torque, 229, 230
Transferring moments of inertia, 95
Triangular fan truss, 31
Triangular loading, 148
Truss, Belgian, 31
    fan, 31
    Howe, 29
    Pratt, 29, 36
    reactions, 26, 28, 29
    stress diagram for, 31
Two-force members, 38
Types of beams, 114

Ultimate strength, 66, 68
Unequal leg angles, 111
Uniformly distributed loads, 116

Vectors, 6
Vertical shear, 116

Wall, cantilever, 268
    counterfort, 268
    gravity, 268
    retaining, 268
Water pressure, 273
Web reinforcement, 255
Weights of materials, 68
Welding, 219
Welds, butt, 224
    fillet, 219
    plug and slot, 225
Wide-flange sections, 106, 107
Wood columns, 194
Work, 234
Working unit stress, 81
Wrought iron, 68

Yard lumber and timbers, 112
Yield point, 72